# PICTURE PUZZLES

# 1. Freaky Footprints

Which monster left this footprint?

# 2. Mumbo Jumbo

Spot the difference between the six elephants. Who is the odd one out?

# 3. Shadow Bats

Which shadow matches the vampire bat?

# 4. Crossroads

You're lost! Study the clues to find which road to take.

**Clues**

**1.** Avoid hens, cows and sheep.
**2.** Don't go North.
**3.** Head for the hills.
**4.** Go the opposite way from the wood.

# 5. Speedboat

Which skier is attached to the speedboat?

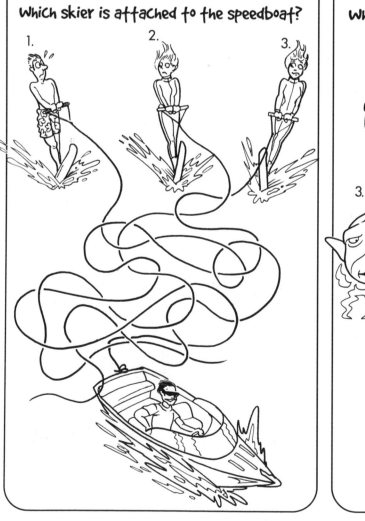

# 6. Jaws

Which shark took a bite out of the raft?

# 7. Haunted House

Circle the ten spooks hiding in the haunted house.

# 8. Mystery Tour

Which route should the mystery tour bus take to get out of the maze?

# 9. Spider's Web

Which spider's web trail leads to the center of the web?

1.

2.

# 10. Snakes Alive

Which snake has a rattle on the end of its tail?

# 11. Silly Sheep

How many sheep are there in the picture?

# 12. Spot the Difference

Spot the dog has lost seven spots. Circle where they are missing.

# 13. Bungee Monkey

Which monkey has the longest bungee cord?

# 14. Mosquito Match

Two of these mosquitoes match. Which two are identical?

1.
2.
3.
4.
5.
6.

# 15. Goo Who?

Who is covered in goo?

1.
2.
3.
4.
5.
6.

# 16. Alien Eyeballs

How many eyeballs does the alien have? Follow the eyeball trails to see which ones are connected to its head.

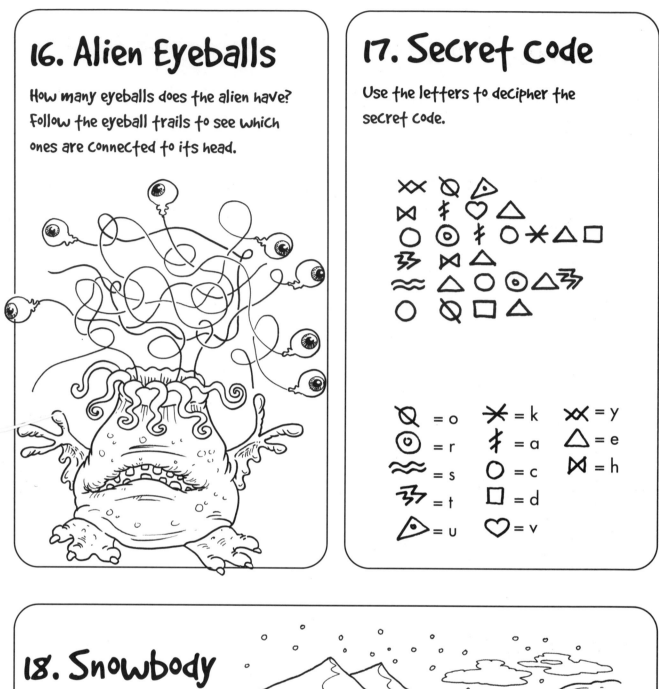

# 17. Secret Code

Use the letters to decipher the secret code.

⬲ = o       ✳ = k       ⬲ = y
◉ = r       ⱡ = a       △ = e
〰 = s       ○ = c       ⋈ = h
⚡ = t       □ = d
▷ = u       ♡ = v

# 18. Snowbody There

oh yes there is! Five polar bears are hiding in the snowscene. Can you find them?

# 19. Cat Splat

Which splat mark did the crazy cat make?

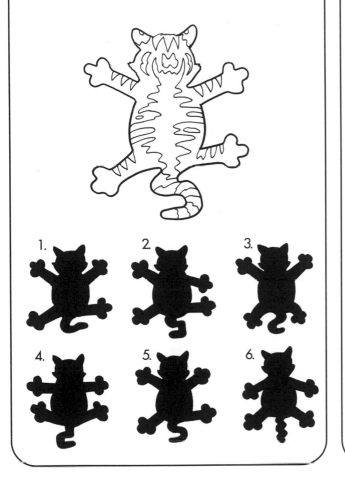

1. 2. 3.
4. 5. 6.

# 20. Witches' Hats

Draw three straight lines across the box to leave three different witches' hats in each part.

# 21. Top Secret

Use the secret code to read the message on the computer.

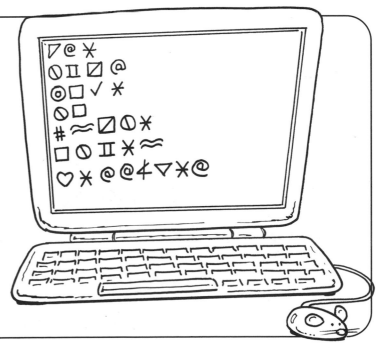

✚ = a
@ = s
✓ = d
✳ = e
▽ = g
Ⅱ = h
▱ = i

♡ = m
▢ = o
≈ = r
◎ = c
◍ = t
▽ = u
# = w

# 22. Mummy Mummy!

Can you spot the two identical mummies?

# 23. Bubble Trouble

Oops! Someone has used too much bubble bath. Who is it?

# 24. Laughing Hyenas

How many hyenas are smiling in the picture?

# 25. Blackout!

How many animals are hiding in the dark?

# 26. Howl at the Moon

Can you spot the two pictures that are identical?

1.
2.
3.
4.
5.
6.

# 27. Bugs!

Draw along the dotted lines to form five equal-sized portions. Each portion should contain only one of each bug.

## 28. Mad Mars

Is there life on Mars? How many Martians can you see?

## 29. Wizard!

Can you help the wizard find his way out of the maze?

## 30. Crazy Castle

Which road leads to the crazy castle?

## 31. Computer Connection

Which game controller is connected to the computer?

A.    B.    C.

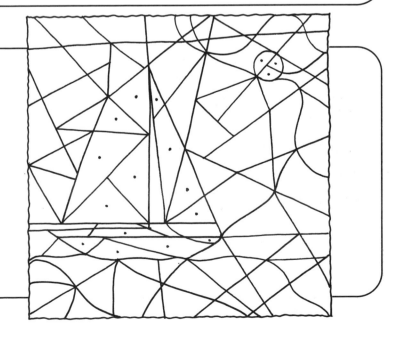

## 32. Nine Dots

Use a pencil to join all nine dots without lifting your pencil off the page and without going back on any lines you've made. You can only draw four lines.

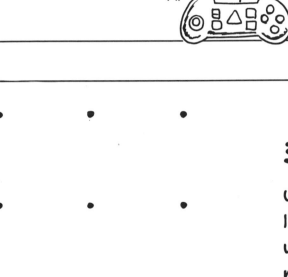

## 33. Over the Waves

Shade in all the shapes marked with a dot to find the shape hidden in the picture.

# 34. Under the Sea

Shade in all the shapes marked with a dot to find the shape hidden in the picture.

# 35. River Rapids

Which river rapid will take you safely to the lagoon?

A.          B.          C.

# 36. Sailing Boat

Without lifting your pencil off the page, start at the big dot and join the dots to make a sailing boat.

# 37. Clown Shapes

How many circles, triangles and squares can you see in the picture of the clown?

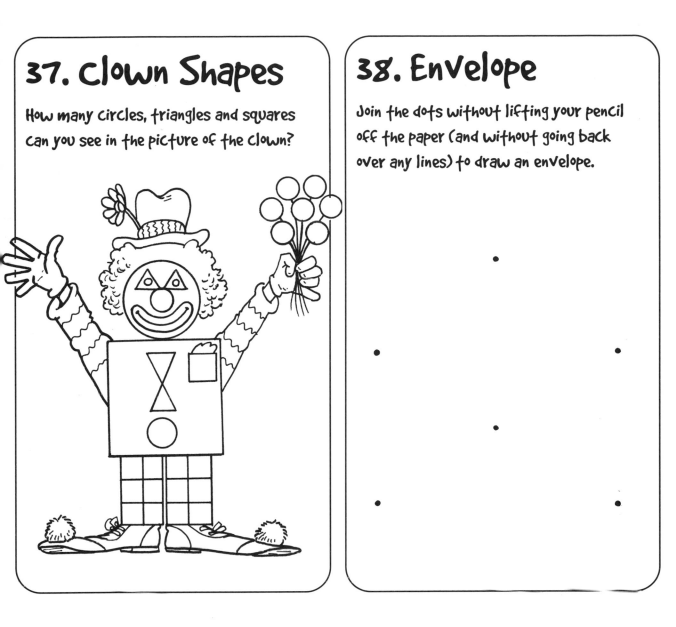

# 38. Envelope

Join the dots without lifting your pencil off the paper (and without going back over any lines) to draw an envelope.

# 39. Manic Monkeys

How many monkeys are there in the picture?

# 40. Space Rocket

Two of these rockets are the same. Can you spot them?

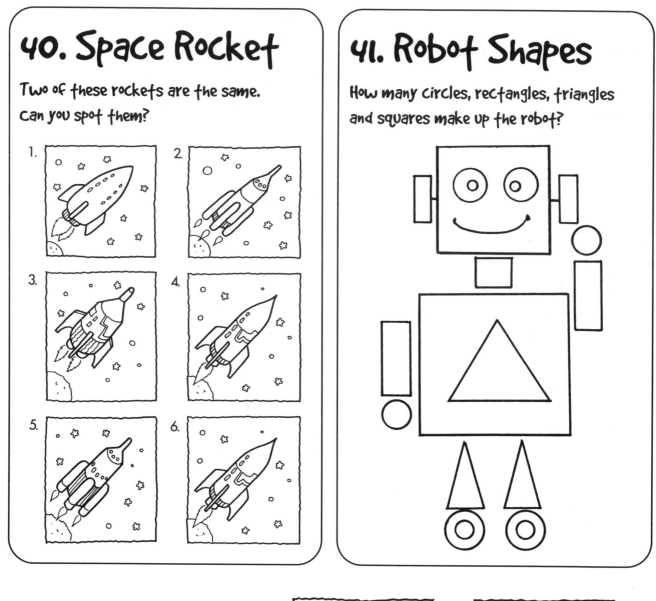

1.

2

3.

4.

5.

6.

# 41. Robot Shapes

How many circles, rectangles, triangles and squares make up the robot?

# 42. Sweet Boxes

Which two sweets are in every box?

# 43. Shadow Match

Draw lines to join each item to its matching shadow.

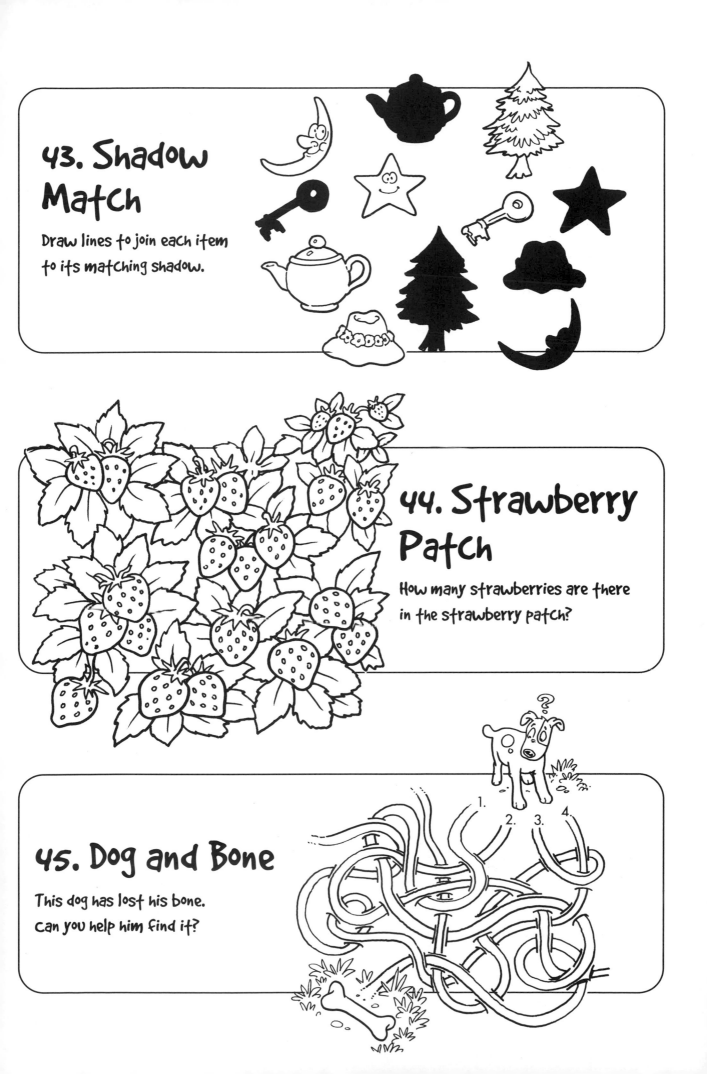

# 44. Strawberry Patch

How many strawberries are there in the strawberry patch?

# 45. Dog and Bone

This dog has lost his bone. Can you help him find it?

# 46. Underwater

Spot the ten differences in the picture. Circle them with a pencil.

# 47. Snowman

Which snowman is the odd one out?

1.
2.
3.
4.
5.
6.

# 48. Cake Puzzle

Draw two straight lines across the box to leave three different cakes in each part.

## 49. Flight of Fright

Shade in all the shapes marked with a dot to find the shape hidden in the picture.

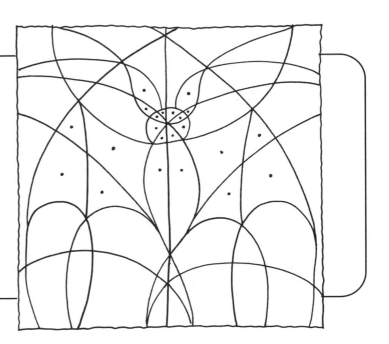

## 50. Fit for a King

Shade in all the shapes marked with a dot to find the shape hidden in the picture.

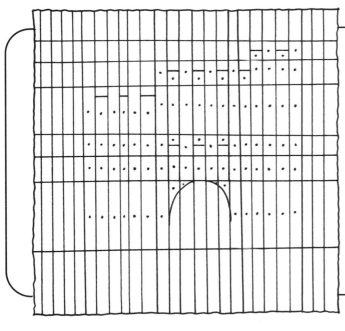

## 51. Top Secret

Follow the lines to find the key that opens the top secret file.

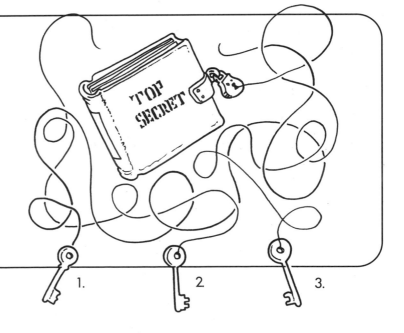

# 52. Treasure Trail

Which route leads to the treasure trove?

# 53. Splish Splat!

Two of these splish splats are identical. Can you spot them?

1.

2.

3.

4.

5.

6.

# 54. Smiling Faces

Draw three straight lines (which can cross each other) to divide the circle into six parts. Each part must contain three different faces.

## 55. High-Five Spider

Can you spot the ten differences between these two pictures?

## 56. Bats' Castle

How many bats are hiding in and around the castle?

## 57. Star Gazing

How many stars can you see in the picture?

## 58. Alien Adventure

Which route should the alien spaceship take to reach its home planet?

## 59. Blast off

Shade in all the shapes marked with a dot to find the shape hidden in the picture.

## 60. Kick It

Shade in all the shapes marked with a dot to find the shape hidden in the picture.

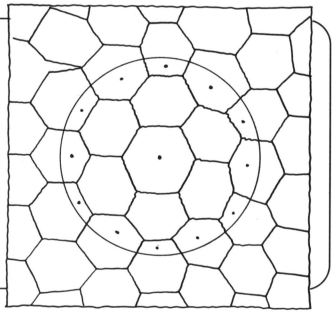

# 61. Cat Calling

Who is the cat phoning? Follow the lines to find out if it is the duck, the gerbil or the dog.

# 62. Oodles of Doodles

Two of these doodles are identical. Which two?

1.

2.

3.

4.

5.

6.

# 63. Jungle Trap

You are trapped in the jungle. Can you find your way out?

START

## 64. Sun, Moon and Stars

Draw three straight lines (which can cross each other) to divide the box into five parts. Each part must contain one sun, one moon and one star.

## 65. Zippy the Snail

Zippy is in a hurry to get out of the snail maze. Which route is the fastest?

## 66. Cat Nap

How many cats are napping in this picture?

# 67. Wibbly Wobbly

Two of these wibbly wobbly men are identical. Can you spot them?

1.   2.   3.   4.   5.   6.

# 68. Walkies

Shade in the shapes marked with a dot to find the shape hidden in the picture.

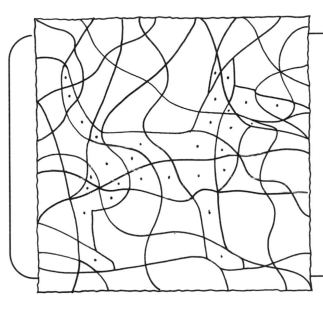

# 69. Home Sweet Home

Shade in all the shapes marked with a dot to find the shape hidden in the picture.

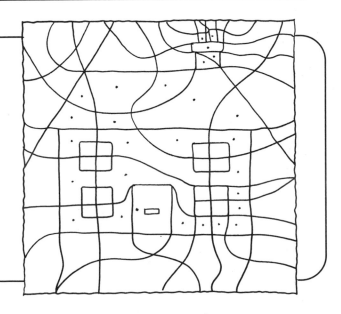

# ANSWERS

## 1. Freaky footprints

5.

## 3. Shadow Bats

4.

## 2. Mumbo Jumbo

## 4. Crossroads

Highlands

## 5. Speedboat

Skier number 3

3.

## 6. Jaws

Shark number 3

## 7. Haunted House

## 8. Mystery Tour

## 9. Spider's Web

2.

## 10. Snakes Alive

Snake number 2

## 11. Silly Sheep

16 sheep

## 12. Spot the Difference

## 13. Bungee Monkey

Monkey number 2

## 14. Mosquito Match

Mosquito numbers 2 and 5

## 15. Goo Who?

Number 4

## 16. Alien Eyeballs

There are three eyeballs

## 17. Secret code

You
have
cracked
the
secret
code

## 18. Snowbody There

## 19. Cat Splat

Shadow number 5

## 20. Witches' Hats

## 21. Top Secret

Use this code to write other messages

## 22. Mummy Mummy!

Mummies number 1 and 6

## 23. Bubble Trouble

Number 4, the lion

## 24. Laughing Hyenas

11 Hyenas

## 25. Blackout!

15 animals

## 26. Howl at the Moon

Pictures 3 and 6 match

## 27. Bugs!

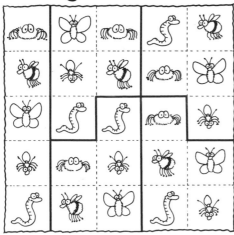

## 28. Mad Mars

10 Martians

## 29. Wizard!

# 30. Crazy Castle

Road A

# 31. Computer Connection

Controller A

# 32. Nine Dots

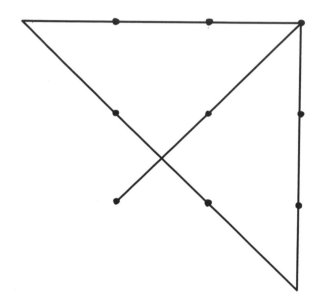

# 33. Over the Waves

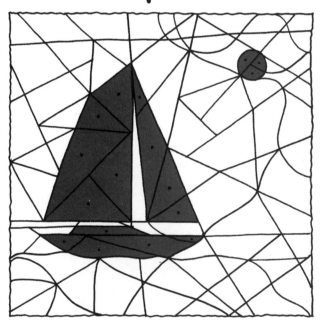

# 34. Under the Sea

# 35. River Rapids

River B

# 36. Sailing Boat

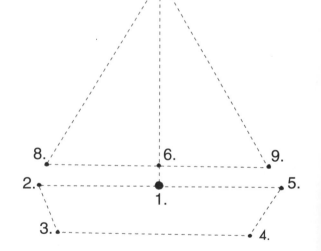

1–2–3–4–5–1–6–7–8–9–7

# 37. Clown Shapes

12 circles
4 triangles
14 squares

# 38. Envelope

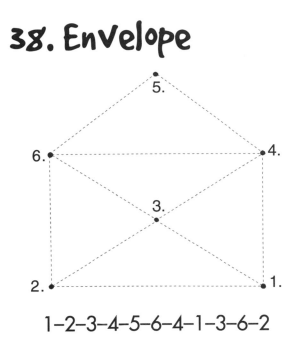

1–2–3–4–5–6–4–1–3–6–2

# 39. Manic Monkeys

14 monkeys

# 40. Space Rocket

Rockets 4 and 6

# 41. Robot Shapes

10 circles
4 rectangles
3 triangles
3 squares

# 42. Sweet Boxes

# 43. Shadow Match

# 44. Strawberry Patch

22 strawberries

# 45. Dog and Bone

Route 1

## 46. Underwater

## 47. Snowman

Snowman number 4

## 48. Cake Puzzle

## 49. Flight of Fright

## 50. Fit for a King

## 51. Top Secret

Key 3

## 52. Treasure Trail

## 53. Splish Splat!

Splish Splats 3 and 4

# 54. Smiling Faces

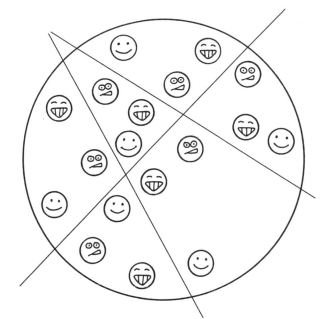

# 55. High-Five Spider

# 56. Bats' Castle

18 bats

# 57. Star Gazing

32 stars

# 58. Alien Adventure

Route Z

# 59. Blast Off

# 60. Kick It

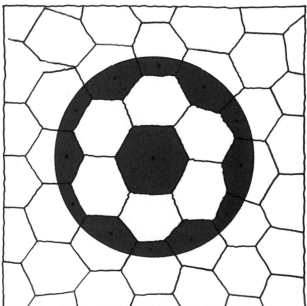

# 61. Cat Calling

The gerbil

## 62. Oodles of Doodles

Doodles 1 and 5

## 63. Jungle Trap

## 64. Sun, Moon and Stars

## 65. Zippy the Snail

Route C

## 66. Cat Nap

14 cats napping

## 67. Wibbly Wobbly

Wibbly wobbly men 4 and 6

## 68. Walkies

## 69. Home Sweet Home

# 1. FISHY TAILS

Go fishing! How many can you catch?

CLAMS
COD
CRAB
HADDOCK
HAKE
HERRING

LOBSTER
MACKEREL
MUSSELS
OYSTERS
PRAWNS
SALMON

SCAMPI
SKATE
SOLE
SQUID
TURBOT

| T | P | Y | E | H | C | Z | S | Q | U | I | D |
|---|---|---|---|---|---|---|---|---|---|---|---|
| H | R | O | A | B | A | L | O | E | H | T | L |
| H | A | D | D | O | C | K | L | W | F | F | M |
| V | W | G | N | I | R | R | E | H | C | A | L |
| S | N | R | L | O | T | O | M | Z | C | L | E |
| E | S | A | L | M | O | N | E | L | V | X | R |
| S | M | M | O | V | J | D | S | K | A | T | E |
| M | O | T | B | E | O | B | L | S | E | I | K |
| A | D | A | S | C | A | M | P | I | N | S | C |
| L | R | G | T | U | R | B | O | T | S | T | A |
| C | S | L | E | S | S | U | M | E | I | N | M |
| F | T | S | R | E | T | S | Y | O | R | B | D |

# 2. DESSERT DELIGHT

There are plenty of desserts and pastries for you here!

CHEESECAKE
CUSTARD        MOUSSE
FLAN           PASTRY
JELLO          PIE            SORBET
MERINGUE       SEMOLINA       SUNDAE

| C | H | E | E | S | E | C | A | K | E | J | A |
|---|---|---|---|---|---|---|---|---|---|---|---|
| U | N | L | S | O | T | N | G | H | C | K | C |
| S | E | M | O | L | I | N | A | T | I | I | J |
| T | A | O | B | F | T | G | H | R | R | O | O |
| A | C | U | A | E | T | A | G | I | K | F | S |
| R | S | S | C | W | C | T | S | F | L | A | N |
| D | U | S | X | O | Z | P | O | L | A | P | L |
| E | N | E | I | E | C | E | R | E | E | A | O |
| D | D | P | C | P | K | E | B | A | V | S | L |
| Z | A | P | P | Y | P | I | E | W | L | T | L |
| T | E | E | A | G | E | J | T | V | M | R | E |
| F | R | M | E | R | I | N | G | U | E | Y | J |

# 3. SUPERSTARS

Find the ten superstars hidden in the puzzle.

STARBURST      STARFLOWER     STARSHINE
STARDOM        STARGAZE       STARSHIP
STARDUST       STARLIGHT
STARFISH       STARRY

| S | T | A | R | L | I | G | H | T | A | S | C |
|---|---|---|---|---|---|---|---|---|---|---|---|
| T | C | G | C | K | N | V | V | A | T | T | E |
| A | E | T | H | A | M | A | S | A | S | A | H |
| R | N | P | S | T | A | R | R | Y | T | R | A |
| B | I | A | T | O | T | F | Y | O | A | F | W |
| U | H | R | Z | I | I | P | Y | O | R | L | T |
| R | S | T | T | S | S | T | A | R | D | O | M |
| S | R | Y | H | A | R | V | E | S | U | W | O |
| T | A | P | R | O | V | I | S | T | S | E | R |
| P | T | O | P | L | A | N | S | G | T | R | N |
| C | S | T | A | R | S | H | I | P | E | D | E |
| D | A | T | E | E | Z | A | G | R | A | T | S |

# 4. SPACE MISSION

Your mission is to find the words in this cosmic puzzle.

| | | |
|---|---|---|
| AURORA | MOON | STAR |
| COMET | NEPTUNE | SUN |
| COSMOS | ORBIT | TELESCOPE |
| GALAXY | PLANET | UNIVERSE |
| JUPITER | ROCKET | URANUS |
| MARS | SATURN | VENUS |

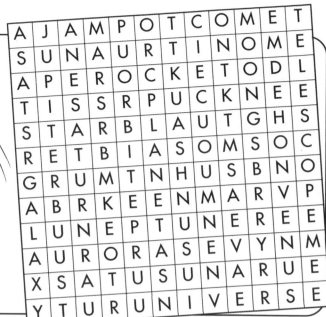

```
A J A M P O T C O M E T
S U N A U R T I N O M E
A P E R O C K E T O D L
T I S S R P U C K N E E
S T A R B L A U T G H S
R E T B I A S O M S O C
G R U M T N H U S B N O
A B R K E E N M A R V P
L U N E P T U N E R E E
A U R O R A S E V Y N M
X S A T U S U N A R U E
Y T U R U N I V E R S E
```

# 5. MAGIC WORDSEARCH

These words are linked to Halloween and magic!

| | | |
|---|---|---|
| ABRACADABRA | HALLOWEEN | VANISH |
| BROOM | MAGIC | WAND |
| CAULDRON | POTION | WARLOCK |
| CHARM | PUMPKIN | WISH |
| CLOAK | SPELLS | WITCH |
| DISAPPEAR | TRICK | WIZARD |

```
P K H S L L E P S H A R
H C A U L D R O N R V Y
S I L W I S H T P P A Z
I R L O N E C I G A M P
N T O A V B R O O M O U
A Z W S C E Y N Z T E M
V U E W W A R L O C K P
C R E T I I N C L O A K
W E N S T W Z O O P A I
A B R A C A D A B R A N
N A R C H A R M R B C L
D I S A P P E A R D D E
```

# 6. SCHOOL IS COOL!

Have fun playing this school word puzzle.

| | | |
|---|---|---|
| ART | CRAYONS | PLAYGROUND |
| ASSEMBLY | DESK | READING |
| BLACKBOARD | GRADES | TEACHER |
| BOOKS | HOMEWORK | |
| CALCULATOR | MATH | |
| CHALK | PENCILS | |
| CLASS | | |
| COMPUTER | | |

```
O X C C S H T A M A R W
L C A L C U L A T O R I
D O E A R A O S S R E B
E M M S A C C S V A H L
K P A S Y K S E D R C A
R U S K O O B M N E A C
O T L L N A S B N A E K
W E I A S U E L B D T B
E R C H U N D Y P I O O
M A N C T R A R T N O A
O L E Y U I R A T G I R
H C P L A Y G R O U N D
```

# 7. WHAT'S THE BUZZ?

Find the noises animals and creatures make.

BARK
BELLOW
BLEAT
BUZZ
CACKLE
CHIRP
COO

GROWL
GRUNT
HISS
HOOT
HOWL
MOO
PURR

QUACK
SNARL
SNIFF
SNORT
SQUEAK
WARBLE
WOOF

| P | U | Z | I | W | O | E | L | B | R | A | W |
|---|---|---|---|---|---|---|---|---|---|---|---|
| B | U | Z | Z | E | O | F | F | R | E | D | O |
| E | T | R | G | T | K | C | A | U | Q | A | O |
| L | C | J | R | A | A | C | R | L | T | A | F |
| L | A | I | E | E | M | O | O | W | F | E | V |
| O | C | P | W | L | S | K | S | O | F | L | E |
| W | K | R | A | B | A | W | G | R | U | N | T |
| P | L | A | P | E | S | U | N | G | H | B | T |
| Z | E | T | U | S | N | A | R | L | E | B | R |
| Q | U | Q | I | P | Y | T | O | W | A | J | O |
| A | S | N | I | F | F | T | O | O | H | O | N |
| C | H | I | R | P | F | Y | Q | H | I | S | S |

# 8. HAUNTED HOUSE

Who is in the haunted house?

GARGOYLES
GHOSTS
GHOULS
MONSTERS

PHANTOMS
SKELETONS
SPECTERS
SPOOKS

VAMPIRES
WEREWOLF
ZOMBIES

| G | A | R | G | O | Y | L | E | S | P | I | E |
|---|---|---|---|---|---|---|---|---|---|---|---|
| H | A | P | P | A | M | S | P | O | O | K | S |
| S | O | N | E | Y | L | I | H | P | T | O | N |
| P | S | E | R | I | P | M | A | V | S | S | M |
| E | A | Y | R | N | T | W | N | O | S | C | O |
| C | A | L | G | H | O | S | T | S | S | A | N |
| T | T | I | H | L | Q | W | O | E | E | R | S |
| E | C | K | O | R | O | E | M | E | I | V | T |
| R | C | E | U | O | Q | A | S | H | B | E | E |
| S | K | M | L | W | U | L | L | K | M | C | R |
| F | T | U | S | K | E | L | E | T | O | N | S |
| F | L | O | W | E | R | E | W | A | Z | H | P |

# 9. TREASURE CHEST

What gems and jewels are hidden in the treasure chest?

AMBER
AMETHYST
BANGLE
BRACELET
CORAL
DIAMOND

EMERALD
JADE
NECKLACE
PENDANT
RING
RUBY

SAPPHIRE
TOPAZ
TURQUOISE
ZIRCON

| D | A | Z | Z | A | M | E | T | H | Y | S | T |
|---|---|---|---|---|---|---|---|---|---|---|---|
| R | R | Z | A | E | K | E | G | A | N | D | U |
| U | D | I | A | M | O | N | D | S | T | O | R |
| B | R | R | P | E | L | O | N | S | N | T | Q |
| Y | W | C | K | R | E | B | M | A | A | O | U |
| B | C | O | C | A | S | C | O | P | D | P | O |
| A | H | N | Z | L | G | T | L | P | N | A | I |
| N | L | O | G | D | J | N | C | H | E | Z | S |
| G | A | V | V | S | H | E | I | I | P | A | E |
| L | R | T | E | L | E | C | A | R | B | A | T |
| E | O | A | J | M | I | N | T | E | D | A | J |
| E | C | A | L | K | C | E | N | A | C | G | O |

# 10. FAB FRUIT

Gather as many of these pieces of fruit as you can.

APRICOT
BANANA
CHERRY
DATES
GOOSEBERRY
GRAPES

KIWI
LEMON
MELON
ORANGE
PEACH
PEAR

PINEAPPLE
PLUM
RASPBERRY
STRAWBERRY

| C | R | O | O | R | A | N | G | E | Y | E | S |
|---|---|---|---|---|---|---|---|---|---|---|---|
| H | A | B | A | N | A | N | A | A | T | L | T |
| E | S | N | O | O | R | Y | P | N | Q | P | R |
| R | E | J | O | V | A | R | B | W | Q | P | A |
| R | S | T | P | L | U | M | O | T | T | A | W |
| Y | R | R | E | B | E | S | O | O | G | E | B |
| S | H | R | A | N | O | M | E | L | D | N | E |
| C | A | G | R | A | P | E | S | O | F | I | R |
| I | W | I | K | I | R | I | W | I | R | P | R |
| F | A | T | R | A | S | P | B | E | R | R | Y |
| T | O | C | I | R | P | A | A | R | H | A | Y |
| D | P | E | A | C | H | S | E | T | A | D | O |

# 11. COLOR CRAZY

All these words are brightly colored!

BALLOONS
CARNIVAL
CLOWN
CRAYONS
FIREWORKS

FRUIT
GEMS
MARBLES
NEON
PAINTS

PARROT
RAINBOW
SUNRISE
SUNSET

| F | R | O | L | L | A | V | I | N | R | A | C |
|---|---|---|---|---|---|---|---|---|---|---|---|
| I | J | E | E | S | W | O | B | N | I | A | R |
| R | A | M | C | S | C | R | F | T | E | D | A |
| E | B | A | Q | D | G | E | M | S | S | E | Y |
| W | M | R | U | C | A | T | H | U | H | H | O |
| O | T | B | A | L | L | O | O | N | S | T | N |
| R | O | L | E | O | J | R | G | R | O | O | S |
| K | M | E | R | W | T | R | C | I | T | H | O |
| S | A | S | E | N | H | A | H | S | U | O | M |
| R | S | T | N | I | A | P | I | E | P | O | C |
| I | F | W | H | H | F | W | L | N | E | O | N |
| T | E | S | N | U | S | F | R | U | I | T | S |

# 12. CANDY SHOP

Seek the treats inside the candy shop.

CANDY
CARAMELS
CHEWS
CHOCOLATE
FUDGE

GUMDROPS
LICORICE
LOLLIPOPS
MARSHMALLOW
MINTS

SHERBET
TOFFEE

| C | A | N | D | Y | B | R | L | Y | T | L | S |
|---|---|---|---|---|---|---|---|---|---|---|---|
| A | E | T | T | E | B | R | E | H | S | O | L |
| R | I | U | Q | C | E | K | I | T | S | L | I |
| A | S | G | U | M | D | R | O | P | S | L | C |
| M | X | R | T | I | A | R | T | W | O | I | O |
| E | F | T | F | N | S | E | H | N | C | P | R |
| L | G | O | S | T | H | C | C | S | S | O | I |
| S | V | F | I | S | M | M | S | S | V | P | C |
| I | X | F | R | S | N | B | B | W | O | S | E |
| E | J | E | G | D | U | F | O | S | E | Z | E |
| G | U | E | E | T | A | L | O | C | O | H | C |
| M | A | R | S | H | M | A | L | L | O | W | C |

# 13. FLOWER GARDEN

Find the flowers hidden in the garden.

BLUEBELL          LILAC          ROSE
BUTTERCUP         LILY           SNOWDROP
CROCUS            MARIGOLD       SWEET PEA
DAISY             PANSY
HOLLYHOCK         POPPY

| M | A | R | I | G | O | L | D | B | O | R | O |
| D | C | A | L | B | A | E | D | L | R | O | J |
| V | B | U | T | T | E | R | C | U | P | S | K |
| A | R | V | T | H | A | S | T | E | T | E | S |
| E | O | Q | D | S | T | W | E | B | I | V | U |
| P | O | C | A | L | I | L | V | E | M | T | C |
| T | G | W | I | A | R | R | E | L | B | S | O |
| E | F | Y | S | N | A | P | U | L | E | E | R |
| E | R | P | Y | G | O | O | O | E | I | C | C |
| W | O | P | Z | O | I | N | M | A | V | L | E |
| S | N | O | W | D | R | O | P | M | I | L | Y |
| T | M | P | K | C | O | H | Y | L | L | O | H |

# 14. TREEHOUSE

What are the childrens' treehouses made of?

APPLE          FIR          POPLAR
BIRCH          OAK          ROWAN
CEDAR          PALM         SYCAMORE
CHERRY         PEAR         WALNUT
CHESTNUT       PLUM         WILLOW

| T | R | H | C | R | I | B | I | S | C | K | S |
| E | E | C | H | E | S | T | N | U | T | A | T |
| H | U | H | W | C | D | C | A | P | U | R | S |
| B | O | E | T | G | P | A | L | M | K | T | E |
| T | S | R | S | R | A | T | R | W | M | E | R |
| U | E | R | R | A | L | P | O | P | O | O | O |
| N | B | Y | L | U | H | I | W | I | H | K | M |
| L | E | Q | U | K | R | S | A | S | T | E | A |
| A | F | I | Z | A | A | E | N | H | M | I | C |
| W | I | L | L | O | W | C | R | H | U | I | Y |
| A | R | L | A | R | O | Z | O | O | L | A | S |
| A | P | P | L | E | B | R | A | E | P | I | E |

# 15. SEASHORE SEARCH

Search the seashore for the hidden words.

BOAT          SEAWEED        TIDES
CRAB          SHELLS         WAVES
JELLYFISH     STARFISH
ROCKPOOL      SURF
SANDCASTLE    SWIMMERS

| O | S | E | L | T | S | A | C | D | N | A | S |
| S | T | T | S | W | I | U | G | A | V | E | E |
| C | A | H | U | C | R | D | A | V | D | W | A |
| W | R | E | R | W | A | V | E | S | R | S | W |
| O | F | S | F | C | R | E | P | S | U | P | E |
| T | I | R | O | C | K | P | O | O | L | L | E |
| L | S | H | O | L | I | D | O | S | C | I | D |
| I | H | I | S | H | D | T | A | O | B | S | X |
| L | F | P | S | L | K | S | K | Y | A | I | U |
| O | S | W | I | M | M | E | R | S | R | E | T |
| S | H | E | L | L | S | F | I | V | C | S | P |
| M | A | J | H | S | I | F | Y | L | L | E | J |

# 16. WILD WEATHER

What's hidden in the weather chart?

CLOUDY
COOL
CYCLONE
FREEZING
FOG
FROST
HAILSTORM

HAZY
HOT
HURRICANE
ICY
LIGHTNING
MIST
RAIN

SNOW
THUNDER
TORNADO
WET
WINDY

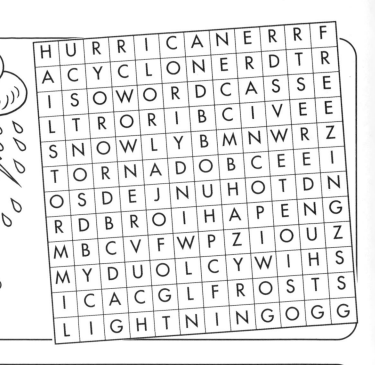

| H | U | R | R | I | C | A | N | E | R | R | F |
| A | C | Y | C | L | O | N | E | R | D | T | R |
| I | S | O | W | O | R | D | C | A | S | S | E |
| L | T | R | O | R | I | B | C | I | V | E | E |
| S | N | O | W | L | Y | B | M | N | W | R | Z |
| T | O | R | N | A | D | O | B | C | E | E | I |
| O | S | D | E | J | N | U | H | O | T | D | N |
| R | D | B | R | O | I | H | A | P | E | N | G |
| M | B | C | V | F | W | P | Z | I | O | U | Z |
| M | Y | D | U | O | L | C | Y | W | I | H | S |
| I | C | A | C | G | L | F | R | O | S | T | S |
| L | I | G | H | T | N | I | N | G | O | G | G |

# 17. FUNNY WORDS

Enjoy searching for these humorous words.

| S | N | I | G | G | E | R | H | G | A | G | C |
| W | A | V | E | R | C | C | A | Y | K | I | T |
| E | W | K | A | L | A | J | O | K | E | S | E |
| L | A | U | G | H | T | E | P | T | U | U | M |
| T | I | W | I | V | B | S | Z | L | W | O | H |
| R | C | W | G | B | O | T | Q | M | K | R | Y |
| A | L | Y | G | I | C | A | R | T | O | O | N |
| H | E | N | L | J | X | D | O | Y | R | M | U |
| C | O | M | E | D | Y | J | J | E | A | U | P |
| A | V | L | O | Z | Y | N | N | U | F | H | M |
| B | R | I | D | A | Y | L | R | O | R | F | N |
| Y | S | U | O | I | R | A | L | I | H | J | O |

CARTOON
COMEDY
FUNNY
GAG
GIGGLE

HILARIOUS
HOWL
HUMOROUS
JEST
JOKE

LAUGH
PUN
SNIGGER
WIT

# 18. ANIMALS

Can you find the hiding animals?

CAT
CHICKENS
COW
DOG
DONKEY
DUCKS
GEESE
GOATS

HAMSTER
HORSE
LAMBS
MICE
PIG
RABBITS
RATS
SHEEP

| S | T | S | C | C | G | H | E | O | O | P | V |
| T | A | H | D | O | G | S | Y | T | T | L | A |
| I | R | E | I | W | R | A | E | S | R | O | H |
| B | V | E | T | H | D | E | K | O | P | C | A |
| B | E | P | I | G | I | R | N | U | I | N | M |
| A | V | C | A | M | O | T | O | A | R | V | S |
| R | R | E | A | X | S | T | D | F | C | A | T |
| E | Y | S | N | E | K | C | I | H | C | S | E |
| S | S | K | C | U | D | H | S | R | O | U | R |
| O | Z | E | H | F | S | B | M | A | L | A | M |
| M | I | C | E | I | L | A | T | T | E | Y | P |
| P | R | O | G | G | O | A | T | S | N | Q | M |

# 19. TOYS!

See how many toys you can find.

BALL
BAT
BICYCLE
BOAT
CRAYONS

DOLL
GAMES
KITE
PAINTS

RATTLE
SKATES
TRAIN
YOYO

| O | T | A | O | B | O | O | C | K | I | B | E |
|---|---|---|---|---|---|---|---|---|---|---|---|
| O | R | R | I | K | N | B | F | E | E | B | T |
| R | A | T | T | L | E | H | O | U | Z | I | T |
| Q | I | U | V | S | N | O | Y | A | R | C | M |
| S | N | O | W | B | R | I | O | X | X | Y | O |
| R | I | A | D | O | L | L | Y | M | K | C | O |
| S | O | W | O | N | L | H | O | P | C | L | N |
| K | H | E | I | M | A | U | W | A | A | E | B |
| A | I | O | T | A | B | S | B | I | L | B | O |
| T | M | C | G | R | A | I | T | N | T | H | N |
| E | B | O | A | P | R | V | E | T | I | K | N |
| S | E | M | A | G | A | Z | Y | S | K | N | E |

# 20. SUPERMARKET

Can you find the items hidden in the store?

BACON
BEANS
BISCUITS
BREAD
BUTTER
CHEESE
COFFEE

EGGS
JAM
MARGARINE
MARMALADE
MILK
PEPPER
SOUP

SUGAR
TEA

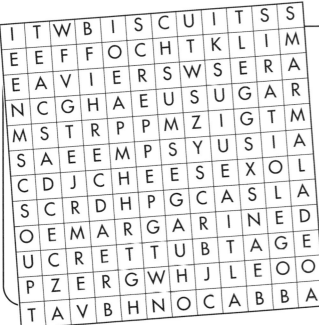

| I | T | W | B | I | S | C | U | I | T | S | S |
|---|---|---|---|---|---|---|---|---|---|---|---|
| E | E | F | F | O | C | H | T | K | L | I | M |
| E | A | V | I | E | R | S | W | S | E | R | A |
| N | C | G | H | A | E | U | S | U | G | A | R |
| M | S | T | R | P | P | M | Z | I | G | T | M |
| S | A | E | E | M | P | S | Y | U | S | I | A |
| C | D | J | C | H | E | E | S | E | X | O | L |
| S | C | R | D | H | P | G | C | A | S | L | A |
| O | E | M | A | R | G | A | R | I | N | E | D |
| U | C | R | E | T | T | U | B | T | A | G | E |
| P | Z | E | R | G | W | H | J | L | E | O | O |
| T | A | V | B | H | N | O | C | A | B | B | A |

# 21. VEGETABLE PATCH

Find the selection of vegetables here.

ARTICHOKE
BROCCOLI
CABBAGE
CARROT
CAULIFLOWER

KALE
LEEKS
ONION
POTATOES
SPINACH

SPROUTS
SQUASH

| J | E | Z | U | C | C | H | I | N | I | V | E |
|---|---|---|---|---|---|---|---|---|---|---|---|
| O | E | R | T | S | Q | U | A | S | H | I | R |
| F | S | S | K | A | L | E | F | R | E | D | E |
| E | I | L | O | C | C | O | R | B | O | E | W |
| S | S | E | D | E | A | U | O | A | L | N | O |
| E | P | G | A | A | R | W | N | O | D | J | L |
| O | I | A | B | U | R | N | I | P | C | E | F |
| T | N | B | E | L | O | Z | O | O | E | Q | I |
| A | A | B | E | T | T | K | N | K | B | X | L |
| T | C | A | T | F | F | J | S | F | B | S | U |
| O | H | C | E | K | O | H | C | I | T | R | A |
| P | A | S | T | U | O | R | P | S | Z | X | C |

# 22. OCEANS AND SEAS

Go sailing! Find the oceans and seas in the grid.

ADRIATIC
ARCTIC
ATLANTIC
ANTARCTIC
BALTIC

BLACK
CARIBBEAN
CASPIAN
DEAD
INDIAN

NORTH
PACIFIC
RED

| | | | | | | | | | | | |
|---|---|---|---|---|---|---|---|---|---|---|---|
| D | E | R | A | H | O | U | B | L | A | C | K |
| R | E | F | B | I | A | T | E | R | R | T | G |
| E | C | A | S | P | I | A | N | O | C | H | P |
| F | I | T | C | P | P | U | F | W | T | I | A |
| C | T | L | D | J | I | V | G | L | I | P | C |
| I | L | A | E | K | E | W | A | K | C | N | I |
| T | A | N | T | A | R | C | T | I | C | A | F |
| A | B | T | F | L | Q | X | G | D | M | I | I |
| I | D | I | K | M | R | Y | I | A | A | D | C |
| R | E | C | A | R | I | B | B | E | A | N | L |
| D | V | U | G | N | S | Z | J | D | W | I | N |
| A | T | H | T | R | O | N | K | T | I | M | O |

---

| | | | | | | | | | | | |
|---|---|---|---|---|---|---|---|---|---|---|---|
| T | H | I | M | B | L | V | K | N | I | S | U |
| O | S | E | L | I | T | E | W | S | T | P | Q |
| P | U | R | R | S | H | A | M | P | O | O | H |
| H | R | Q | U | H | S | A | P | R | I | N | T |
| O | B | W | S | O | A | P | T | S | L | G | A |
| R | H | W | R | W | A | N | T | I | E | E | B |
| D | T | O | W | E | L | C | H | I | T | G | E |
| E | O | E | D | R | L | H | A | F | U | O | L |
| N | O | F | A | U | C | E | T | G | H | I | B |
| T | T | O | O | T | H | P | A | S | T | E | B |
| A | C | A | T | Y | H | O | T | F | A | U | U |
| M | I | R | R | O | R | F | A | T | B | O | B |

# 23. WHAT'S IN THE BATHROOM?

How many things can you find in the bathroom?

BUBBLE BATH
FAUCET
MAT
MIRROR
SHAMPOO

SHOWER
SINK
SOAP
SPONGE
TILES

TOILET
TOOTHBRUSH
TOOTHPASTE
TOWEL

# 24. WHAT'S IN THE KITCHEN?

How many things can you find in the kitchen?

BLENDER
FREEZER
GRILL
KETTLE

MICROWAVE
OVEN
PANS
POTS

REFRIGERATOR
SINK
STOVE
TOASTER

| | | | | | | | | | | | |
|---|---|---|---|---|---|---|---|---|---|---|---|
| R | O | L | P | D | O | T | R | I | F | E | C |
| E | V | S | T | O | V | E | E | B | R | I | I |
| F | E | K | P | K | E | E | D | E | E | A | N |
| R | P | C | I | O | N | S | N | L | E | L | K |
| I | I | W | J | S | E | R | E | A | Z | H | A |
| G | N | P | G | R | I | L | L | C | E | O | Y |
| E | C | O | J | P | U | T | B | K | R | B | L |
| R | E | T | S | A | O | T | O | P | P | U | S |
| A | C | S | S | N | O | T | H | A | T | I | I |
| T | V | A | R | S | S | G | E | H | E | R | N |
| O | X | I | I | P | E | E | L | T | T | E | K |
| R | Z | E | V | A | W | O | R | C | I | M | K |

## 25. BIRDS

How many birds can you spot?

BLACKBIRD
BUDGIE
CANARY
DOVE
HAWK

LAPWING
LARK
LINNET
MAGPIE
NIGHTINGALE

PARROT
PIGEON

| A | C | T | I | C | B | U | N | S | X | Z | N |
|---|---|---|---|---|---|---|---|---|---|---|---|
| P | A | R | R | O | T | Q | R | E | N | V | I |
| R | N | A | T | W | L | A | P | W | I | N | G |
| D | A | R | E | I | B | E | E | F | O | G | H |
| R | R | C | N | B | N | T | X | W | I | N | T |
| I | Y | H | N | C | O | E | W | D | I | R | I |
| B | A | A | I | R | M | P | I | G | E | O | N |
| K | R | A | L | J | A | N | T | A | R | T | G |
| C | W | O | P | S | G | O | G | H | R | S | A |
| A | C | A | T | X | P | W | B | L | O | R | L |
| L | A | T | H | W | I | N | A | D | O | V | E |
| B | U | D | G | I | E | E | W | N | W | F | R |

## 26. GO NUTS!

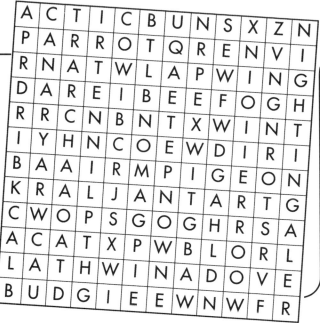

This puzzle will drive you nuts!

ACORN
ALMOND
BRAZIL
CASHEW
CHESTNUT
COCONUT

FILBERT
GROUNDNUT
HAZEL
MACADAMIA
PEANUT
PECAN

PISTACHIO
WALNUT

| G | R | M | A | N | H | C | A | S | H | E | W |
|---|---|---|---|---|---|---|---|---|---|---|---|
| N | X | A | A | L | L | R | T | R | E | U | A |
| B | A | C | O | R | N | L | B | F | U | E | L |
| A | E | A | G | O | F | I | O | I | R | G | N |
| P | S | D | Z | H | A | Z | E | L | I | G | U |
| E | E | A | E | A | H | A | I | B | T | R | T |
| A | L | M | O | N | D | R | P | E | U | D | S |
| N | I | I | T | S | T | B | H | R | N | H | W |
| U | A | A | B | F | S | D | P | T | O | J | R |
| T | N | T | U | N | T | S | E | H | C | K | H |
| G | P | I | S | T | A | C | H | I | O | S | D |
| T | U | N | D | N | U | O | R | G | C | W | R |

## 27. PRIVATE DETECTIVE

Become a private detective and track down these words.

CASE
CLUES
CRIME
DATA
FACTS
FINGERPRINTS
FORENSIC
GUMSHOE

HUNT
IDENTITY
PROOF
SEARCH

SLEUTH
SOLVE

| T | R | F | A | C | T | S | E | E | V | J | K |
|---|---|---|---|---|---|---|---|---|---|---|---|
| O | T | C | R | I | M | E | E | S | T | V | M |
| Y | S | L | E | U | T | H | N | A | V | A | U |
| I | L | U | J | E | V | J | K | M | R | I | T |
| C | E | E | V | E | J | I | G | Y | T | C | Y |
| I | M | S | E | O | N | E | U | T | N | U | H |
| S | J | F | O | O | R | P | O | I | Z | A | C |
| N | A | O | H | L | Q | A | R | T | R | A | I |
| E | C | I | S | K | V | T | E | N | S | O | R |
| R | C | G | M | D | D | E | T | E | T | Y | O |
| O | A | R | U | Y | A | T | A | D | J | A | C |
| F | I | N | G | E | R | P | R | I | N | T | S |

# 28. ROBOTS

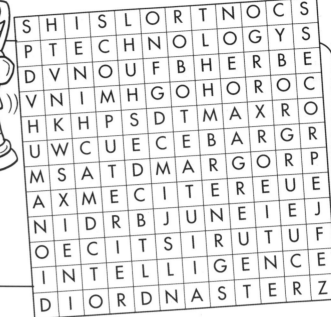

Find the words linked to robots.

ANDROID
COMPUTER
CONTROLS
CYBORG
FUTURISTIC

HUMANOID
INTELLIGENCE
MACHINE
MEMORY
PROCESS

PROGRAM
ROBOT
TECHNOLOGY

| S | H | I | S | L | O | R | T | N | O | C | S |
|---|---|---|---|---|---|---|---|---|---|---|---|
| P | T | E | C | H | N | O | L | O | G | Y | S |
| D | V | N | O | U | F | B | H | E | R | B | E |
| V | N | I | M | H | G | O | H | O | R | O | C |
| H | K | H | P | S | D | T | M | A | X | R | O |
| U | W | C | U | E | C | E | B | A | R | G | R |
| M | S | A | T | D | M | A | R | G | O | R | P |
| A | X | M | E | C | I | T | E | R | E | U | E |
| N | I | D | R | B | J | U | N | E | I | E | J |
| O | E | C | I | T | S | I | R | U | T | U | F |
| I | N | T | E | L | L | I | G | E | N | C | E |
| D | I | O | R | D | N | A | S | T | E | R | Z |

# 29. AROUND THE WORLD

Find the continents and countries in the puzzle.

AFRICA
AMERICA
AUSTRALIA
BELGIUM
BRITAIN
CHINA

EGYPT
FRANCE
GERMANY
ICELAND
ITALY
JAPAN

NORWAY
RUSSIA
SPAIN
SWEDEN

| S | P | A | I | N | Y | I | N | A | P | A | J |
|---|---|---|---|---|---|---|---|---|---|---|---|
| W | K | I | C | O | M | M | M | J | F | M | R |
| E | E | S | E | S | O | U | S | X | E | E | D |
| D | C | S | L | P | N | I | A | T | I | R | B |
| E | D | U | A | L | O | G | H | P | W | I | U |
| N | S | R | N | A | R | L | O | Y | A | C | Z |
| E | C | M | D | V | W | E | U | G | C | A | E |
| C | H | O | A | C | A | B | S | E | I | S | S |
| N | I | T | A | L | Y | E | E | V | R | R | C |
| A | N | D | R | H | I | T | R | E | F | R | I |
| R | A | U | S | T | R | A | L | I | A | I | C |
| F | R | O | I | L | Y | N | A | M | R | E | G |

# 30. GLOBE TROTTERS

Can you find these countries?

AUSTRIA
BRAZIL
CANADA
DENMARK
FINLAND
GREECE

GREENLAND
HOLLAND
HUNGARY
INDIA
MEXICO
PERU

PORTUGAL
SWITZERLAND
THAILAND
TURKEY

| I | A | V | A | L | L | C | A | N | A | D | A |
|---|---|---|---|---|---|---|---|---|---|---|---|
| N | H | M | E | X | I | C | O | F | I | N | U |
| D | U | Y | O | R | Z | N | R | O | B | A | S |
| I | N | E | K | R | A | M | N | E | D | L | T |
| A | G | K | G | R | R | E | A | T | N | R | R |
| X | A | R | E | X | B | W | D | H | A | E | I |
| E | R | U | T | D | F | E | Z | A | L | Z | A |
| C | Y | T | R | U | E | T | E | I | N | T | R |
| E | P | O | R | T | U | G | A | L | I | I | V |
| E | Q | E | R | C | V | G | H | A | F | W | A |
| R | P | C | H | O | L | L | A | N | D | S | L |
| G | R | E | E | N | L | A | N | D | J | R | O |

# 31. CREEPY-CRAWLY

This puzzle is full of creepy-crawly creatures.

BEETLE
BUG
CATERPILLAR
CENTIPEDE
COCKROACH
EARWIG

LADYBUG
NIT
PARASITE
SCORPION
SLUG
SPIDER

TARANTULA
WEEVIL
WORM

| B | I | R | F | S | L | U | G | A | L | O | R |
|---|---|---|---|---|---|---|---|---|---|---|---|
| C | E | G | R | E | A | C | U | T | Y | O | A |
| O | K | E | X | D | G | U | B | Y | D | A | L |
| C | A | A | T | I | Q | I | O | T | R | S | L |
| K | K | R | R | L | M | R | O | W | I | C | I |
| R | D | W | A | E | E | W | L | E | F | G | P |
| O | O | I | J | S | P | I | D | E | R | B | R |
| A | K | G | A | P | T | O | V | V | W | X | E |
| C | A | Y | P | A | R | A | S | I | T | E | T |
| H | T | A | R | A | N | T | U | L | A | R | A |
| A | I | H | E | D | E | P | I | T | N | E | C |
| J | N | O | I | P | R | O | C | S | Z | O | I |

# 32. INCREDIBLE INSECTS!

Can you find the insects?

ANT
BLUEBOTTLE
BUTTERFLY
FIREFLY
FLEA

GNAT
GREENFLY
HORNET
LOCUST
MIDGE

MOSQUITO
MOTH
TICK
WASP

| F | I | R | E | F | L | Y | T | H | O | C | E |
|---|---|---|---|---|---|---|---|---|---|---|---|
| L | P | R | I | B | C | Z | W | T | A | N | G |
| E | S | H | O | R | N | E | T | R | E | P | D |
| A | S | T | I | R | S | H | I | J | L | O | I |
| I | G | M | O | O | C | W | C | I | T | N | M |
| T | R | D | O | P | A | R | K | V | T | M | A |
| P | E | D | O | T | I | U | Q | S | O | M | R |
| T | E | P | Z | O | H | I | V | S | B | V | T |
| P | N | S | S | I | G | M | T | O | E | T | O |
| T | F | A | H | A | R | L | O | C | U | S | T |
| X | L | W | A | F | R | E | R | S | L | U | S |
| I | Y | L | F | R | E | T | T | U | B | U | H |

# 33. GOBBLEDYGOOK

All these words mean utter nonsense!

BLAH
BLETHER
DAFT
DRIVEL
FABLE
FLAPDOODLE
GOBBLEDYGOOK

FLIMFLAM
NONSENSE
PRATTLE
ROT
SILLY
STUPID

| Z | A | H | P | P | Y | L | L | I | S | Y | O |
|---|---|---|---|---|---|---|---|---|---|---|---|
| A | N | S | A | B | R | B | B | U | H | R | O |
| G | O | B | B | L | E | D | Y | G | O | O | K |
| M | N | O | W | T | B | L | A | G | H | T | F |
| M | S | C | A | R | T | E | B | F | S | L | B |
| A | E | H | F | A | B | L | E | M | T | A | L |
| L | N | A | F | L | E | T | B | I | U | N | E |
| F | S | F | L | E | S | T | E | T | P | C | T |
| M | E | Q | I | V | A | A | L | U | I | E | H |
| I | A | U | N | I | N | R | G | L | D | T | E |
| L | Z | I | B | R | R | P | I | B | D | U | R |
| F | L | A | P | D | O | O | D | L | E | I | R |

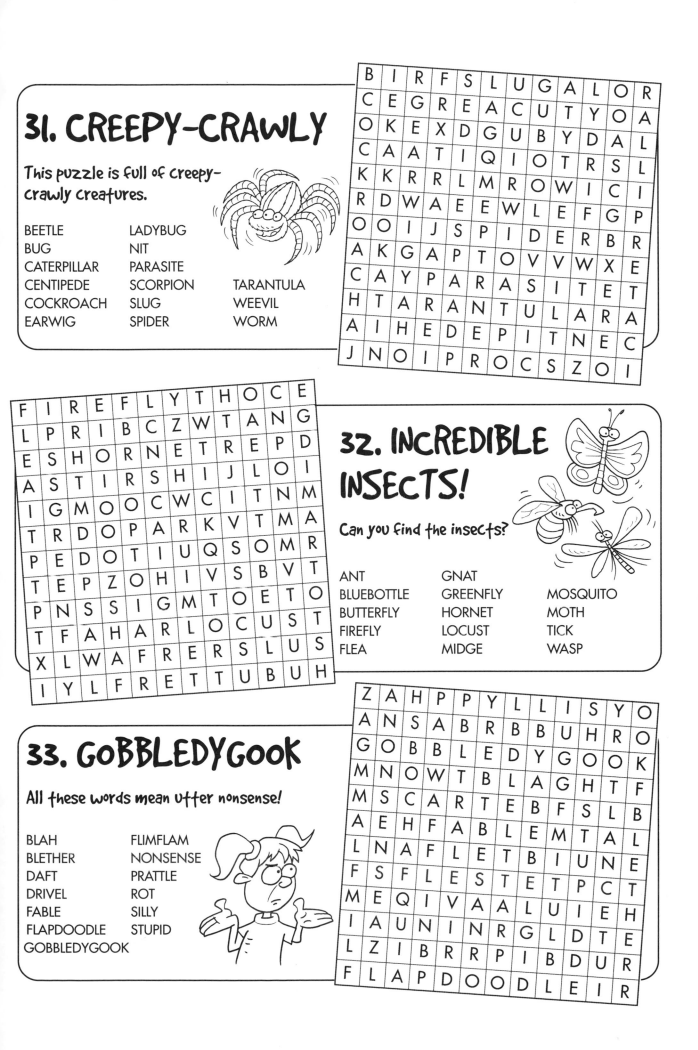

# 34. MUSICAL INSTRUMENTS

Can you find the instruments?

BAGPIPES
BANJO
BELLS
FLUTE
GUITAR

HARMONICA
KAZOO
KEYBOARD
OBOE
PIANO

RECORDER
TAMBOURINE
VIOLA
VIOLIN

| | | | | | | | | | | | |
|---|---|---|---|---|---|---|---|---|---|---|---|
| B | R | I | P | J | U | S | O | O | Z | A | K |
| A | G | U | I | T | A | R | S | R | I | E | E |
| C | T | N | A | A | R | U | O | E | P | N | Y |
| I | E | R | N | W | T | L | I | D | M | I | B |
| N | I | L | O | I | V | E | L | R | W | R | O |
| O | R | A | I | T | I | S | R | O | Q | U | A |
| M | B | A | N | J | O | O | L | C | U | O | R |
| R | E | O | D | F | L | U | T | E | O | B | D |
| A | L | R | E | F | A | Y | R | R | I | M | R |
| H | L | U | T | E | I | T | G | N | S | A | A |
| L | S | V | E | S | H | O | P | I | E | T | T |
| O | S | C | S | E | P | I | P | G | A | B | H |

# 35. 'A' WORDS

All these words start with the letter A.

ABACUS
ACROBAT
ALADDIN
ALASKA
AMAZON
AMBER

APOLLO
APRIL
AQUAMARINE
ART
ASTRONAUT
ASTRONOMY

ATLAS
AUGUST
AZURE

| | | | | | | | | | | | |
|---|---|---|---|---|---|---|---|---|---|---|---|
| A | S | T | R | O | N | A | U | T | G | O | R |
| S | P | R | V | E | A | T | D | R | C | J | N |
| T | A | Q | U | A | M | A | R | I | N | E | C |
| R | P | A | T | A | B | O | R | C | A | B | E |
| O | R | A | C | U | E | A | W | T | K | L | D |
| N | I | A | R | C | R | T | C | S | J | O | S |
| O | L | L | O | P | A | A | Z | U | R | E | A |
| M | R | A | N | A | L | B | A | G | S | R | L |
| Y | O | D | I | D | O | S | O | U | O | S | A |
| F | W | D | N | O | Z | A | M | A | L | V | S |
| D | L | I | S | C | I | T | R | O | L | W | K |
| M | M | N | B | B | S | A | L | T | A | Q | A |

# 36. MORE 'A' WORDS

Again, every word begins with the letter A.

ACTION
ADVENTURE
ALMOND
ALPHABET
APPLE
APRICOT
APRON
ARCADE

ARCTIC
ARENA
ARITHMETIC
ASTEROID
ATMOSPHERE
ATTIC
AUBURN

| | | | | | | | | | | | |
|---|---|---|---|---|---|---|---|---|---|---|---|
| H | E | R | E | H | P | S | O | M | T | A | U |
| A | M | I | L | K | I | R | O | S | E | R | H |
| D | N | O | M | L | A | A | R | C | T | I | C |
| V | B | E | W | A | A | P | P | L | E | T | O |
| E | U | A | S | T | E | R | O | I | D | H | U |
| N | Z | N | T | M | C | I | T | T | A | M | S |
| T | Z | E | I | A | R | C | A | D | E | E | R |
| U | R | S | T | P | K | O | H | A | W | T | C |
| R | A | N | E | R | A | T | K | I | T | I | Z |
| E | S | E | I | O | N | N | O | I | T | C | A |
| A | T | O | M | N | R | U | B | U | A | S | Q |
| A | L | P | H | A | B | E | T | K | A | J | U |

# 37. BIRTHDAYS!

All these words are associated with birthdays.

CAKE
CANDLES
CELEBRATE
DANCING
DECORATIONS
FRIENDS

FUN
GAMES
GIFTS
HAPPY
HATS
ICING

MUSIC
PARTY
PRESENTS
SINGING
WISH

| S | R | I | B | O | G | I | F | T | S | N | S |
|---|---|---|---|---|---|---|---|---|---|---|---|
| I | C | I | N | G | O | R | D | E | N | U | F |
| N | W | H | I | T | E | B | L | A | C | O | K |
| G | N | I | C | N | A | D | T | R | I | P | S |
| I | S | C | E | L | E | B | R | A | T | E | H |
| N | H | A | P | P | Y | C | H | D | A | R | O |
| G | E | K | S | T | N | E | S | E | R | P | R |
| M | E | E | R | Y | A | W | O | R | O | L | P |
| U | S | T | A | H | D | R | A | S | C | L | A |
| S | L | A | R | T | S | G | A | M | E | S | R |
| I | C | R | O | F | R | I | E | N | D | S | T |
| C | A | N | D | L | E | S | W | F | G | H | Y |

# 38. DOGS

Find the dogs in the word puzzle.

BASSET
BEAGLE
CHOW
CORGI
DACHSHUND

DOBERMAN
LABRADOR
PEKINESE
POMERANIAN
ROTTWEILER

SETTER
SHEEPDOG
WOLFHOUND

| R | E | L | G | A | E | B | D | B | P | W | Y |
|---|---|---|---|---|---|---|---|---|---|---|---|
| O | G | J | A | L | S | A | T | I | O | N | O |
| T | O | N | S | O | S | S | X | H | M | W | A |
| T | E | A | M | V | H | S | C | T | E | O | B |
| W | E | M | H | H | E | E | A | M | R | L | E |
| E | R | R | I | E | E | T | S | I | A | F | S |
| I | S | E | S | R | P | O | J | H | N | H | E |
| L | A | B | R | A | D | O | R | T | I | O | N |
| E | Z | O | L | G | O | R | M | T | A | U | I |
| R | D | D | R | I | G | R | O | C | N | N | K |
| A | R | D | N | U | H | S | H | C | A | D | E |
| A | S | E | T | T | E | R | H | A | P | I | P |

# 39. MORE DOGS

Discover the dogs hidden here.

AIREDALE
BLOODHOUND
BOXER
BULLDOG
CHIHUAHUA

COLLIE
DALMATIAN
GREYHOUND
NEWFOUNDLAND
HUSKY

POODLE
PUG
SPANIEL
WHIPPET

| A | D | O | G | I | L | E | I | N | A | P | S |
|---|---|---|---|---|---|---|---|---|---|---|---|
| C | A | I | R | E | D | A | L | E | I | O | T |
| D | L | E | E | A | D | E | R | S | T | O | B |
| N | M | A | V | C | R | O | I | L | C | D | L |
| U | A | U | B | O | X | E | R | A | H | L | O |
| O | T | B | U | L | L | D | O | G | I | E | O |
| H | I | I | K | L | S | C | U | E | H | I | D |
| Y | A | W | H | I | P | P | E | T | U | U | H |
| E | N | C | O | E | T | E | A | C | A | L | O |
| R | M | P | U | T | Y | K | S | U | H | A | U |
| G | E | R | B | I | E | F | O | P | U | C | N |
| N | E | W | F | O | U | N | D | L | A | N | D |

# 40. TRAIN STATION

Find the words associated with trains.

CARS
DRIVER
LOCO
PASSENGERS
PLATFORM

RAILROAD
SHUNTER
SIGNALS
SLEEPER

TICKETS
TIMETABLE
WHISTLE

| B | S | D | A | O | R | L | I | A | R | H | W |
|---|---|---|---|---|---|---|---|---|---|---|---|
| R | E | A | D | S | T | E | K | C | I | T | H |
| S | D | R | I | V | E | R | I | V | A | I | I |
| R | E | E | A | W | I | F | E | A | L | M | S |
| E | A | P | S | I | G | N | A | L | S | E | T |
| F | V | E | E | I | L | O | C | O | L | T | L |
| F | I | E | S | T | B | S | D | E | P | A | E |
| X | P | L | A | T | F | O | R | M | D | B | P |
| B | S | S | U | N | N | E | A | W | S | L | P |
| A | R | U | R | E | T | N | U | H | S | E | A |
| W | A | R | G | H | O | R | G | S | Q | U | I |
| T | C | S | R | E | G | N | E | S | S | A | P |

# 41. FOOTBALL CRAZY

Search for the football words.

BALL
COACH
DEFENSE
END ZONE
FIELD
FLAG

HUDDLE
KICK
PASS
PENALTY
POINTS
REFEREE

TACKLE
TEAM
TOUCHDOWN

| R | S | T | B | S | L | P | A | S | S | E | E |
|---|---|---|---|---|---|---|---|---|---|---|---|
| I | M | A | E | T | U | H | U | E | D | S | N |
| T | L | C | W | E | V | E | O | F | O | U | D |
| L | M | K | I | N | E | L | F | E | R | B | Z |
| I | R | L | H | T | M | D | I | R | D | S | O |
| K | R | E | I | I | A | D | E | E | B | E | N |
| S | E | F | K | N | N | U | L | E | O | S | E |
| T | F | T | O | U | C | H | D | O | W | N | I |
| N | E | F | L | A | G | C | I | K | A | E | O |
| I | R | A | R | E | E | R | O | C | S | F | N |
| O | E | C | O | A | C | H | K | I | N | E | A |
| P | E | N | A | L | T | Y | E | K | E | D | F |

# 42. COWBOY RANCH

Find the ranching words.

BRONCO
CATTLE
CHAPS
COWBOY
HORSE
LARIAT
LASSO
PRAIRIE

RANCH
RANGER
SADDLE
SHEEP
SPURS
STETSON
TROUGH

| R | E | G | N | A | R | D | R | H | A | W | R |
|---|---|---|---|---|---|---|---|---|---|---|---|
| A | S | C | A | R | F | B | R | O | N | C | O |
| R | T | R | U | E | B | E | X | R | I | O | U |
| S | E | I | R | I | A | R | P | S | E | V | J |
| T | R | O | U | G | H | V | E | E | A | C | B |
| E | E | C | A | T | T | L | E | L | G | F | E |
| T | W | O | D | B | A | V | H | O | U | S | A |
| S | E | W | I | S | O | B | S | R | E | S | H |
| O | I | B | S | V | P | L | S | P | A | H | C |
| N | E | O | A | E | V | U | P | A | R | K | N |
| S | D | Y | D | S | L | A | R | I | A | T | A |
| J | O | J | E | L | D | D | A | S | W | O | R |

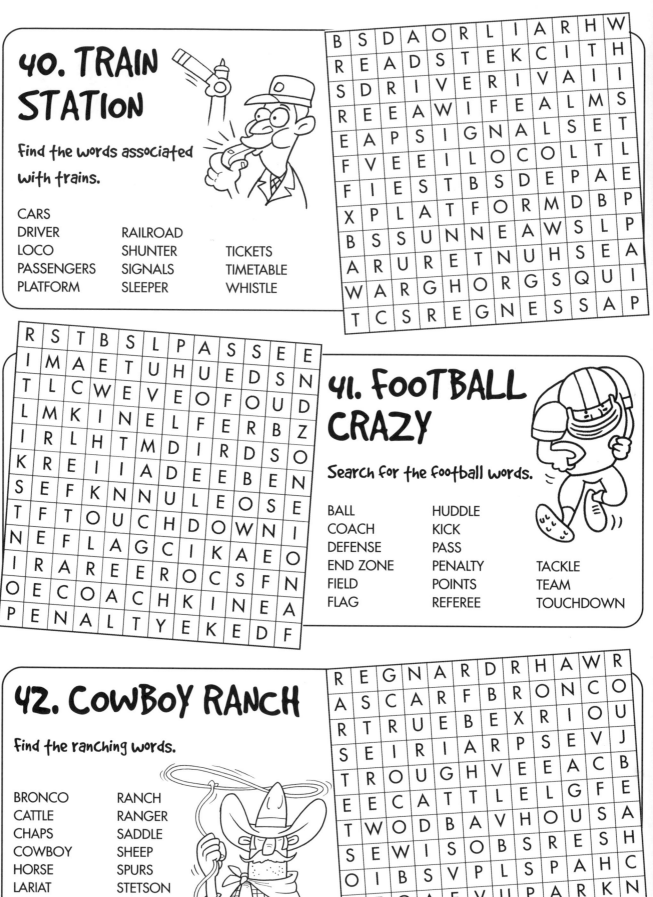

# 43. CIRCUS

Find the words linked to the circus.

ACROBAT     JUGGLE     SHOWS
ACTS     LIONS     TIGERS
CLOWNS     MAGIC     TRAINER
ELEPHANTS     RIGGING     TRAPEZE
HORSES     RING     TENT

| E | L | G | G | U | J | I | G | Z | I | P | Z |
|---|---|---|---|---|---|---|---|---|---|---|---|
| L | W | I | P | T | R | A | P | E | Z | E | B |
| E | C | M | A | G | I | C | R | T | D | Y | I |
| P | J | R | F | E | N | P | J | A | C | T | S |
| H | G | N | I | G | G | I | R | B | L | E | H |
| A | S | D | F | N | E | O | F | O | O | S | O |
| N | E | O | R | D | S | B | K | R | W | U | W |
| T | S | E | S | R | O | H | Z | C | N | J | S |
| S | A | R | E | S | D | S | T | A | S | G | K |
| R | O | G | W | J | A | E | W | E | B | E | E |
| L | I | O | N | S | R | T | Q | V | N | F | N |
| T | R | A | I | N | E | R | R | A | R | T | O |

# 44. COMPUTERS

Use your skills to find the computer words.

| | | |
|---|---|---|
| COMPUTER | KEYBOARD | |
| DESKTOP | INPUT | MOUSE |
| DISK | LAPTOP | NET |
| FONT | MAIL | PRINTER |
| GAMES | MEMORY | SOFTWARE |
| HARDWARE | MODEM | WEB |

| D | E | R | D | R | A | O | B | Y | E | K | U |
|---|---|---|---|---|---|---|---|---|---|---|---|
| E | I | D | R | E | T | N | I | R | P | S | D |
| S | E | V | R | R | E | S | U | O | M | I | R |
| K | R | I | F | I | F | D | Z | M | C | D | O |
| T | C | B | I | O | S | E | U | E | R | O | H |
| O | R | A | N | V | E | S | E | M | A | G | A |
| P | O | T | P | A | L | N | H | A | M | R | R |
| R | A | I | U | T | O | I | P | Y | E | R | D |
| T | H | W | T | T | I | T | A | E | D | G | W |
| N | Z | B | R | E | T | U | P | M | O | C | A |
| R | E | V | L | E | M | K | L | T | M | A | R |
| W | A | T | F | S | O | F | T | W | A | R | E |

# 45. STAR SIGNS

Search for the star signs in this zodiac puzzle.

| | | |
|---|---|---|
| ARIES | GOAT | |
| AQUARIUS | LEO | |
| BULL | LIBRA | SCORPIO |
| CAPRICORN | LION | TAURUS |
| CRAB | PISCES | TWINS |
| FISH | RAM | VIRGO |
| GEMINI | SAGITTARIUS | ZODIAC |

| S | C | O | R | P | I | O | T | L | A | M | D |
|---|---|---|---|---|---|---|---|---|---|---|---|
| A | S | A | R | D | N | W | A | R | I | E | S |
| G | O | A | T | A | I | W | U | A | Y | O | V |
| I | E | S | E | N | M | R | R | M | T | E | N |
| T | A | V | S | L | E | P | U | H | I | L | E |
| T | A | R | F | E | G | E | S | C | L | T | P |
| A | R | B | I | L | G | R | P | A | L | E | O |
| R | E | A | S | C | O | H | I | I | U | T | G |
| I | B | R | H | W | I | J | S | D | B | O | R |
| U | U | C | A | P | R | I | C | O | R | N | I |
| S | Q | U | E | R | T | E | E | Z | I | S | V |
| A | Q | U | A | R | I | U | S | H | I | P | Y |

# 46. HERBS

Find the herbs hidden in the puzzle.

BASIL
BAY LEAF
CHERVIL
CHIVES
CORIANDER
DILL

FENNEL
MARJORAM
MINT
PARSLEY
ROSEMARY
SAGE

SAVORY
THYME

| S | E | T | A | F | A | E | L | Y | A | B | L |
|---|---|---|---|---|---|---|---|---|---|---|---|
| A | M | A | R | J | O | R | A | M | C | A | R |
| L | Y | S | P | E | P | O | R | I | C | S | O |
| R | H | S | A | T | M | A | N | N | H | I | S |
| E | T | K | I | G | M | I | X | T | E | L | E |
| D | O | F | E | X | E | E | M | J | R | K | M |
| N | R | L | E | N | N | E | F | D | V | D | A |
| A | J | L | O | E | V | A | Z | A | I | T | R |
| I | C | I | Q | Z | P | A | R | S | L | E | Y |
| R | E | D | R | L | I | F | T | E | X | E | R |
| O | S | T | S | A | V | O | R | Y | O | U | W |
| C | H | I | V | E | S | O | N | D | A | R | O |

# 47. CHRISTMAS

Find these Christmas time words.

CARDS
CAROLS
CHIMNEY
CHRISTMAS
DECEMBER
ELVES
GARLANDS

GIFTS
HOLLY
MISTLETOE
SLEIGH
TINSEL
TOYS
TREE

# 48. FESTIVE FUN

And these festive ones, too!

BAUBLES
CANDLES
CHESTNUTS
COLD
DECORATIONS
FAIRY
FEAST

LIGHTS
REINDEER
RUDOLPH
SANTA
SNOW
STAR
YULETIDE

| S | D | R | A | C | B | S | U | V | K | A | Y |
|---|---|---|---|---|---|---|---|---|---|---|---|
| V | E | A | T | R | R | E | A | K | F | A | S |
| M | C | H | R | I | S | T | M | A | S | D | S |
| I | E | Q | E | C | E | B | D | E | R | Y | T |
| S | M | Y | E | R | S | C | A | R | O | L | S |
| T | B | J | T | I | M | H | N | T | A | T | D |
| L | E | K | N | H | G | I | E | L | S | N | N |
| E | R | K | A | S | R | M | A | E | S | M | A |
| T | I | L | E | P | H | N | P | S | R | W | L |
| O | U | V | N | D | F | E | V | N | F | A | R |
| E | L | H | O | L | L | Y | D | I | Y | I | A |
| E | D | H | S | T | D | B | S | T | F | I | G |

| R | U | D | O | L | P | H | F | A | I | R | Y |
|---|---|---|---|---|---|---|---|---|---|---|---|
| E | A | R | T | C | H | J | K | E | S | W | U |
| I | F | A | V | R | T | S | T | H | G | I | L |
| N | E | V | E | Y | J | T | S | Z | S | H | E |
| D | S | E | L | B | U | A | B | A | T | T | T |
| E | C | R | S | I | S | R | T | N | U | A | I |
| E | H | T | F | E | A | S | T | A | N | S | D |
| R | A | T | M | E | L | E | M | O | T | N | E |
| W | T | I | F | W | M | D | S | A | S | H | U |
| O | N | C | O | L | D | B | N | M | E | F | D |
| R | A | N | F | A | D | R | D | A | H | J | K |
| K | S | N | O | I | T | A | R | O | C | E | D |

# 49. FIRE STATION

All the words here are linked to a fire station.

AXE
BELL
ENGINE
FIRE
FOAM
HELMETS
HOSE
LADDER
MASKS
POLE
RADIO
RESCUE
TURNTABLE
UNIFORM
WATER

```
W O F F U N I F O R M I
D R A I T E R E T A W I
A R K O R I F T C D O D
J O N R S E C B L I V E
E L O P S L V R E O S N
F A A S L B E L L A K T
O D L O S A R A H S S R
R D T B O T I C B T A E
E E N G I N E H U O M S
S R D D N R A S T A G C
H E A R Y U S K O S X U
H E L M E T S F R H U E
```

# 50. 'B' WORDS

Find the words starting with the letter B.

BAMBOOZLE
BANANA
BAT
BAUBLE
BEAUTY
BEEHIVE
BILLION
BINOCULARS
BLOSSOM
BLUEBELL
BOAT
BONFIRE
BOOK
BOX
BOY
BREAD
BREAKFAST
BUBBLE
BUTTER
BUZZ

```
F B H B I B M B L B T A
B I N O C U L A R S A C
L L E N B T M N I M O T
O L V F L T D A E R B T
S I I I U E O N L A J S
S O H R E R R A U J K A
O N E E B I N B O Y Y F
M S E V E X L U O R T K
R S B K L E A J B F U A
X A O G I C K G U I A E
B O B A M B O O Z L E R
B U B B L E V R Z S B B
```

# 51. PUZZLE WORDS

All these words have something to do with puzzles.

ANSWER
CLUES
CODE
CRYPTIC
ENIGMA
GRID
JIGSAW
LOGIC
MAZE
MIND
MYSTERY
PUZZLE
RIDDLE
QUIZ
SOLUTIONS
WORDSEARCH

```
W A I C R Y P T I C R O
O K E J C R U Z O O C E
R Y N A R A Z A Q U I Z
D N I M E B Z X G D G A
S R G R W A L C L U O M
E R M Y S T E R Y F L A
A A A A N E J I G S A W
R H Z D A I E D O C K O
C R B R I V E D L L S O
H P O T B R W L D U D F
Q U E O M I G E W E R I
A S N O I T U L O S O H
```

# 52. COOL!

This wordsearch is really cool.

ARCTIC
CHILLY
COLD
COOL
FREEZING
FROSTBITE

GLACIER
HAILSTONE
ICELAND
POLAR
SLEET
SNOWFLAKE

SNOWSTORM
WINTRY

| I | C | H | I | L | L | Y | D | D | V | I | W |
|---|---|---|---|---|---|---|---|---|---|---|---|
| R | R | B | A | L | K | R | G | J | Y | C | I | N |
| I | A | S | N | O | W | F | L | A | K | E | N |
| R | L | N | I | U | N | R | L | R | O | L | T |
| C | O | O | E | C | O | O | L | C | A | A | R | Y |
| S | P | W | V | O | Y | S | U | T | I | N | Y |
| T | E | S | I | L | J | T | R | I | O | D | E |
| E | D | T | H | D | N | B | I | C | T | L | L |
| E | N | O | T | S | L | I | A | H | V | E | A |
| L | J | R | N | I | O | T | R | H | X | S | E |
| S | T | M | I | O | R | E | I | C | A | L | G |
| B | R | U | E | G | N | I | Z | E | E | R | F |

# 53. IT'S A JUNGLE!

Find the animals and creatures hidden here.

CHEETAH
CHIMP
COUGAR
GECKO
GIRAFFE

GORILLA
JAGUAR
MONKEY
MOSQUITO
PANTHER

TIGER
VIPER
VULTURE
ZEBRA

| M | O | S | Q | U | I | T | O | L | D | G | W |
|---|---|---|---|---|---|---|---|---|---|---|---|
| O | S | T | K | T | A | K | W | I | W | O | I |
| N | O | R | T | K | C | A | J | K | E | R | F |
| K | V | T | I | E | E | F | F | A | R | I | G |
| E | I | H | G | R | H | O | L | R | O | L | E |
| Y | R | I | E | E | C | G | D | B | L | L | R |
| E | I | M | R | P | C | H | E | E | T | A | H |
| D | P | O | M | I | O | I | H | Z | U | S | W |
| A | C | I | F | V | U | L | T | U | R | E | H |
| D | H | U | S | A | G | I | R | I | L | P | A |
| C | R | P | A | J | A | G | U | A | R | Z | V |
| R | A | F | X | E | R | E | H | T | N | A | P |

# 54. JUNGLE FUN!

Hunt for even more hidden animals and creatures.

ANTELOPE
APE
COBRA
CROCODILE
ELEPHANT
HIPPO
HYENA
LEOPARD

LION
OCELOT
PIRANHA
SNAKE
SPIDER
RHINO

| S | A | N | D | S | R | U | C | O | B | R | A |
|---|---|---|---|---|---|---|---|---|---|---|---|
| P | I | R | A | N | H | A | R | D | A | X | X |
| I | A | R | V | A | E | D | O | N | I | H | R |
| D | G | H | H | K | J | T | C | S | H | L | O |
| E | O | A | M | E | D | B | O | P | P | I | H |
| R | R | N | O | O | Y | J | D | I | F | O | R |
| I | B | T | N | G | I | E | I | I | O | N | O |
| A | N | E | Y | H | L | S | L | D | C | Z | S |
| S | F | L | J | L | R | E | E | M | E | D | E |
| L | E | O | P | A | R | D | D | O | L | L | S |
| E | M | P | P | N | I | C | N | W | O | L | I |
| M | A | E | L | E | P | H | A | N | T | I | G |

# 55. 'C' WORDS

All these words begin with the letter C.

CAFE
CALCULATOR
CALENDAR
CANDLE
CARAMEL
CARNIVAL

CARTOON
CAT
CAVE
CHARM
CHEF
CHERRY

CHOCOLATE
CINDERELLA
CINEMA
COCOA
COMET
CREAM

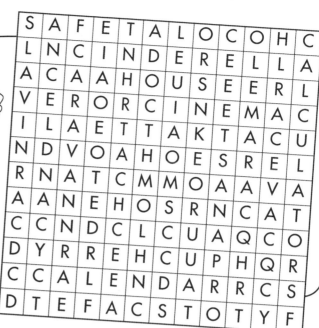

| S | A | F | E | T | A | L | O | C | O | H | C |
|---|---|---|---|---|---|---|---|---|---|---|---|
| L | N | C | I | N | D | E | R | E | L | L | A |
| A | C | A | A | H | O | U | S | E | E | R | L |
| V | E | R | O | R | C | I | N | E | M | A | C |
| I | L | A | E | T | T | A | K | T | A | C | U |
| N | D | V | O | A | H | O | E | S | R | E | L |
| R | N | A | T | C | M | M | O | A | A | V | A |
| A | A | N | E | H | O | S | R | N | C | A | T |
| C | C | N | D | C | L | C | U | A | Q | C | O |
| D | Y | R | R | E | H | C | U | P | H | Q | R |
| C | C | A | L | E | N | D | A | R | R | C | S |
| D | T | E | F | A | C | S | T | O | T | Y | F |

| S | E | L | Z | Z | A | D | F | R | E | S | I |
|---|---|---|---|---|---|---|---|---|---|---|---|
| E | S | V | D | E | C | E | M | B | E | R | F |
| C | T | R | O | I | R | S | U | D | H | U | R |
| R | G | A | O | D | A | S | P | D | O | A | O |
| E | G | R | D | A | D | E | O | A | U | S | G |
| D | N | D | L | D | A | R | K | R | R | O | H |
| A | I | C | E | F | G | T | G | J | S | N | E |
| I | W | Y | E | M | D | Y | N | A | M | I | C |
| S | A | L | L | P | P | A | A | L | E | D | N |
| Y | R | I | A | D | I | L | S | L | V | T | A |
| S | D | A | N | D | E | L | I | O | N | F | D |
| W | I | D | H | G | E | O | N | D | U | C | K |

# 56. 'D' WORDS

Look for the words beginning with the letter D.

DAILY
DAIRY
DAISY
DANCE
DANDELION
DARK

DATE
DAZZLE
DECEMBER
DESSERT
DINOSAUR
DOODLE

DOVE
DRAWING
DUCK
DYNAMIC

# 57. DESERT

Have a look for these desert words.

CACTI
CAMELS
DATES
DESERT
DUNES
DRY

GOATS
HAZE
HEAT
LIZARDS
MIRAGE
OASIS

PALMS
SAHARA
SANDSTORM
SCORPION
WATER

| Z | O | N | E | R | K | R | E | T | A | W | E |
|---|---|---|---|---|---|---|---|---|---|---|---|
| H | A | P | P | M | I | R | A | G | E | E | R |
| S | T | U | A | H | C | A | C | T | I | P | D |
| A | E | Y | Y | L | A | C | T | I | R | G | U |
| N | R | Q | U | E | M | S | D | A | M | O | N |
| D | A | T | E | S | E | S | S | I | N | A | E |
| S | H | D | N | V | L | N | D | H | J | T | S |
| T | E | B | D | E | S | E | R | T | N | S | T |
| O | A | S | I | S | A | H | A | R | A | O | R |
| R | T | T | R | S | C | E | Z | A | H | S | I |
| M | R | S | C | O | R | P | I | O | N | I | S |
| H | A | W | T | R | I | X | L | F | I | N | G |

## 58. BIRDS

How many birds can you spot?

CUCKOO     ROBIN
CROW     ROOK
DUCK     SPARROW
FLAMINGO     STORK
JACKDAW     SWALLOW
RAVEN     VULTURE

| G | E | T | A | W | A | F | R | O | B | I | N |
|---|---|---|---|---|---|---|---|---|---|---|---|
| R | O | O | K | F | F | E | R | S | W | E | Z |
| A | M | T | R | O | R | S | E | T | O | K | I |
| V | R | E | O | E | E | R | U | T | L | U | V |
| E | L | Q | T | T | N | H | X | N | L | I | P |
| N | I | U | S | Y | K | I | E | C | A | B | M |
| A | N | D | J | A | C | K | D | A | W | O | T |
| V | S | U | Y | U | R | E | L | E | S | S | I |
| A | E | C | C | W | O | K | U | S | T | O | P |
| L | P | K | R | E | W | O | R | R | A | P | S |
| O | O | R | T | I | N | I | R | A | S | R | Y |
| O | G | N | I | M | A | L | F | L | U | P | T |

## 59. PIZZA PICK

Pick out all the different toppings and types of pizza.

ANCHOVY     MOZZARELLA
BACON     OLIVES
CHEESE     ONIONS     PINEAPPLE
FROZEN     PAN     SAUSAGE
GARLIC     PEPPERONI     SPICY
HAM     PEPPERS     TOMATO

| S | G | E | C | U | F | V | B | A | C | O | N |
|---|---|---|---|---|---|---|---|---|---|---|---|
| O | Y | V | O | H | C | N | A | C | R | R | O |
| G | O | O | G | L | H | A | N | T | H | E | L |
| A | P | E | P | P | E | R | O | N | I | M | O |
| R | I | C | E | D | E | A | V | E | N | M | T |
| L | N | U | D | G | S | X | S | F | E | E | A |
| I | E | A | L | L | E | R | A | Z | Z | O | M |
| C | A | S | N | S | X | Z | U | I | O | N | O |
| S | P | A | R | R | S | M | S | H | R | I | T |
| S | P | I | C | Y | O | R | A | S | F | O | W |
| O | L | I | V | E | S | G | G | H | R | N | W |
| P | E | P | P | E | R | S | E | T | E | S | I |

## 60. SUMMER

Search for the summer words.

HAPPY     JULY
HEATWAVE     MIDSUMMER     SUMMERTIME
HOLIDAY     PICNIC     SUNSHINE
HOT     SAND     SWIMMING
JUNE     SEA     WARM

| E | V | A | W | T | A | E | H | S | G | O | O |
|---|---|---|---|---|---|---|---|---|---|---|---|
| D | E | L | O | V | J | R | S | W | A | R | M |
| S | G | C | D | J | U | N | E | I | S | T | I |
| E | U | S | N | A | L | V | N | M | A | R | D |
| S | Y | N | A | R | Y | O | R | M | D | U | S |
| S | A | A | S | P | I | C | N | I | C | S | U |
| A | D | L | J | H | K | O | P | N | V | I | M |
| L | I | R | H | A | I | I | N | G | U | M | M |
| G | L | D | T | P | B | N | E | A | R | S | E |
| N | O | O | C | P | L | E | E | T | H | V | R |
| U | H | R | D | Y | Y | O | G | M | I | S | S |
| S | S | U | M | M | E | R | T | I | M | E | T |

# 61. HALLOWEEN

It's Halloween! Can you find the ghostly words?

APPLES
BAT
CANDLES
COSTUME
GHOSTS

HALLOWEEN
LANTERN
MASK
OCTOBER
PARTY

PUMPKIN
WARLOCK
WITCH

| C | U | P | U | M | P | K | I | N | G | S | H |
|---|---|---|---|---|---|---|---|---|---|---|---|
| H | C | T | I | W | H | A | P | O | H | H | K |
| A | P | R | I | E | M | U | T | S | O | C | B |
| L | A | N | T | E | R | N | R | Y | S | A | L |
| L | I | Y | W | N | E | A | E | Y | T | I | U |
| O | N | P | A | Y | T | R | A | P | S | V | E |
| W | C | I | R | C | L | E | C | R | O | V | F |
| E | D | T | L | H | S | E | L | D | N | A | C |
| E | O | B | O | S | E | A | E | I | B | S | I |
| N | L | O | C | B | S | E | L | P | P | A | R |
| M | A | S | K | D | E | A | V | A | L | S | E |
| G | I | R | L | M | L | R | H | A | F | I | M |

---

# 62. SCARY STUFF!

Monsters, ghouls, and werewolves! See if you can find them.

BEASTS
BROOMS
CREEPY
EERIE
FAIRIES
GHOULS

GOBLINS
HAUNTED
MONSTERS
SPELLS
TREATS
WEBS

WEIRD
WEREWOLF
WIZARD

| R | E | W | R | F | L | O | W | E | R | E | W |
|---|---|---|---|---|---|---|---|---|---|---|---|
| M | O | E | X | A | L | E | D | E | F | T | I |
| O | F | B | V | I | I | D | E | C | B | S | Z |
| N | T | S | H | R | A | G | Y | R | C | T | A |
| S | E | J | D | I | D | R | H | G | I | A | R |
| T | B | W | S | E | H | A | U | N | T | E | D |
| E | C | K | S | S | S | G | H | S | H | R | R |
| R | R | J | H | T | X | L | V | M | A | T | A |
| S | L | L | E | P | S | D | U | O | R | J | A |
| Q | E | A | R | C | Y | A | I | O | K | F | C |
| Y | P | E | E | R | C | D | E | R | H | R | O |
| Z | X | D | T | S | N | I | L | B | O | G | O |

---

# 63. SWEET TREATS

See how many things you can find in the shop.

BISCUITS
CANDY
CUPCAKE
ECLAIR
FLAN
MALLOWS

MERINGUE
MUFFINS
PASTRIES
PIE
ROLLS
SCONE

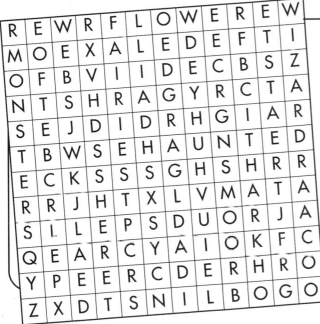

| I | S | I | R | S | N | I | F | F | U | M | S |
|---|---|---|---|---|---|---|---|---|---|---|---|
| E | T | L | G | H | D | E | I | P | A | J | M |
| X | I | H | L | O | V | E | L | K | E | O | I |
| S | U | A | R | O | O | Z | Q | I | T | Y | R |
| S | C | O | N | E | R | R | X | J | A | C | G |
| E | S | U | M | M | E | R | I | N | G | U | E |
| I | I | N | J | A | M | T | R | F | B | P | P |
| R | B | P | R | L | C | R | I | A | L | C | E |
| T | M | A | C | L | V | I | G | H | D | A | S |
| S | T | E | H | O | A | F | D | W | G | K | N |
| A | T | E | A | W | M | L | T | E | Y | E | D |
| P | T | A | E | S | F | C | A | N | D | Y | I |

# 64. BAKERY

How many cakes and buns can you see?

BUNS
CAKES
CHEESECAKE
COOKIES
CRUMPETS
DOUGHNUTS
GINGERBREAD
MACAROONS
PANCAKES
PIES
SHORTBREAD
TARTS

```
Z S H O R T B R E A D A
C P I E S B I R D J A C
H A T D S D U T Y H E T
M N T O P M I N U O R C
A C R U M P E T S U B H
C A I G L U U A E S R Y
A K C H S A T R I E E U
R E L N O E W T K S G R
O S D U S E K S O J N F
B E T I C E A O A I I
N R I S C O N E C M G F
S G E K A C E S E E H C
```

# 65. POST OFFICE

What can you find at the post office?

ADDRESS
CARDS
DELIVER
ENVELOPES
LETTERS
MAILBAG
MAILBOX
MESSAGE
NAMES
PACKAGE
PARCEL
STAMPS
TELEGRAMS

```
T E N V E L O P E S I K
H S H O A E I A E M P X
S E M A N T I R A A U Q
A F M G H T I C A R D S
D E L I V E R E D G S S
W A R F L R B L B E T G
S P M A T S E J R L E A
T L O P I R N D E E D B
H J E N B R D N N T O L
O M E S S A G E B L E I
R E G A K C A P I N K A
F I F E V X O B L I A M
```

# 66. WINTERTIME

Find the words linked to the winter season.

BLIZZARD
COLD
COZY
DECEMBER
FREEZING
FROSTY
GALES
HOLLY
ICY
RAIN
SANTA
SKATING
SKIING
SNOWMAN
STORMS
TOBOGGAN

```
W I N S G N I Z E E R F
T D E S K A T I N G R P
G G L T C I O S L D R A
S A T O I L I A C H E I
N I A R C O P N R I B R
O C D M I S T T G E M S
W Y T S O R F A S T E Y
M I L V S Z X Y Z O C L
A R S U E R E M I S E L
N F G B L I Z Z A R D O
B E A U A T T R A E S H
T O B O G G A N H H N I
```

# 67. CLOTHES CLUES

Find the clothes hidden in the grid.

BLOUSE
CAPE
COAT
GLOVES
HAT

JACKET
JEANS
MITTS
SCARF
SHIRT

SOCKS
TIE
TIGHTS

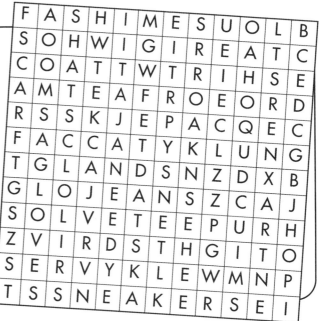

| F | A | S | H | I | M | E | S | U | O | L | B |
|---|---|---|---|---|---|---|---|---|---|---|---|
| S | O | H | W | I | G | I | R | E | A | T | C |
| C | O | A | T | T | W | T | R | I | H | S | E |
| A | M | T | E | A | F | R | O | E | O | R | D |
| R | S | S | K | J | E | P | A | C | Q | E | C |
| F | A | C | C | A | T | Y | K | L | U | N | G |
| T | G | L | A | N | D | S | N | Z | D | X | B |
| G | L | O | J | E | A | N | S | Z | C | A | J |
| S | O | L | V | E | T | E | E | P | U | R | H |
| Z | V | I | R | D | S | T | H | G | I | T | O |
| S | E | R | V | Y | K | L | E | W | M | N | P |
| T | S | S | N | E | A | K | E | R | S | E | I |

# 68. RUMMAGE SALE

| S | W | E | A | T | E | R | I | R | T | F | G |
|---|---|---|---|---|---|---|---|---|---|---|---|
| S | A | V | N | I | G | H | R | E | D | A | A |
| S | Q | U | O | R | S | U | M | E | B | R | L |
| R | A | C | R | S | S | H | J | K | T | E | O |
| E | A | R | A | W | E | A | N | I | A | F | S |
| P | B | S | K | I | R | T | N | L | O | G | H |
| P | L | A | U | A | D | E | I | E | C | A | E |
| I | A | S | H | S | H | O | P | U | T | I | S |
| L | C | T | R | O | X | S | E | R | S | R | O |
| S | H | O | E | S | O | E | R | U | I | O | N |
| K | T | O | W | I | N | D | R | R | A | W | S |
| I | A | B | L | A | Z | E | R | T | W | E | D |

How many items of clothing can you find in the puzzle?

ANORAK
BLAZER
BOOTS
CAP
DRESS
GALOSHES

HOOD
SHOES
SKIRT
SLIPPERS
SUIT
SWEATER

# 69. 'G' WORDS

Find the words starting with the letter G.

GALAXY
GAMES
GERBIL
GIANTS
GIGGLE
GINGER

GIRAFFE
GOAT
GOSSIP
GREAT
GREEN
GRAY

GRILL
GYM

| E | M | P | O | C | G | R | E | E | N | G | R |
|---|---|---|---|---|---|---|---|---|---|---|---|
| L | L | I | R | G | V | E | N | S | Y | H | S |
| Y | E | N | J | G | A | F | U | M | P | K | C |
| O | B | S | E | E | Z | F | G | C | I | H | G |
| G | E | E | G | R | E | A | T | C | S | E | B |
| R | A | M | H | B | Y | R | O | A | S | D | D |
| A | Y | A | A | I | Y | I | T | T | O | G | G |
| G | I | G | G | L | E | G | I | N | G | E | R |
| S | O | A | V | E | A | D | X | B | E | R | A |
| G | I | A | N | T | S | G | A | L | A | X | Y |
| A | S | Q | T | I | P | A | C | E | J | C | A |
| A | R | V | H | G | E | H | A | W | E | H | R |

# ANSWERS

## 1. FISHY TAILS

```
T P Y E N C Z S Q U I D
H R O A B A L O E H T L
H A D D O C K R W F F M
V W G N I R R E H C A L
S N R L O T O M Z C L E
E S A L M O N E L V X R
S M M O V J D S K A T E
M O T B E O B L S E I K
A D A S C A M P I N S C
L R G T U R B O T S T A
C S L E S S U M E I N M
F T S R E T S Y O R B D
```

## 4. SPACE MISSION

```
A J A M P O T C O M E T
S U N A U R T I N O M E
A P E R O C K E T O D L
T I S S R P U C K N E E
S T A R B L A U T G H S
G R U M T N H U S B N O
A B R K E E N M A R V P
L U N E P T U N E R E E
A U R O R A S E V Y N M
X S A T U S U N A R U E
Y T U R U N I V E R S E
```

## 3. SUPERSTARS

```
S T A R L I G H T A S C
C G C K N V V A T T E H
A E T H A M A S A S A A
R N P S T A R R Y T R A
B I A T O T F Y O A F W T
U H R Z I I P Y O R I T
R S T T S S T A R D O M
S R Y H A R V E S U W O
T A P R O V I S T S T R N
P T O P L A N S G T R N
C S T A R S H I P E D E
D A T E E Z A G R A T S
```

## 2. DESSERT DELIGHT

```
C H E E S E C A K E J A
U N L S O T N G H C K C
S E M O L I N A T I I J
T A O B F T G H R R O O
A C U A E T A G X K F S
R S S C W C T S F L A N
D U S X O Z P O L A P L
E N E I E C E R E E A O
D D P C P K E B A V S L
Z A P P Y P I E W L T I
T E E A G E J V M R E
F R M E R I N G U E Y I
```

## 5. MAGIC WORDSEARCH

```
P K H S L L E P S H A R
H C A U L D R O N R V Y
S I L W I S H T P P A Z
I R L O N E C C A M P
N T O A V B R O O M O U
A Z W S C E Y N Z T E M
V U E W W A R L O C K P
C R E T I N C L O A K
W E N S T W Z O O P A
A B R A C A D A B R A N
N A R C H A R M R B C L
D I S A P P E A R D D E
```

# 6. SCHOOL IS COOL!

```
O X C C S H T A M A R W
L C A L C U L A T O R I
D O E A R A O S S R E B
E M M S A C C S V A H L
K P A S Y K S E D R C A
R U S S O O B M N E A C
O T L N A S N A E K B K
W E I A S U E L B D T B
E R C H U N D Y P O O B
M A N C T R A R T N O A
O L E Y U I R A T G I R
H C P L A Y G R O U N D
```

# 9. TREASURE CHEST

```
D A Z Z A M E T H Y S T
R R Z A E K E G A N D U
U D I A M O N D S T O R
B R R P E L O N S N T Q
Y W C K R E B M A A O U
B C O C A S C O P D P O
A H N Z L G T L P N A I
N L O G D J N C H E Z S
G A V V S H E T P A E E
L R T E L E C A R B A T
E O A J M I N T E D A J
E C A L K C E N A C G O
```

# 7. WHAT'S THE BUZZ?

```
R U Z I W O E L B R A W
B U Z Z E O F F R E D O
E T R G K C A U Q A O I
L C J R A A C R L T A F
L A I E E M O O W F E V
O C P W L S K S Q F L E
W K R A B A W G R U N T
P L A P E S U N G H B T
Z E T U S N A R L E B R
Q U Q I P Y T O W A J O
A S N I F F T O O H O N
C H I R P F Y Q H I S H
```

# 10. FAB FRUIT

```
C R O O R A N G E Y F S
H A B A N A N A A T L T
E S N O O R Y P N Q P R
R E J O V A R B W Q P A
R S T P L U M O T T A W
Y R R E B E S O O G E B
S H R A N O M E L D N E
C A G R A P E S O F R
T W I K I R I W I R P R
F A T R A S P B E R R Y
T O C I R P A A R H A Y
D P E A C H S E T A D O
```

# 8. HAUNTED HOUSE

```
G A R G O Y L E S P I E
H A P P A M S P O O K S
S O N E Y L I H P T O N
P S E R I P M A V S S M
E A Y R N T W N O S C O
C A L G H O S T S S A N
T I H L Q W O E E R S
E C K O R O E M E I V R
R C E U O Q A S H B E E
S K M L W U L L K M C R
F T U S K E L E T O N S
F L O W E R E W A Z H P
```

# 11. COLOR CRAZY

```
F R O L L A V I N R A C
I J E E S W O B N I A R
R A M C S C R F T E D A
E B A Q D G E M S S E Y
W M R U C A T H U H H O
O T B A L L O O N S T N
R O L E O J R G R O O S
K M E R W T R C I T H O
S A S E N H A H S U O M
R S T N I A P I P O C
I F W H H F W L N E O N
T E S N U S F R U I T S
```

# 12. CANDY SHOP

```
C A N D Y B R L Y T L S
A E T T E B R E H S O I
R I U Q C E K I T S L I
A S G U M D R O P S L C
M X R T A R T W O I O
E F T F N S E H N C P R
L G O S T H C C S S O
S V F I S M M S S V P C
I X F R S N B B W O S E
E J E G D U F O S E Z E
G U E E T A L O C O H C
M A R S H M A L L O W
```

# 13. FLOWER GARDEN

```
M A R I G O L D B O R O
D C A L B A E D L R O J
V B U T T E R C U P S K
A R V T H A S T E T E S
E O Q D S T W E B I V U
P O C A L I L V E M T C
T G W A R R E L B S O
E F Y S N A P U Y E R
R P Y G O O O E I C C
W O P Z O I N M A V L E
S N O W D R O P M I L Y
T M P K C O H Y L L O H
```

# 14. TREEHOUSE

| T | R | H | C | R | I | B | I | S | C | K | S |
|---|---|---|---|---|---|---|---|---|---|---|---|
| E | E | C | H | E | S | T | N | U | T | A | T |
| H | U | H | W | C | D | C | A | P | U | R | S |
| B | O | E | T | G | P | A | L | M | K | T | E |
| T | S | R | S | R | A | T | R | W | M | E | R |
| U | E | R | R | A | L | P | O | P | O | O | O |
| N | B | Y | L | U | H | I | W | I | H | K | M |
| L | E | Q | U | K | R | S | A | S | T | E | A |
| A | F | I | Z | A | A | E | N | H | M | I | C |
| W | I | L | L | O | W | C | R | H | U | I | Y |
| A | R | L | A | R | O | Z | O | O | L | A | S |
| A | P | P | L | E | B | R | A | E | P | I | E |

# 15. SEASHORE SEARCH

| O | S | E | L | T | S | A | C | D | N | A | S |
|---|---|---|---|---|---|---|---|---|---|---|---|
| S | T | T | S | W | I | U | G | A | V | E | E |
| C | A | H | U | C | R | D | A | V | D | W | A |
| W | R | E | R | W | A | V | E | S | R | S | W |
| O | F | S | F | C | R | E | P | S | U | P | E |
| T | S | R | O | C | K | P | O | O | L | P | E |
| L | S | H | O | L | I | D | O | S | C | I | D |
| I | H | I | S | H | D | T | A | O | B | S | X |
| L | F | P | S | L | K | S | K | Y | A | I | U |
| O | S | W | I | M | M | E | R | S | R | E | T |
| S | H | E | L | L | S | F | I | V | C | S | P |
| M | A | J | H | S | I | F | Y | L | L | E | J |

# 16. WILD WEATHER

| H | U | R | R | I | C | A | N | E | R | R | F |
|---|---|---|---|---|---|---|---|---|---|---|---|
| A | C | Y | C | L | O | N | E | R | D | T | R |
| I | S | Q | W | O | R | D | C | A | S | S | E |
| L | T | R | O | R | I | B | C | V | E | E |  |
| S | N | O | W | L | Y | B | M | N | W | R | Z |
| T | O | R | N | A | D | O | B | C | E | E |  |
| O | S | D | E | J | N | U | H | O | T | D | N |
| R | D | B | R | O | H | A | P | E | N | G |  |
| M | B | C | V | F | W | P | Z | I | O | U | Z |
| M | Y | D | U | O | L | C | Y | W | I | H | S |
| I | C | A | C | G | L | F | R | O | S | T | S |
| L | I | G | H | T | N | I | N | G | O | G | G |

# 17. FUNNY WORDS

| S | N | I | G | G | E | R | H | G | A | G | C |
|---|---|---|---|---|---|---|---|---|---|---|---|
| W | A | V | E | R | C | C | A | Y | K | I | T |
| E | W | K | A | L | A | J | O | K | E | S | E |
| L | A | U | G | H | T | E | P | T | U | U | M |
| T | I | W | I | V | B | S | Z | L | W | O | H |
| R | C | W | G | B | O | T | Q | M | K | R | Y |
| A | L | Y | G | I | C | A | R | T | O | O | N |
| H | E | N | L | J | X | D | O | Y | R | M | U |
| C | O | M | E | D | Y | J | J | E | A | U | P |
| A | V | L | O | Z | Y | N | N | U | F | H | M |
| B | R | I | D | A | Y | L | R | O | R | F | N |
| Y | S | U | O | I | R | A | L | I | H | J | O |

# 18. ANIMALS

| S | T | S | C | C | G | H | E | O | O | P | V |
|---|---|---|---|---|---|---|---|---|---|---|---|
| T | A | H | D | O | G | S | Y | T | T | L | A |
| I | R | E | I | W | R | A | E | S | R | O | H |
| B | V | E | T | H | D | E | K | O | P | C | A |
| E | P | I | G | I | R | N | U | I | N | M |  |
| A | V | C | A | M | O | T | O | A | R | V | S |
| R | R | E | A | X | S | T | D | F | C | A | T |
| E | Y | S | N | E | K | C | I | H | C | S | E |
| S | S | K | C | U | D | H | S | R | O | U | R |
| O | Z | E | H | F | S | B | M | A | L | A | M |
| M | I | C | E | I | L | A | T | T | E | Y | P |
| P | R | O | G | G | O | A | T | S | N | Q | M |

# 19. TOYS!

| O | T | A | O | B | O | O | C | K | I | B | E |
|---|---|---|---|---|---|---|---|---|---|---|---|
| O | R | R | I | K | N | B | F | E | E | B | T |
| R | A | T | T | L | E | H | O | U | Z | I | T |
| Q | U | V | S | N | O | Y | A | R | C |  |  |
| S | N | O | W | B | R | I | O | X | X | Y | O |
| R | I | A | D | O | L | L | Y | M | K | C | O |
| S | O | W | O | N | L | H | O | P | C | L | N |
| K | H | E | I | M | A | U | W | A | A | E | B |
| A | I | O | T | A | B | S | B | I | L | B | O |
| T | M | C | G | R | A | I | T | N | T | H | N |
| E | B | O | A | P | R | V | E | T | I | K | N |
| S | E | M | A | G | A | Z | Y | S | K | N | E |

# 20. SUPERMARKET

| I | T | W | B | I | S | C | U | I | T | S | S |
|---|---|---|---|---|---|---|---|---|---|---|---|
| E | F | F | O | C | H | T | K | L | I | M |  |
| E | A | V | I | E | R | S | W | S | E | R | A |
| N | C | G | H | A | E | U | S | U | G | A | R |
| M | S | T | R | P | P | M | Z | I | G | T | M |
| S | A | E | E | M | P | S | Y | U | S | I | A |
| C | D | L | C | H | E | E | S | E | X | O | L |
| S | C | R | D | H | P | G | C | A | S | L | A |
| O | E | M | A | R | G | A | R | I | N | E | D |
| U | C | R | E | T | T | U | B | T | A | G | E |
| P | Z | E | R | G | W | H | J | L | E | O | O |
| T | A | V | B | H | N | O | C | A | B | B | A |

# 21. VEGETABLE PATCH

| J | E | Z | U | C | C | H | I | N | I | V | E |
|---|---|---|---|---|---|---|---|---|---|---|---|
| O | E | R | T | S | Q | U | A | S | H | I | R |
| F | S | S | K | A | L | E | F | R | E | D | E |
| E | I | L | O | C | C | O | R | B | O | E | W |
| S | S | E | D | E | A | U | D | A | L | N | O |
| E | P | G | A | A | R | W | N | O | D | J |  |
| O | O | A | B | U | R | N | I | P | C | E | F |
| N | B | E | L | O | Z | O | O | E | Q | I |  |
| A | A | B | E | T | T | K | N | K | B | X |  |
| T | C | A | T | F | F | J | S | F | B | S | U |
| O | H | C | E | K | O | H | C | I | T | R | A |
| P | A | S | T | U | O | R | P | S | Z | X | C |

## 22. OCEANS AND SEAS

```
D E R A H O U B L A C K
R E F B I A T E R R T G
E C A S P I A N O C H P
F I T C P P U F W I I A
C T L D J I V G L P C C
I L A E K E W A K C N I
I A N T A R C T I C A F
B B F L Q X G D M I C I
D I K M R Y I A A D C C
R E C A R I B B E A N L
D V U G N S Z J D W I N
A T H T R O N K T I M O
```

## 25. BIRDS

```
A C T I C B U N S X Z N
P A R R O T Q R E N V
R N A T W L A P W I N G
D A R E I B E E F O G H
R R C N B N T X W I N T
Y H N C O E W D I R
B A A I R M P I G E O N
K R A L J A N T A R T G
C W O P S G O G H R S A
A C A T X P W B L O R
L A T H W N A D O V E
B U D G I E E W N W F R
```

## 23. WHAT'S IN THE BATHROOM?

```
T H I M B L V K N I S U
O S E L I T E W S T P Q
P U R R S H A M P O O H
H R Q U H S A P R I N T
O B W S O A P T S L G A
R H W R W A N T I E E F
D T O W E L C H I T G E
E O E D R L H A F U O L
N O F A U C E T G H I B
T T O O T H P A S T E R
A C A T Y H O T F A U U
M I R R O R F A T B O B
```

## 26. GO NUTS!

```
G R M A N H C A S H E W
N X A A L L R T R E U A
B A C O R N I B F U E L
A E A G O F I O R G N
I S D Z H A Z E L I G U
E E A E A H A I B R T
A L M O N D R P E U D S
N I I T S T B H R N H W
U A A B F S D P T O J R
I N T U N T S E H C K H
G P I S T A C H I O S D
T U N D N U O R G C W R
```

## 24. WHAT'S IN THE KITCHEN?

```
R O L P D O T R I F E C
E S T O V E E B R I I
F E K P K E E D E E A N
R P C I O N S N L E L K
I I W J S E R E A Z H A
G N P G R I L L C E O Y
E C O J P U T B K R B L
R E T S A O T O P P U S
A C S S N O T H A T I
T V A R S S G E H E R N
O X I I P E E L T T E K
R Z E V A W O R C I M K
```

## 27. PRIVATE DETECTIVE

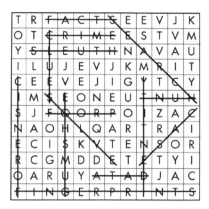

```
T R F A C T S E E V J K
O T C R I M E E S T V M
Y S L E U T H N A V A U
I L U J E V J K M R I T
C E E V E J I G Y T C Y
I M S E O N E U I N U N
S J F O R P O I Z A C
N A O H L Q A R I R A I
E C I S K Y T E N S O R
R C G M D D E T E T Y I
O A R U Y A T A D J A C
F I N G E R P R I N T S
```

## 28. ROBOTS

```
S H I S L O R T N O C S
P T E C H N O L O G Y S
D V N O U F B H E R B E
V N I M H G O H O R O C
H K H P S D T M A X R O
U W C U E C E B A R G R
M S A T D M A R G O R P
A X M E C I T E R E U E
N I D R B J U N E I E J
O E C I T S I R U T U F
N T E L L I G E N C E
D I O R D N A S T F R Z
```

## 29. AROUND THE WORLD

```
S P A I N Y I N A P A J
W K I C O M M M J F M R
E E S E S O U S X E E D
D C S L P N A T I R B
E D U A L O G H P W U
N S R N A R L O Y A C Z
E C M D V W E U G C A E
C H O A C A B S E I S S
N I T A L Y E E V R R C
A N D R H I T R E F R I
R A U S T R A L I A I C
F R O I L Y N A M R E G
```

# 30. GLOBE TROTTERS

```
I A V A L L C A N A D A
N H M E X L C O F I N U
D U Y O R Z N R O B A S
I N E K R A M N E D L T
A G K G R R E A T N R R
X A R E X B W D H A E
E R U T D F E Z A L Z A
C Y T R U E T E N T R
E P O R T U G A L V
E Q E R C V G H A F W A
R P C H O L L A N D S L
G R E E N L A N D J R O
```

# 35. 'A' WORDS

```
A S T R O N A U T G O R
S P R V E A T D R C J N
T A Q U A M A R I N E C
R P A T A B O R C A B E
O R A C U E A W T K L D
N A R C R T C S J O S
O L O P A A Z U R E A
M R A N A L B A G S R
Y O D I D O S O U O S A
F W D N O Z A M A L V S
D L S C I T R O L W K
M M N B B S A L T A Q A
```

# 33. GOBBLEDYGOOK

```
Z A N P P Y L L I S Y O
A N S A B R B B U H R O
G O B B L E D Y G O O K
M N O W T B L A G H T F
M S C A R T E B F S L B
A E H F A B L E M A N
L N A F L E T B I U N E
F S F L E S T E T P C T
M E Q I V A A L U E H
A U N N R G L D T
L Z I G R R P I B D U R
F L A P D O O D L E I R
```

# 31. CREEPY-CRAWLY

```
B I R F S L U G A L O R
C E G R E A C U T Y O A
O K I X D G U B Y D A L
C A A T I Q U O T R S L
K K R R L M R O W I C
R D W A E E W L E F G P
O O J S P I D E R B R
A K G A P T O V V W X E
C A Y P A R A S I T E T
H I T A R A N T U L A R A
A A H E D E P I T N E C
J N O I P R O C S Z O I
```

# 34. MUSICAL INSTRUMENTS

```
B R I P J U S O O Z A K
A G U I T A R S R I E E
C T N A A R U O E P N Y
I E R N W T L I D M B
N I L O I V E L R W R O
O R A I T I S R O Q U A
M B A N J O O L C U O R
R E Q D F L U T E O B D
A L R E F A Y R P I M R
H L U T E I T G N S A A
L S V E S H O P I E T T
O S C S E P I P G A B H
```

# 36. MORE 'A' WORDS

```
H E R E H P S O M T A U
A M I L K I R O S E R H
D N O M L A A R C T C O
V B E W A A P P L E T H U
E U A S T E R O I D H U
N Z N T M C T T A M S
T Z E I A R C A D E E R
U R S T P K O H A W C
R A N E R A T K I T Z
F S E I O N N O I T C A
A T O M N R U B U A S Q
A L P H A B E T K A J U
```

# 32. INCREDIBLE INSECTS!

```
F I R E F L Y T H O C E
L P R I B C Z W T A N G
E S H O R N E T R E P D
A S T I R S H J J L O
I G M O O C W C I T N M
T R D O P A R K V T M A
P E D O T I U Q S O M R
E T P Z O N I V S B V T
P N S S I G M T O E T O
T F A H A R L O C U S T
X L W A F R E R S U S
I Y L F R E T T U B U H
```

# 37. BIRTHDAYS!

```
S R I B O G I F T S N S
C I N G O R D E N U F
N W H I T E B L A O C K
G N I C N A D T R P S
I S C E L E B R A T E
N H A P P Y C H D A R O
G E K S T N E S E R P R
M E E R Y A W O R O L P
U S T A N D R A S C L A
S L A R T S G A M E S
C R O F R I E N D S
C A N D L E S W F G H Y
```

# 38. DOGS

```
R E L G A E B D B P W Y
O G J A L S A T I O N O
T O N S O S S X H M W A
T E A M V H S C T E O B
W E M H H E E A M R L E
E R I E E T S I A F S
S E S R P O J H N H E
L A B R A D O R T I O N
E Z O L G O R M T A U
R D D R I C R O C N N K
A R D N U H S H C A D E
A S E T T E R H A P I P
```

# 39. MORE DOGS

```
A D O G I L E I N A D S
C A I R E D A L E I O T
D L E E A D E R S T O B
N M A V C R O I L C D
A U B O X E R A H L O
O T B U L L D O G I E
H I K S C U E H I D
Y A W H P R E T U U H
E N C O E T E A C A L O
R M P U T Y K S U H A U
G E R B I E F O P U C N
N E W F O U N D L A N D
```

# 40. TRAIN STATION

```
B S D A O R L I A R H W
R E A D S T E K C I T H
S D R I V E R I V A I
R E E A W I F E A L M S
E A P S I G N A L S E T
F V E E I L O C O B T
F I E S T B S D E P A E
U P L A T F O R M D B P
B S S U N N E A W S
A R U R E T N U H S E A
W A R G H O R G S Q U I
T C S R E G N E S S A P
```

# 41. FOOTBALL CRAZY

```
R S T B S L P A S S E E
I M A E T U H U E D S N
T L C W E V E O F O U D
L M K I N E L F E R B Z
I R L H T M D R D S O
K R E I I A D E E B E N
S E F K N N U L E O S E
T F T O U C H D O W N I
N E F L A G C I K A E O
I R A R E E R O C S F N
O E C O A C H K N E A
P E N A L T Y E K E D F
```

# 42. COWBOY RANCH

```
R E G N A R D R H A W R
A S C A R F B R O N C O
R T R U E B E X R I O U
S E I R I A R P S E V J
T R O U G H V E E A C B
E E C A T T L E L G F E
T W O D B A V H O U S A
S E W I X O B S R E S H
O I B S V R L S P A H C
N E D A E V U P A R K N
S D Y D S L A R I A T A
J O J E L D D A S W O R
```

# 43. CIRCUS

```
E L G G U J I G Z I P Z
L W I P T R A P E Z E B
E C M A G C R T D Y I
P J R F E N P J A C T S
H C N I G G R I B L E H
A S D F N E O F O O S O
N E O R D S B K R W U W
S E S R O H Z C N J S
S A R E S D S T A S G K
R O G W J A E W E B E E
L I O N S R T Q V N F N
T R A I N E R R A R T O
```

# 44. COMPUTERS

```
D E R D R A O B Y E K U
E I D R E T N I R P S D
S E V R R E S U O M R O
K R I F I Z D Z M C D O
T C B I S E U E R O H
O R A N V E S E M A G A
P O T P A L N H A M R R
R A I U T O I P Y E R D
T H W T I T A E D G W
N Z B R E T U P M O C A
R V L E M K L T M A R
W A T F S O F T W A R E
```

# 45. STAR SIGNS

```
S C O R P I O T L A M D
A S A R D N W A R I E S
G O A T A W U A Y O V
I E S E N M R R M T E N
T A V S L E P U H I L E
T A R F E G E S C L T P
A R B L G R P A T E O
R E A S C O H U T G
B R H W I J S D B O R
U U C A P R I C O R N
S Q U E R T E E Z I S
A Q U A R I U S H I P Y
```

## 46. HERBS

```
S E T A F A E L Y A D L
A M A R J O R A M C A R
L Y S P E P O R C S O S
R H S A T M A N N H I I
E T K I G M I X T E L E
D O F E X E E M J R K M
N R L E N N E F D V D A
A J L O E V A Z A I T R
I C I Q Z P A R S L E Y
R E D R L I F T E X E R
O S T S A V O R Y O U W
C H I V E S O N D A R O
```

## 47. CHRISTMAS

```
S D R A C B S U V K A Y
V E A T R R E A K F A S
M C H R I S T M A S D S
I E Q C E B D E R Y T
S M Y E R S C A R O L S
T B J T I M H N T A T D
L E K N H O L L S N N
E R K A S R M A E S M A
I L E P H N P S R W L
O U Y N D F E V N F A R
F L H O L L Y D I Y I A
E D H S T D B S T F I G
```

## 48. FESTIVE FUN

```
R U D O L P H F A I R Y
E A R T C H J K E S W U
I F A V R T S T H G I L
N E V E Y J I S Z S H E
D S E L B U A B A I T
E C R S I S R T N U A
E H T F E A S T A N S D
R A T M E L E M O T N E
W T I F W M D S A S H U
O N C O L D B N M E F D
R A F A D R D A H J K
K S N O I T A R O C E D
```

## 49. FIRE STATION

```
W O F F U N I F O R M I
D R A I T E R E T A W I
A R K O R I F T C D O D
J O N R S E C B L I V E
E L O P S L V R E O S N
F A A S L B E L L A K T
O D L O S A R A H S S R
R D T B O T I C B T A E
E E N G I N E H U O M S
S R D D N R A S T X G C
H E A R Y U S K O S X U
H E L M E T S P R N U E
```

## 50. 'B' WORDS

```
F B H B I B M B L B T A
B I N O C U L A R S A C
L E N B T M N I M O T
O L V F T D A E R B T
S I I U E O N L A J S
S O H R R R A U J K A
O N E E B I N B O Y Y F
M S E V E X L U O R T K
R S B K L E A J B F U A
X A O G C K G U I A E
B O B A M B O O Z L E R
B U B B L E V R I S B B
```

## 51. PUZZLE WORDS

```
W A I C R Y P T I C R O
O K E J C R U Z O O C E
R Y N A P A Z A Q U I Z
D N I M E B Z X G D G A
S R G R W A L C L U O M
E R M Y S T E R Y F L A
A A A A N E J I G S A W
R H Z D A I E D O C K O
C R B R I V E D L L S O
H P O T B R W L D U D F
Q U E O M I G E W E R I
A S N O I T U L O S O H
```

## 52. COOL!

```
I C H I L L Y D D V W
R R B A L K R G J Y C
I A S N O W F L A K E N
C O D E C O O L C A A R
S P W V O Y S U T I N Y
E D T H D N B I C T L L
E N O T S L A H V E A
J R N I O T R H X S E
S T M I O R E I C A L G
B R U E G N I Z E E R F
```

## 53. IT'S A JUNGLE!

```
M O S Q U I T O L D G W
O S T K T A K W I W O I
N O R T K C A J K E R F
K V T K E F F A R I G
E I H G R H O L R O L E
Y R I E E C G D B L L R
E I M R Y C H E E T A H
D P O M O I H Z U S W
A C I F V U L T U R E H
D H U S A G I R I L P A
C R P A J A G U A R Z V
R A F X E R E H T N A P
```

## 54. JUNGLE FUN!

```
S A N D S R U C O B R A
P I R A N H A R D A X X
I A R V A E D O N I H R
D G H H K J T C S H L O
E O A M E D B O P P I H
R R N O O Y J D I F O R
I B I N G I E I O N O S
A N E Y H L S L D C Z S
S F L J L R E E M E D E
L E O P A R D D O I L S
E M P N I C N W O L I G
M A E L E P H A N T I G
```

## 55. 'C' WORDS

```
S A F E T A L O C O H C
I N C I N D E R E L L A
A C A A H O U S E E R L
V E P O R C I N E M A C
I L A E T T A K T A C U
N D V Q A H O E S R E L
R N A T C M M Q A A V A
A A N E H O S R N C A T
C C N D C L Q U A Q C O
D Y R R E U C U P H Q R
C C A L E N D A R R C S
D T E F A C S T O T Y F
```

## 56. 'D' WORDS

```
S E L Z Z A D F R E S I
E S V D E C E M B E R F
C T R O I R S U D H U R
R G A O D A S P D O A G
E G R D A D E O A U S G
D N D I C E F G T J S N E
A I C E F G T J S N E
W Y E M D Y N A M I C E
S A L L P P A A L E D N
Y R A D I L S L V T A
S D A N D E L I O N F D
W I D H G E O N D U C K
```

## 57. DESERT

```
Z O N E R K R E T A W E
H A R P M I R A G E E R
S T U A H C A C T I P D
A E Y Y L A C T I R G U
N R Q U E M S D A M O N
B A T E S E S S I N A E
S H D N V L N D H J S
T E B D E S E R T N S T
O A S I S A H A R A O R
R T R S C E Z A H S I S
M R S C O R P I O N I S
H A W T R I X L F I N G
```

## 58. BIRDS

```
G E T A W A F R O B I N
R O O K F F E R S W E Z
A M T R O R S E T O K I
V R E O E E R U T L U V
E L Q T T N H X N L I P
N I U S Y K I E C A B M
A N D J A C K D A W O T
V S U Y U R E L E S S I
A E C C W O K U S T O P
L P K R E W O R R A P S
O O R T I N I R A S R Y
O G N I M A L F L U P T
```

## 59. PIZZA PICK

```
S G E C U F V B A C O N
O Y V O H C N A C R R O
G O O G L H A N T H E L
A P E P P E R O N I M O
R I C E D E A V E N M T
L N U D G S X S F E E A
I E A L L E R A Z Z O M
C A S M S X Z U I O N O
S P A R R S M S H R I T
S P I C Y O R A S F O W
O L I V E S G G R N R W
P E P P E R S E T E S I
```

## 60. SUMMER

```
E V A W T A E H S G O O
D E L O V I R S W A R M
X G C D J U N E I S T
E U S N A L V N M A R D
S Y N A R Y O R M D U S
A D L J H K O P N V I M
L R H A I N G U M M E
G L D P B N E A R S E
N O O C P L E E T H V R
U H R D Y Y O G M I S S
S S U M M E R T I M E T
```

## 61. HALLOWEEN

```
C U P U M P K I N G S H
H C T I W H A P O H H K
A P R I E M U T S O C B
L A N T E R N R Y S A L
L I Y W N E A E Y I U
O N P A Y T R A P S V E
W C I R C L E C R O V F
E D T L H S E D N A C
E O B O S E A E I B S I
N L O C B S E L P P A R
M A S K D E A V A L S E
G I R L M L R H A F I M
```

# 62. SCARY STUFF!

```
R E W R F L O W E R E W
M O E X A L X D E F T S
O F B V X D E C B S Z
N T S H R A G Y R C T A
S E J D R H G A R A
T B W S E H A U N T E D
E C K S S S G H S H R R
R R J H T X L V M A T A
S L L E P S D U O R J A
Q E A R C Y A I O K F C
Y P E E R C D E R H R O
Z X D T S N I L B O G O
```

# 65. POST OFFICE

```
T E N V E L O P E S I K
H S H O A E I A E M P X
S E M A N T I R A A U Q
A F M G H T I C A R D S
D E L I V E R E D G S S
W A R F L R B I B F T G
S P M A T S E J R L E A
T L O P I R N D E E D B
H J E N B R D N N T O L
O M E S S A G E B L E
R E G A K C A P I N K A
F I F E V X O B L I A M
```

# 63. SWEET TREATS

```
I S I R S N I F F U M S
E T L G H D E I P A J M
X I H L O V E L K E O I
S U A R O O Z Q I T Y R
S C O N E R R X J A C G
E S U M M E R I N G U E
  I N J A M T R E B P P
R B P R L C R I A L C E
T M A C L V A G H D A S
S T E H O A F D W G K N
A T E A W M L T E Y E D
P T A E S F C A N D Y I
```

# 64. BAKERY

```
Z S H O R T B R E A D A
C P I E S B I R D J A C
H A T D S D U T Y H E T
M N T O P M I N U O R C
A C R U M P E T S U B H
C A I G L U U A E S R Y
R E L N O E W I K S G R
O S D U S E K S O J N F
O B E T I C E A O A I
N R I S C O N E C M G F
S G E K A C E S E E H C
```

# 66. WINTERTIME

```
W I N S G N I Z E E R F
T D E S K A T I N G R P
G G L T C I O S L D R A
S A T O I L I A C H E I
N I A R O P N R I B R
O C D M I S T T G E M S
W Y T S O R F A S T E Y
M I L V S Z X Y Z O C
A R S U E R E M I S E
N F G B L I Z Z A R D
B E A U A T T R A E S H
T O B O G G A N H H N I
```

# 67. CLOTHES CLUES

```
F A S H I M E S U O L B
S O H W I G I R E A T C
C O A T T W F R I H S E
A M T E A F R O E O R D
R S K J E P A C Q E C
F A C C A T Y K L U N G
T G L A N D S N Z D X F
G L O J E A N S Z C A J
S O L V E T E E P U R H
Z V I R D S T H G I T O
S E R V Y K L E W M N P
T S S N E A K E R S E I
```

# 68. RUMMAGE SALE

```
S W E A T E R I R T F G
S A V N I G H R E D A A
S Q U O R S U M E B R L
R A C R S S H J K T E O
E A R A W E A N I A F S
K B S K I R T N L O G H
P L A U A D E I E C A E
I A S S H O P U T I S
L C T R O U S E R S R O
S H O E S Q E R U I O N
K T O W I N D R R A W S
I A B L A Z E R T W E D
```

# 69. 'G' WORDS

```
E M P O C G R E E N O R
L L I R G V E N S Y H S
Y E N J G A F U M P K C
O B S E E Z F G C H G
G E E G R E A T C S E B
R A M H B Y R O A S D D
A Y A A Y T T O G G
G I G G L E G I N G E R
S O A V E A D X B E R A
G I A N T S G A L A X Y
A S Q T I P A C E J C A
A R V H G E H A W E H R
```

# BRAINBENDER PUZZLES

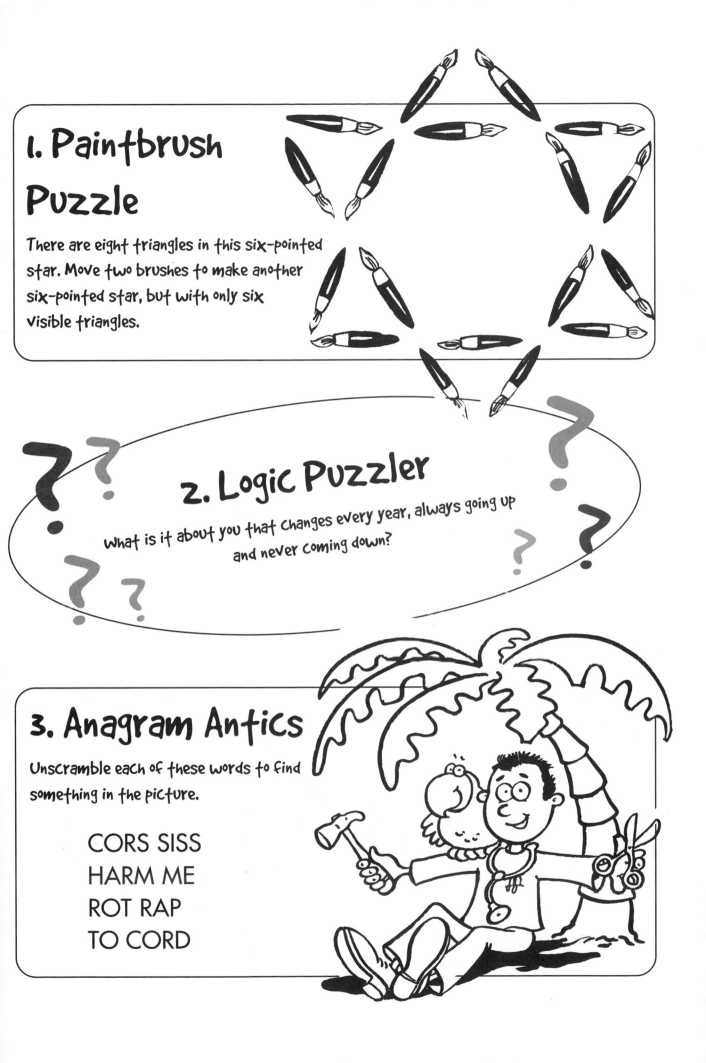

# 1. Paintbrush Puzzle

There are eight triangles in this six-pointed star. Move two brushes to make another six-pointed star, but with only six visible triangles.

# 2. Logic Puzzler

What is it about you that changes every year, always going up and never coming down?

# 3. Anagram Antics

Unscramble each of these words to find something in the picture.

CORS SISS
HARM ME
ROT RAP
TO CORD

# 4. Number Search

Two numbers between one and twenty are missing from the box. Can you find them?

# 5. Baffling Bet

A man was sitting in a cafe enjoying a drink when the waiter came over to him and said "I'll bet you $2 that if you give me $2, I will give you $3 in return." The man was puzzled as he thought about it. Should he accept the bet or not?

# 6. Word Play

Look at the clues and see if you can make new words by changing just one letter in each of these words.

Change FORK to a kind of meat.
Change SHOW to the opposite of fast.
Change HARD to a thick type of paper.

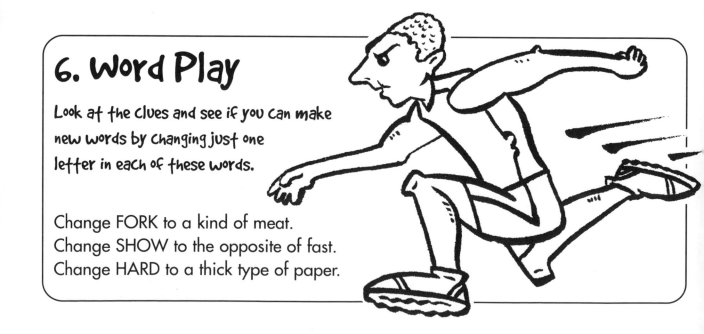

# 7. Age Question

When asked how old she was, Rosie replied "In two years I will be twice as old as I was five years ago." How old is she?

# 8. Number Cross

Fill in the numbers in the number grid by solving the clues.

## Across

**1.** Number of days in three weeks.
**3.** Six times seven.
**4.** 888 divided by four.
**6.** Half of seventy-six.
**8.** Four times seventeen.
**9.** Seven down plus eleven across.
**10.** 125 divided by five.
**11.** Eight + fourteen + eighteen.

## Down

**1.** 121 doubled.
**2.** Thirty-six divided by three.
**4.** Half of fifty-two.
**5.** Eight across minus eleven across.
**6.** Four times eight.
**7.** Three across plus six across.
**9.** Half of 300.
**10.** Number of hours in a day.

# 9. Driving Dilemma

Bill was sitting in his car on an ordinary road pointing north. He turns to his friend and says "Even though we are pointing north, I can drive this car for one mile and end up one mile south of where we started from." How?

## 10. Wild Wordsearch

Find these ten animals in the wordsearch.

| | | | | | | | | | | | |
|---|---|---|---|---|---|---|---|---|---|---|---|
| M | D | Y | T | A | F | W | U | Q | D | J | P |
| K | O | I | R | C | E | S | H | O | Z | K | S |
| T | B | U | J | O | C | I | G | L | B | D | Y |
| A | Z | Y | S | K | V | S | O | B | C | W | E |
| O | A | C | N | E | C | E | X | Y | I | N | K |
| G | I | P | L | K | F | S | N | A | C | R | N |
| F | O | S | J | F | T | D | D | O | F | L | O |
| H | R | C | A | W | I | B | K | S | I | Q | M |
| I | P | R | Q | U | X | N | T | H | P | L | X |
| K | I | Y | T | E | R | E | S | R | O | H | A |
| G | T | D | A | Z | C | I | O | J | U | C | B |
| R | W | A | C | F | L | X | B | D | R | I | B |

GIRAFFE     HORSE
CAT     PIG
DOG     MONKEY
MOUSE     BIRD
LION     GOAT

## 11. Letter Change

Turn REAL into BELT by changing one letter at a time by following the clues.

1. Cotton and films come on this.
2. Sense of touch.
3. You walk on these.
4. A sort of pen tip.

REAL

_ _ _ _

_ _ _ _

_ _ _ _

_ _ _ _

BELT

## 12. Number Sequence

What's the next number in the sequence?

11 10 8 7 13 5

## 13. Ridiculous Riddle

Which source of heat is black when you buy it, red when you use it and gray when you throw it away?

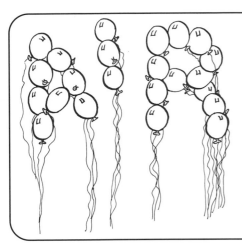

## 14. Alphabet Puzzle

Put a different letter or letters in front of the word AIR each time to solve the clues.

**1.** Strands of this are on your head.     _AIR
**2.** At this you can go on different rides.     _AIR
**3.** You sit on this.     _AIR

## 15. Letter Assembler

Rearrange these letters to make a ten-letter word meaning 'all.'

THIEVE GRYN

## 16. What Am I?

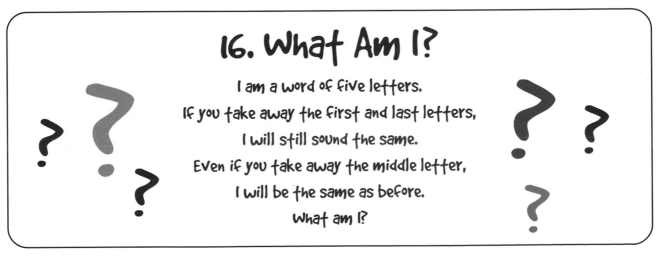

I am a word of five letters.
If you take away the first and last letters,
I will still sound the same.
Even if you take away the middle letter,
I will be the same as before.
What am I?

# 17. Mix And Match

Put the words below into their correct pairs.

| | |
|---|---|
| Swan | Foal |
| Bear | Chick |
| Cow | Cygnet |
| Kangaroo | Cub |
| Rooster | Joey |
| Horse | Calf |

# 18. Spot The Difference

Study the picture carefully for one minute. Then look at the same picture on the opposite page. Spot five things which are missing from the picture.

1. _____

2. _____

3. _____

4. _____

5. _____

# 19. Solve The Mystery

It's the middle of winter and five pieces of coal, a carrot, and a scarf are lying on the lawn. Nobody put them there but there is a perfectly good explanation why they are there. What is it?

# 20. Word Change

Look at the clues and make new words by changing just one letter in each of these words:

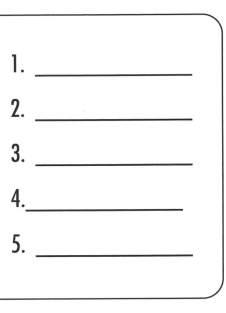

1. Change TALK into a story.
2. Change GATE into something found on a calendar.
3. Change FINE into a number.

# 21. Proverb Puzzler

Rearrange the letters to form a well-known six-word saying. As in the question, there are six letters in the first word of the answer, five letters in the second, three letters in the third, four letters in the fourth, two letters in the fifth, and three letters in the sixth.

## TRIKES HILWE ETH RONI SI THO

# 22. Number Cruncher

The number FIVE as written using block capitals contains exactly ten strokes or segments of a straight line. Can you find a number which, when written out as words, contains as many strokes as the number says. (Clue: it's between twenty and thirty.)

# 23. Word Wizz

Name the flowers that can be found by removing one letter from each word.

1. IRISH   2. ROUSE
3. MASTER   4. VIOLENT

## 24. Pencil Trick

Remove three pencils to leave three equal touching squares.

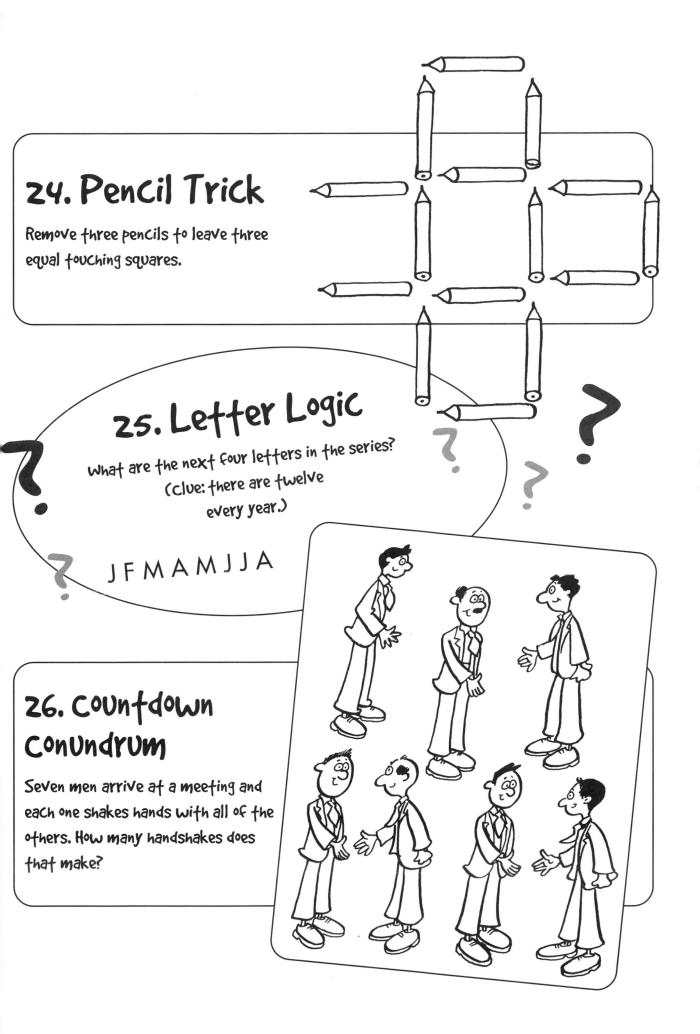

## 25. Letter Logic

What are the next four letters in the series?
(Clue: there are twelve every year.)

J F M A M J J A

## 26. Countdown Conundrum

Seven men arrive at a meeting and each one shakes hands with all of the others. How many handshakes does that make?

# 27. Hidden Countries

In each of the sentences below, the name of a country is hidden. For example, the sentence: 'Interpol and the FBI catch criminals' contains the word Poland. Can you find them?

**1.** Our dog likes his food so much he eats a can a day.
**2.** Always use a pencil when drawing lines in diagrams.
**3.** The king was angry when a thief stole his painting.
**4.** Does the teacher teach in a classroom?
**5.** In anger, many people say things they don't mean.

# 28. Adder

Answer the clues, then create a new word by joining the two answers together. Can you think of any other words that are made up in this way?

|   | NOISE OF A COW |
| + | DANGER COLOR |
| = | SECURED LIKE A BOAT |

# 29. Tricky Words

Which word can be put before all the words below to make four new words?

FAST THROUGH DOWN AWAY

## 30. How Did She Do That?

A woman went outside without an umbrella or a raincoat, yet did not get wet. How's that?

## 31. Upside Down

Which number, written in figures, increases in value by 21 when turned upside down? (clue: it's between 60 and 70)

## 32. Learn The Language

Think of words ending in –GRY. Angry and hungry are two of them. There are only three words in the English language. What is the third word? The word is something that everyone uses every day. If you have read carefully what is written, it already says what it is.

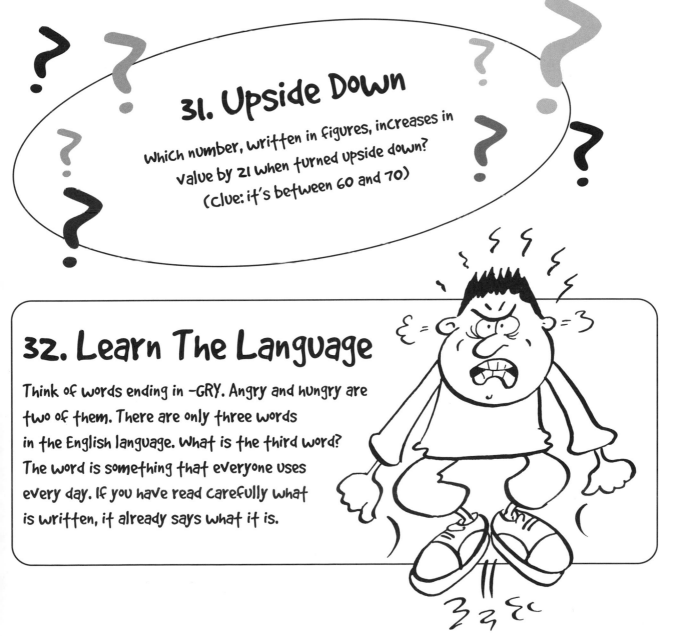

## 33. Match Them Up

Match up the pairs with their rightful owners.

## 34. Mind The Gap

Which single three-letter word completes all of the following words?

_ _ _ WARD

BE _ _ _ E

_ _ _ GED

IN_ _ _ MATION

## 35. Oddly Enough

What is the opposite of NOT OUT?

## 36. Figure It Out

Andy bought a bag of apples on Monday and ate a third of them. On Tuesday he ate half of the remaining apples. On Wednesday he looked in the bag to find he only had two apples left. How many apples were originally in the bag?

## 37. Date Dilemma

How many days is it from Wednesday August 1st to the first Saturday in September?

## 38. Missing Alphabet

Find the two letters missing from the ball.

## 39. Catch A Cat

If six cats can catch six rats in six minutes, how many cats are needed to catch ten rats in ten minutes?

## 40. Deadly Decision

An explorer is caught stealing food by a tribe who order that he must die. But the tribe chief is a reasonable man and allows the explorer to choose the method by which he will be killed. The explorer is asked to make a single statement. If it is true he will be thrown off a high cliff. If it is false he will be eaten by lions. What clever statement does the explorer make that forces the chief to let him go?

## 41. Animal Madness

Can you name the creature missing from the nursery rhyme?

1. Mary had a little ____.

2. With a nicknack paddywhack, give the ___ a bone.

3. Pop goes the _____.

4. The ___ jumped over the moon.

## 42. Wise Words

What is the one thing that all people, no matter how important they are, agree is between heaven and Earth?

## 43. Gambling Games

Tom and Nancy are playing a game of cards for $1 a game. At the end of the evening, Tom has won three games and Nancy has won $3. How many games did they play?

## 44. Put Them Together

Match up these characters with their other halves.

Gretel    Jane    Hermione Granger    Gandalf    Jerry

Harry Potter    Bilbo Baggins    Tom    Tarzan    Hansel

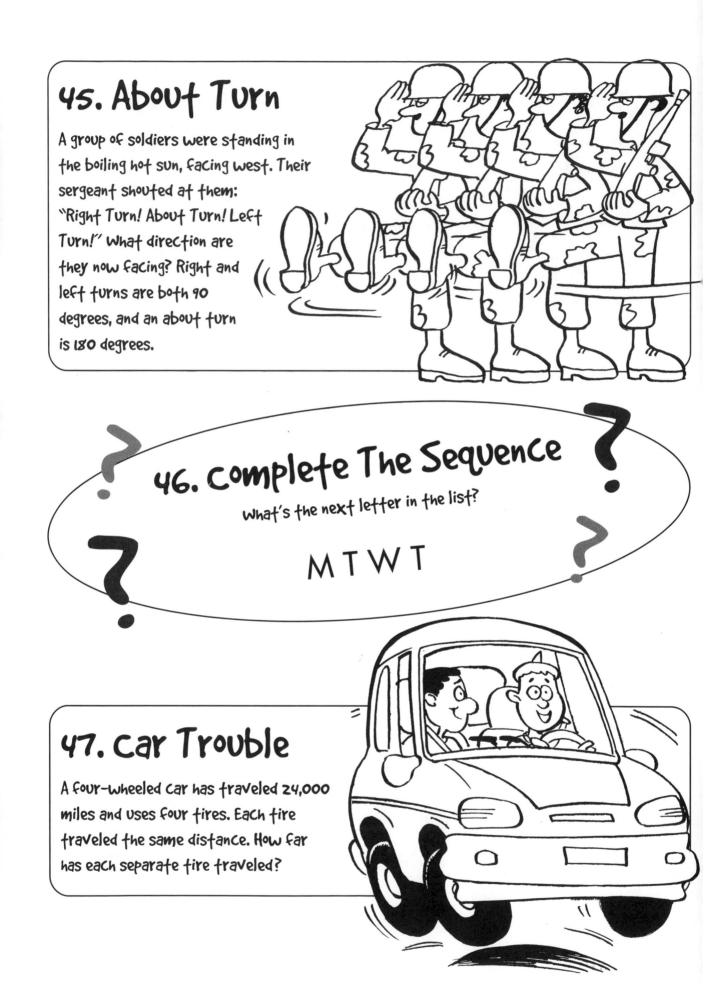

## 45. About Turn

A group of soldiers were standing in the boiling hot sun, facing west. Their sergeant shouted at them: "Right Turn! About Turn! Left Turn!" What direction are they now facing? Right and left turns are both 90 degrees, and an about turn is 180 degrees.

## 46. Complete The Sequence

What's the next letter in the list?

M T W T

## 47. Car Trouble

A four-wheeled car has traveled 24,000 miles and uses four tires. Each tire traveled the same distance. How far has each separate tire traveled?

# 48. Wacky Wordsearch

| N | B | E | R | R | A | Z | I | B | M | F | C |
|---|---|---|---|---|---|---|---|---|---|---|---|
| J | P | U | V | I | Q | P | L | G | R | R | A |
| R | T | W | O | S | H | S | H | E | K | U | O |
| Q | D | F | G | N | N | A | K | E | B | D | D |
| A | B | C | M | I | G | J | G | G | T | E | M |
| Y | T | Z | F | E | J | N | P | G | N | S | Q |
| K | S | H | K | L | A | S | C | D | H | J | G |
| C | D | V | U | R | R | S | M | B | H | P | Z |
| A | O | N | T | D | S | H | O | A | W | N | H |
| W | M | S | S | W | T | B | F | Q | I | S | D |
| P | J | I | D | E | H | V | Z | R | D | K | D |
| C | W | W | E | I | R | D | M | U | B | G | O |

**Find the words:**

STRANGE

WACKY

ODD

WEIRD

BIZARRE

RUDE

# 49. Number Solver

Find two whole numbers which, when multiplied together, give an answer of 61.

# 50. What Am I?

You use me from head to toe, the more I work the thinner I grow. What am I?

## HAND

\_ \_ \_ \_

\_ \_ \_ \_

\_ \_ \_ \_

\_ \_ \_ \_

## FEET

# 51. Letter Game

Go from HAND to FEET by changing only one letter at a time.

1. This is found on a beach.
2. You do this to a letter.
3. You plant this to make a flower grow.
4. To take food in.

# 52. Picture Puzzle

Work out the saying from the picture.

**ARREST**

**YOU'RE**

# 53. Pencil Palaver

Take away six pencils to leave three equal-sized squares.

## 54. Sweet Tooth

Five children were sharing out a box of candy. Bob took five, Peter took five, Joey took five, and Danny took five. That left half the pack, which Natasha took. How many candies were there altogether?

FLUFF

IRAQI

ROBIN

SANTA

TOTAL

## 55. Long List

What's special about the list of words opposite? (Clue: look at the beginning and end of each word.)

## 56. Number Parts

Bill's number is two, Clare's number is three, and Edward's number is five. What is Donna's number?

# 57. Body Parts

Name ten body parts that are spelt with three letters. No slang words!

# 58. Pictionary

Work out the saying from the picture.

# 59. Chocolate Challenge

One boy can eat sixteen chocolates in half a minute, and another can eat half as many in twice the length of time. How many chocolates can both boys eat between them in fifteen seconds?

## 60. Common Factor

What letter do the following numbers have in common?

3, 7, 10, 11, 12

## 61. Sleep Tight

Turn the word SLEEP into DREAM by changing one letter at a time.

**1.** An alarm clock makes this noise.
**2.** What happens when you cut yourself.
**3.** A species of something          .
**4.** Eat this with jelly.
**5.** Not looking forward to something.

SLEEP

_ _ _ _ _

_ _ _ _ _

_ _ _ _ _

_ _ _ _ _

_ _ _ _ _

DREAM

## 62. Sink or Swim

Reposition three pencils to make the fish swim in the opposite direction.

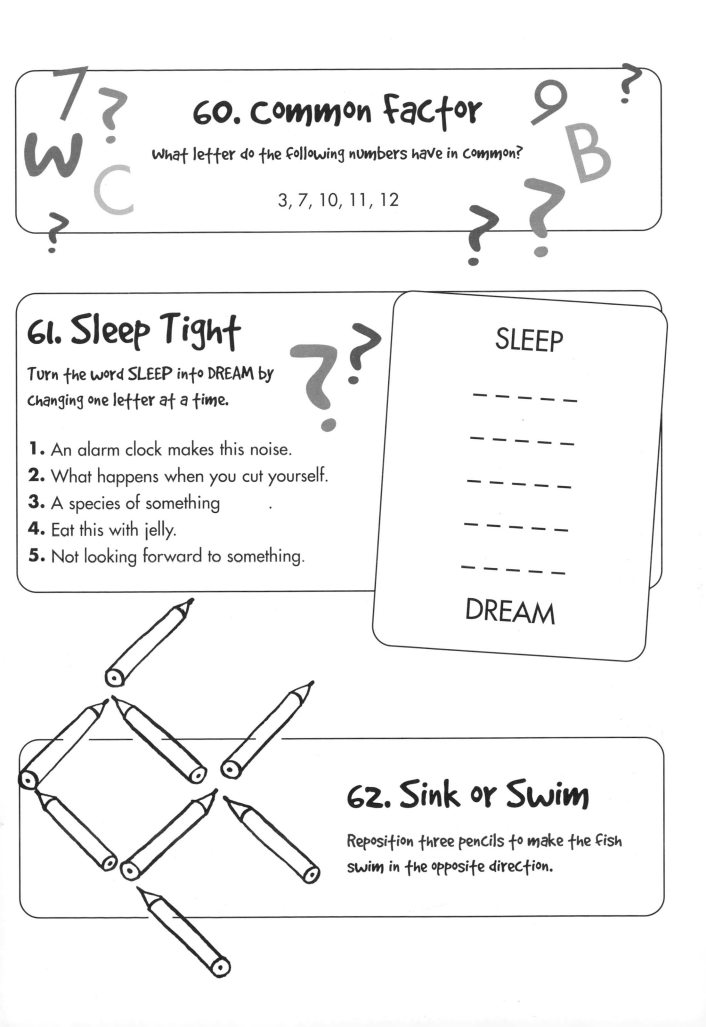

# 63. Picture Guess

Discover the saying from the picture.

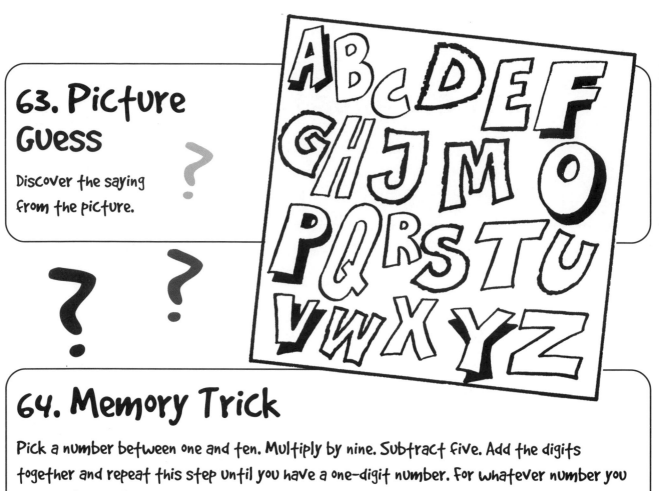

# 64. Memory Trick

Pick a number between one and ten. Multiply by nine. Subtract five. Add the digits together and repeat this step until you have a one-digit number. For whatever number you have, pick that letter of the alphabet. E.g. A = 1, B = 2, etc.

Now think of a country beginning with that letter.

Think of an animal that begins with the second letter of the country.

Think of a color usually associated with the animal. What do you have?

# 65. A Dog's Life

Once there was a dog named Nelly, who lived on a farm. There were three other dogs on the farm. Their names were Blackie, Whitey, and Brownie. What do you think the fourth dog's name was?

# 66. Anagram Anger

Rearrange these letters to give the title of a famous wizard.

## PORT TRAY HER

# 67. Memorize This

Look at the picture below for one minute. Then cover it up (no cheating!) and answer the questions.

**1.** How many loaves of bread are there in the bakery window?
**2.** Whose bakery is it?
**3.** What hairstyles do the twins have?
**4.** What time is it?
**5.** Is the toy shop closed or open?

# 68. Odd One Out

Which of the following words doesn't belong in the group and why?

## LAME    MALE    MEAL    MEAT

# ANSWERS

## 1. Paintbrush Puzzle

## 3. Anagram Antics

Scissors
Hammer
Parrot
Doctor

## 4. Number Search

13 and 19

## 2. Logic Puzzler

Your age.

## 5. Baffling Bet

The man is in a no-win situation—even if he wins the bet he still loses $1 of his money.

# 6. Word Play

Pork
Slow
Card

# 7. Age Question

She's twelve.

# 8. Number Cross

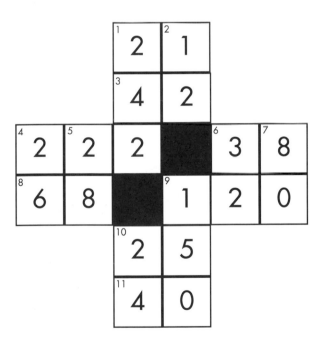

# 9. Driving Dilemma

Bill was driving in reverse.

# 10. Wild Wordsearch

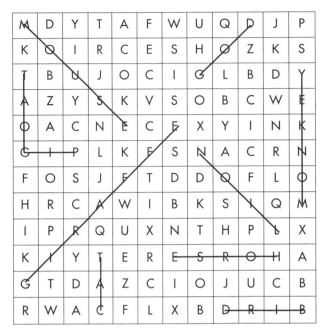

# 11. Letter Change

1. REEL
2. FEEL
3. FEET
4. FELT

# 12. Number Sequence

Fourteen—each time you add on two,
then one, then two, then one and so on.

# 13. Ridiculous Riddle

Coal

# 14. Alphabet Puzzle

1. Hair
2. Fair
3. Chair

# 15. Letter Assembler

Everything

# 16. What Am I?

Empty

# 17. Mix And Match

Swan + cygnet
Bear + cub
Cow + calf
Kangaroo + joey
Rooster + chick
Horse + foal

# 18. Spot The Difference

1. The bottle of drink has gone.
2. The woman's glasses have disappeared.
3. There are now only two balloons.
4. There are only four people queuing for ice cream now.
5. There are five birds in the air now.

# 19. Solve The Mystery

They were used to make a snowman.
The snow has melted.

# 20. Word Change

1. Tale
2. Date
3. Nine or Five

# 21. Proverb Puzzler

Strike while the iron is hot

# 22. Number Cruncher

TWENTY NINE

# 23. Word Wizz

1. IRIS  2. ROSE
3. ASTER  4. VIOLET

# 24. Pencil Trick

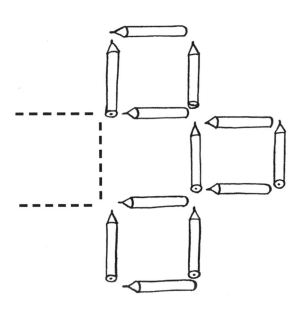

# 25. Letter Logic

S O N D—they are all the first letters of months of the year

# 26. Countdown Conundrum

21

# 27. Hidden Countries

1. Canada—Our dog likes his food so much he eats a **can a da**y.
2. India—Always use a pencil when drawing lines **in dia**grams.
3. Spain—The king was angry when a thief stole hi**s pain**ting.
4. China—Does the teacher tea**ch in a** classroom?
5. Germany—In an**ger, many** people say things they don't mean.

# 28. Adder

Moored

# 29. Tricky Words

They can all have the word BREAK in front of them to make a new word.

## 30. How Did She Do That?

It wasn't raining.

## 31. Upside Down

68 (changes to 89)

## 32. Learn The Language

The key sentences are: There are only three words in the English language. What is the third word? The third word is "language".

## 33. Match Them Up

## 34. Mind The Gap

For

## 35. Oddly Enough

Out!

## 36. Figure It Out

He had six apples to start with and ate two apples on the first day and two on the second.

## 37. Date Dilemma

32—including both dates.

## 38. Missing Alphabet

K and R

## 39. Catch A Cat

Six cats

## 40. Deadly Decision

The explorer makes the statement: "I will be killed by the lions." Now if the chief feeds him to the lions, his statement will be true, so he should be thrown off the cliff. But if he is thrown off the cliff, his statement will be false. The chief has to let the explorer go!

## 41. Animal Madness

1. Lamb
2. Dog
3. Weasel
4. Cow

## 42. Wise Words

AND is between heaven and earth.

## 43. Gambling Games

They played nine games. Tom won three games and Nancy won six games.

## 44. Put Them Together

Hansel and Gretel
Tarzan and Jane
Harry Potter and Hermione Granger
Tom and Jerry
Bilbo Baggins and Gandalf

## 45. About Turn

East

## 46. Complete The Sequence

The next letter is F—the days of the week.

## 47. Car Trouble

They all traveled the same distance—24,000 miles each.

# 48. Wacky Wordsearch

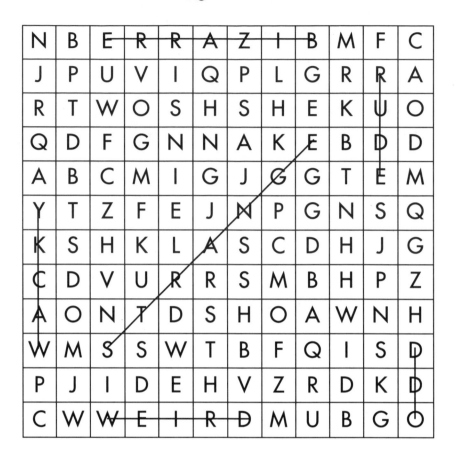

| N | B | E | R | R | A | Z | I | B | M | F | C |
|---|---|---|---|---|---|---|---|---|---|---|---|
| J | P | U | V | I | Q | P | L | G | R | R | A |
| R | T | W | O | S | H | S | H | E | K | U | O |
| Q | D | F | G | N | N | A | K | E | B | D | D |
| A | B | C | M | I | G | J | G | G | T | E | M |
| Y | T | Z | F | E | J | N | P | G | N | S | Q |
| K | S | H | K | L | A | S | C | D | H | J | G |
| C | D | V | U | R | R | S | M | B | H | P | Z |
| A | O | N | T | D | S | H | O | A | W | N | H |
| W | M | S | S | W | T | B | F | Q | I | S | D |
| P | J | I | D | E | H | V | Z | R | D | K | D |
| C | W | W | E | I | R | D | M | U | B | G | O |

# 49. Number Solver

1 x 61

# 50. What Am I?

A bar of soap.

# 51. Letter Game

1. Sand
2. Send
3. Seed
4. Feed

# 52. Picture Puzzle

You're under arrest.

# 53. Pencil Palaver

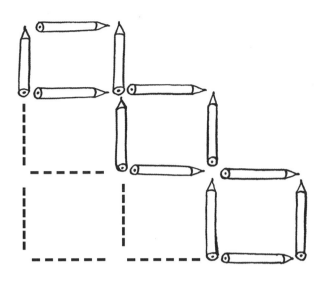

# 54. Sweet Tooth

40

# 55. Long List

The first letters in sequence, spell FIRST, the final letters spell FINAL.

# 56. Number Parts

Four—the first letter of the name has a value with A = 1, B = 2, etc.

# 57. Body Parts

Arm, Ear, Eye, Gum, Hip, Jaw, Lip, Leg, Rib, Toe.
Not: Bum, Gut, Lap!

# 58. Pictionary

Time after time

# 59. Chocolate Challenge

Ten chocolates

# 60. Common Factor

The only vowel they contain when written out fully is the letter E.

# 61. Sleep Tight

1. Bleep
2. Bleed
3. Breed
4. Bread
5. Dread

## 62. Sink or Swim

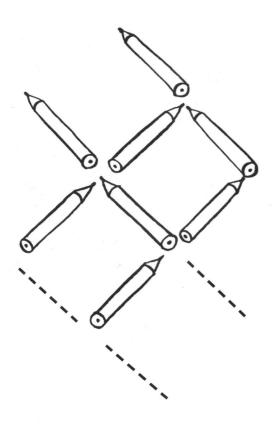

## 63. Picture Guess

Missing Link

## 64. Memory Trick

Do you have a gray elephant from Denmark? Now try it on your friends!

## 65. A Dog's Life

Nelly

## 66. Anagram Anger

Harry Potter

## 67. Memorize This

1. Four
2. Bernie's
3. Plaits
4. 10.30 am
5. Open

## 68. Odd One Out

Meat—all the others are anagrams of each other.

# CROSSWORD SEARCH PUZZLES

```
B Q R S S Q U I R R E L
T H E D G E H O G U T S
L M E J P Z R O L V Q R
Z I R J A C O R N L N Z
O L T K M D A B S T M A
E N P Q A R N A B H L O
A L A D Y B U G D L L O
R A L E A V E S P K A W
T S Y L W A T S M R F D
      D L Q P R V O J I
        O K S M J Q
        T W R L P
```

```
N M C E B O A T M S T S
V O D A F D R O R H U E
H T O L Y I K C E P E T
P O Z C D S R S T N Q A
B R N A A E L S A F L K
A B I A N R C L Z G S S
T I A M A N P T O E R R
G K R Y A R O R B E O E
W E T N I A C U H K T L
S L R A Z N A C Y I A L
U E A M E S R K E B P O
B A I N A V O L I T O R
```

```
M S H L R K T O W E L P
S L D U C W J H V U I S
K L T O F G G X Y E J H
N U R M J R D G R J H G
U G I Z S L L E H S K L
R A S E S S A L G N U S
T E R G H D F D G X U S
J S K M T D H G I B D E
U P O S T C A R D S W N
B S I V W X L G Z J D O
R D L O O P K C O R M T
F S W I M S U I T S H S
```

```
T K G F J L H D F X E R
I E R N K T A E L P V C
A X F C R I M P E R I
L T L E D G N L B
P E I H K F Z W T
H N A L S E H O
C S T J D I D G X E X Z
N I Y M S S R E L R U C
E O N H N V K E H P J I
R N O X O L R F I L F D
F S P F R D N L W G D S
E N H L I C C V Z M R J
```

# 1. Mother Nature

1. A small animal with a bushy tail (8)
2. A tall plant with a trunk and branches (4)
3. A series of tunnels where rabbits live (6)
4. A small red beetle with black spots (7)
5. Season between summer and winter (4)
6. It has a soft body, no bones and lives in the earth (4)
7. Dry soil found in the garden (5)
8. The oval nut of an oak tree (5)
9. They are flat and green and grow on branches (6)
10. A small animal with stiff spines on its back (8)

| B | Q | R | S | S | Q | U | I | R | R | E | L |
|---|---|---|---|---|---|---|---|---|---|---|---|
| T | H | E | D | G | E | H | O | G | U | T | S |
| L | M | E | J | P | Z | R | O | L | V | Q | R |
| Z | I | R | J | A | C | O | R | N | L | N | Z |
| O | L | T | K | M | D | A | B | S | T | M | A |
| E | N | P | Q | A | R | N | A | B | H | L | O |
| A | L | A | D | Y | B | U | G | D | L | L | O |
| R | A | L | E | A | V | E | S | P | K | A | W |
| T | S | Y | L | W | A | T | S | M | R | F | D |
| H | R | A | D | L | Q | P | R | V | O | J | I |
| B | O | T | N | D | J | O | K | S | M | J | Q |
| N | E | R | R | A | W | V | T | W | R | L | P |

# 2. Going Places

1. The capital city of England (6)
2. This is where firefighters work (4, 7)
3. Kings live in this sort of place (6)
4. Where children go to learn new things (6)
5. A place where you can go to swim (8, 4)
6. A place to go when you're very ill or hurt (8)
7. People go here to work on computers (6)
8. Where planes take off and land (7)
9. Here you can see lots of different animals (3)
10. A place where people might go to worship God (6)

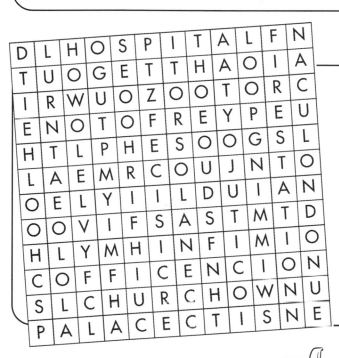

| D | L | H | O | S | P | I | T | A | L | F | N |
|---|---|---|---|---|---|---|---|---|---|---|---|
| T | U | O | G | E | T | T | H | A | O | I | A |
| I | R | W | U | O | Z | O | O | T | O | R | C |
| E | N | O | T | O | F | R | E | Y | P | E | U |
| H | T | L | P | H | E | S | O | O | G | S | L |
| L | A | E | M | R | C | O | U | J | N | T | O |
| O | E | L | Y | I | I | L | D | U | I | A | N |
| O | O | V | I | F | S | A | S | T | M | T | D |
| H | L | Y | M | H | I | N | F | I | M | I | O |
| C | O | F | F | I | C | E | N | C | I | O | N |
| S | L | C | H | U | R | C | H | O | W | N | U |
| P | A | L | A | C | E | C | T | I | S | N | E |

# 3. Getting Around

1. A big vehicle that carries lots of passengers (3)
2. A fast vehicle that runs on tracks (5)
3. This vehicle takes you across the sky (8)
4. A large vehicle that takes objects by road (5)
5. A two-wheeled vehicle that you pedal (4)
6. You drive this small vehicle along the road (3)
7. This vehicle carries people and objects by sea (4)
8. It's larger than a car and smaller than a truck (3)
9. A bike with an engine (9)
10. Wheeled objects attached to feet to get around (6, 6)

| N | M | C | E | B | O | A | T | M | S | T | S |
|---|---|---|---|---|---|---|---|---|---|---|---|
| V | O | D | A | F | D | R | O | R | H | U | E |
| H | T | O | L | Y | I | K | C | E | P | E | T |
| P | O | Z | C | D | S | R | S | T | N | Q | A |
| B | R | N | A | A | E | L | S | A | F | L | K |
| A | B | I | A | N | R | C | L | Z | G | S | S |
| T | I | A | M | A | N | P | T | O | E | R | R |
| G | K | R | Y | A | R | O | R | B | E | O | E |
| W | E | T | N | I | A | C | U | H | K | T | L |
| S | L | R | A | Z | N | A | C | Y | I | A | L |
| U | E | A | M | E | S | R | K | E | B | P | O |
| B | A | I | N | A | V | O | L | I | T | O | R |

# 4. Down on the farm

1. Rolls around in the mud, and has a curly tail (3)
2. This animal's coat is used to make wool (5)
3. An animal with a mane and long tail (5)
4. This hopping animal has soft fur and long ears (6)
5. This animal has feathers and lays eggs (7)
6. They are good at herding sheep (4)
7. A horned animal and some have beards (4)
8. A large animal which goes "moo" (3)
9. A baby goat (3)
10. A male chicken (7)

| S | R | A | B | B | I | T | U | N | T | Y | S |
|---|---|---|---|---|---|---|---|---|---|---|---|
| L | I | N | A | T | C | O | E | S | R | O | H |
| P | M | A | N | T | E | E | N | P | I | D | E |
| E | F | R | E | R | H | E | O | D | N | T | B |
| E | O | M | E | R | K | B | S | E | P | I | G |
| H | V | A | F | C | I | R | H | O | T | R | H |
| S | O | L | I | L | F | D | O | G | S | Z | G |
| T | E | H | Z | D | E | H | D | E | E | F | W |
| O | C | I | L | R | I | T | I | M | T | O | O |
| D | M | Q | T | A | O | G | T | E | H | T | C |
| I | I | G | T | O | N | M | A | N | N | O | I |
| K | R | H | R | O | O | S | T | E | R | W | S |

# 5. Fantastic food

1. A baked dessert which comes in many flavors (4)
2. These small green vegetables grow in a pod (4)
3. Finger-shaped meat found in hot dogs (7)
4. You have this wobbly dessert with ice cream (5)
5. A yellow fruit with spiky green leaves on top (9)
6. Heated bread which has turned brown (5)
7. Sea-living food, often served with fries (4)
8. Hard-shelled food that comes from chickens (3)
9. A vegetable that can be boiled, roasted or fried (6)
10. Breakfast food that is delicious with milk (6)

| L | A | E | R | E | C | A | Y | I | M | F | I |
|---|---|---|---|---|---|---|---|---|---|---|---|
| U | Y | A | S | E | R | D | T | O | A | S | T |
| T | O | R | W | Q | P | O | O | A | N | N | E |
| O | L | L | B | H | E | K | D | J | T | P | H |
| L | O | A | E | G | A | S | U | A | S | I | S |
| L | O | S | I | T | M | C | Y | H | X | Z | I |
| E | H | E | P | O | T | A | T | O | B | S | F |
| J | P | I | N | E | A | P | P | L | E | H | A |
| O | R | Y | W | F | G | L | U | Y | I | K | N |
| T | C | A | K | E | G | U | S | O | U | T | S |
| K | T | O | E | G | V | C | H | P | E | A | S |
| L | A | T | E | R | U | A | P | L | S | E | A |

# 6. Cool colors

1. A mixture of red and blue (6)
2. Light red, the color of fingernails (4)
3. The darkest color (5)
4. The color of "stop" on traffic lights (3)
5. The color of a lemon (6)
6. The lightest color (5)
7. A mixture of red and yellow (6)
8. The color of grass (5)
9. A yellow color, used to make jewelery (4)
10. Another valuable object color (6)

| L | W | R | R | Q | I | E | G | N | A | R | O |
|---|---|---|---|---|---|---|---|---|---|---|---|
| G | H | M | K | E | S | T | L | R | V | T | F |
| E | I | G | G | H | V | I | W | J | R | Z | G |
| P | T | I | K | U | S | L | I | Q | I | O | R |
| E | E | N | T | E | R | U | I | Q | N | S | E |
| L | I | D | E | R | P | H | R | S | G | E | E |
| W | G | O | L | D | T | E | U | M | G | D | N |
| O | E | L | S | V | L | C | K | C | A | L | B |
| L | R | E | W | P | D | K | H | F | P | Z | I |
| L | G | B | R | X | D | N | Y | L | A | N | N |
| E | W | U | E | R | D | I | N | B | S | L | S |
| Y | P | A | V | E | R | P | O | O | A | H | T |

# 7. In the Home

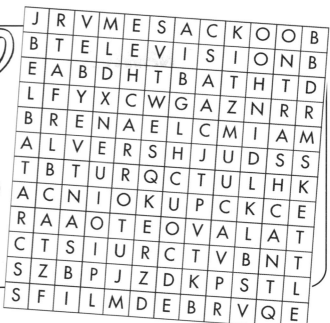

1. An object you put garbage in (8)
2. Something you sleep in (3)
3. What you use to pick up dirt on the floor (6)
4. A four-legged object where food is served (5)
5. Something you lie in to wash or relax (4)
6. You need to go up these to get to the next floor (6)
7. Where books can be stored (8)
8. You heat water in this to make a cup of tea (6)
9. You watch your favorite programs on it (10)
10. A very big chair for two or three people (5)

| J | R | V | M | E | S | A | C | K | O | O | B |
|---|---|---|---|---|---|---|---|---|---|---|---|
| B | T | E | L | E | V | I | S | I | O | N | B |
| E | A | B | D | H | T | B | A | T | H | H | D |
| L | F | Y | X | C | W | G | A | Z | N | R | R |
| B | R | E | N | A | E | L | C | M | I | A | M |
| A | L | V | E | R | S | H | J | U | D | S | S |
| T | B | T | U | R | Q | C | T | U | L | H | K |
| A | C | N | I | O | K | U | P | C | K | C | E |
| R | A | A | O | T | E | O | V | A | L | A | T |
| C | T | S | I | U | R | C | T | V | B | N | T |
| S | Z | B | P | J | Z | D | K | P | S | T | L |
| S | F | I | L | M | D | E | B | R | V | Q | E |

---

| B | A | R | B | I | E | F | G | Q | D | B | R |
|---|---|---|---|---|---|---|---|---|---|---|---|
| S | R | O | Z | T | W | A | S | G | I | J | L |
| S | K | I | P | J | U | M | P | R | O | P | E |
| M | N | O | I | T | A | T | S | Y | A | L | P |
| H | E | R | A | E | B | Y | D | D | E | T | G |
| R | O | C | K | I | N | G | H | O | R | S | E |
| Z | Y | X | D | V | N | H | B | K | K | F | Z |
| Q | N | L | M | C | A | O | A | I | O | H | I |
| O | P | U | W | K | M | B | K | J | O | J | D |
| A | C | T | I | O | N | M | A | N | B | J | O |
| C | O | L | O | R | I | N | G | K | B | K | L |
| R | T | S | E | L | B | R | A | M | F | G | L |

# 8. Toy Store

1. A book with pictures where you fill in the colors (8)
2. A furry toy animal you can cuddle (5, 4)
3. A blond doll who has lots of different outfits (6)
4. Pieces which you put together to see a picture (6)
5. A games console on which you can play (11)
6. A wooden horse you can sit on and ride (7, 5)
7. A hero boy soldier toy you can play with (6, 3)
8. A girl toy you can dress up and style (4)
9. A piece of thick cord with handles to jump over (4, 4)
10. Round pieces of glass flicked at an opponent's (7)

# 9. At the Circus

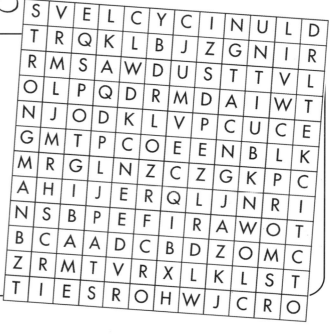

1. A swing on which acrobatics are performed (7)
2. A funny person who does comical tricks (5)
3. The circle in which circus people perform (4)
4. A man who can lift heavy things (6, 3)
5. A bike with one wheel that people do tricks on (8)
6. Powdery wood for animals to walk on (7)
7. This cold treat is sold during the interval (3, 5)
8. You buy one of these to get into the circus (6)
9. A four-legged animal that performers ride on (5)
10. The big tent where the circus is held (3, 3)

| S | V | E | L | C | Y | C | I | N | U | L | D |
|---|---|---|---|---|---|---|---|---|---|---|---|
| T | R | Q | K | L | B | J | Z | G | N | I | R |
| R | M | S | A | W | D | U | S | T | T | V | L |
| O | L | P | Q | D | R | M | D | A | I | W | T |
| N | J | O | D | K | L | V | P | C | U | C | E |
| G | M | T | P | C | O | E | E | N | B | L | K |
| M | R | G | L | N | Z | C | Z | G | K | P | C |
| A | H | I | J | E | R | Q | L | J | N | R | I |
| N | S | B | P | E | F | I | R | A | W | O | T |
| B | C | A | A | D | C | B | D | Z | O | M | C |
| Z | R | M | T | V | R | X | L | K | L | S | T |
| T | I | E | S | R | O | H | W | J | C | R | O |

# 10. Girls' Names

1. Short for Joanne (2)
2. Short for Jennifer (5)
3. This girl's name starts with "T" (6)
4. This name is also the name of a flower (4)
5. This woman was the mother of Jesus (4)
6. This five-letter name begins with "S" (5)
7. This name is the same when it's spelt backwards (4)
8. This name can be shortened to "Maggie" (8)
9. The Queen of England's name (9)
10. This pop star sang "Sometimes" and "Boys" (7)

| Z | E | L | I | Z | A | B | E | T | H | X | O |
|---|---|---|---|---|---|---|---|---|---|---|---|
| X | M | E | I | L | N | D | Z | O | A | W | J |
| B | J | L | N | M | A | R | Y | B | C | T | S |
| M | D | T | E | R | A | G | R | A | M | R | P |
| K | V | R | C | I | B | Q | J | K | Z | O | Y |
| U | H | S | Y | E | N | T | I | R | B | V | E |
| K | A | O | U | S | R | O | J | P | I | H | C |
| L | R | M | K | O | C | M | A | E | P | R | A |
| D | A | B | S | T | Q | I | V | N | F | X | R |
| N | S | E | L | D | K | G | X | A | N | M | T |
| Z | I | V | N | W | O | B | W | B | Z | A | S |
| A | L | M | Z | R | J | E | N | N | Y | R | Z |

## (Writers / Workers grid)

| B | C | N | S | T | W | R | I | T | E | R | S |
|---|---|---|---|---|---|---|---|---|---|---|---|
| F | L | O | R | I | S | T | R | U | N | A | R |
| S | D | O | C | T | O | R | S | U | U | R | E |
| R | Y | H | M | A | E | A | R | F | O | K | T |
| E | N | Y | C | R | I | S | L | T | B | Q | H |
| H | D | D | S | Z | E | O | C | O | W | V | G |
| C | R | K | I | S | L | A | P | L | T | B | I |
| A | T | N | E | D | I | S | E | R | P | E | F |
| E | Q | P | U | L | L | W | M | S | L | M | E |
| T | Z | L | W | R | E | K | M | F | K | I | R |
| F | X | S | R | E | M | R | A | F | Q | R | I |
| S | I | N | G | E | R | S | W | T | I | P | F |

# 11. At Work

1. He runs America (9)
2. They make ill people well again (7)
3. They help doctors (6)
4. They sing very well (7)
5. They help children to learn (8)
6. They grow crops and raise animals (7)
7. They put fires out and rescue people (12)
8. She makes up stories and poems (6)
9. She sells and arranges flowers (7)
10. He plays different parts in movies or plays (5)

# 12. Wild Animals

1. African animal with a very long neck (7)
2. Very large animal with a trunk and tusks (8)
3. This big cat is the fastest land animal (7)
4. Black and white, this looks like a horse (5)
5. A mischievous animal, similar to humans (6)
6. A big cat with a huge roar and a fur mane (4)
7. A black and white sea bird that eats fish (7)
8. A large swimming reptile with lots of teeth (9)
9. A large, heavy animal with thick fur (4)
10. A big river animal with thick skin (12)

| N | Z | R | R | A | E | B | S | E | I | D | D |
|---|---|---|---|---|---|---|---|---|---|---|---|
| Z | Y | E | U | V | X | H | U | L | L | P | C |
| N | B | O | B | R | I | V | M | E | X | V | R |
| H | L | L | D | R | P | Y | A | P | K | G | O |
| A | L | I | S | Z | A | K | T | H | M | I | C |
| T | C | U | O | L | O | N | O | A | N | R | O |
| E | V | K | B | N | I | M | P | N | I | A | D |
| E | O | A | X | U | Z | E | O | T | U | F | I |
| H | S | R | G | U | N | K | P | N | G | F | L |
| C | U | N | A | P | I | N | P | R | N | E | E |
| O | E | L | C | V | R | C | I | T | E | D | R |
| P | M | O | N | K | E | Y | H | B | B | O | L |

# 13. Holidays

1. Presents are left in this at Christmas (8)
2. This is decorated with tinsel and baubles at Christmas (4)
3. Jewish holiday in December (8)
4. Traditional meat eaten at Thanksgiving (6)
5. You are given these at Christmas (8)
6. Father ____, another name for Santa Claus (9)
7. Baby Jesus was laid in this (6)
8. Eat this after the main course (7)
9. These special songs are sung at Christmas (6)
10. Chocolate cake eaten at Christmas (4, 3)

| C | Z | C | S | A | M | T | S | I | R | H | C |
|---|---|---|---|---|---|---|---|---|---|---|---|
| M | M | A | N | G | E | R | O | Y | X | S | R |
| G | P | H | B | T | C | A | R | O | L | S | E |
| N | U | R | I | D | U | A | C | U | M | F | H |
| I | D | Z | H | M | W | R | P | A | T | N | T |
| K | D | A | T | A | V | S | K | M | O | I | A |
| C | I | M | X | L | K | L | Z | E | K | H | F |
| O | N | P | M | E | F | K | M | S | Y | Z | A |
| T | G | O | E | I | B | Q | U | D | F | W | Q |
| S | C | R | P | O | A | X | Y | N | N | W | B |
| N | T | Y | U | L | E | L | O | G | A | Z | X |
| Q | S | T | N | E | S | E | R | P | L | H | H |

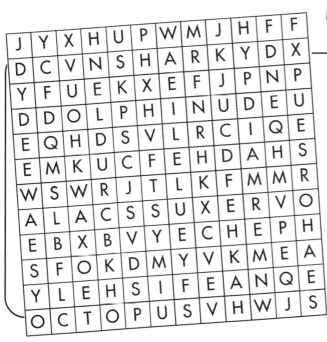

| J | Y | X | H | U | P | W | M | J | H | F | F |
|---|---|---|---|---|---|---|---|---|---|---|---|
| D | C | V | N | S | H | A | R | K | Y | D | X |
| Y | F | U | E | K | X | E | F | J | P | N | P |
| D | D | O | L | P | H | I | N | U | D | E | U |
| E | Q | H | D | S | V | L | R | C | I | Q | E |
| E | M | K | U | C | F | E | H | D | A | H | S |
| W | S | W | R | J | T | L | K | F | M | M | R |
| A | L | A | C | S | S | U | X | E | R | V | O |
| E | B | X | B | V | V | Y | E | C | H | E | P | H |
| S | F | O | K | D | M | Y | V | K | M | E | A |
| Y | L | E | H | S | I | F | E | A | N | Q | E |
| O | C | T | O | P | U | S | V | H | W | J | S |

# 14. Under the Sea

1. Shellfish with large claws (7)
2. Fishy horse (8)
3. Plant that grows in the sea (7)
4. Intelligent animal that plays in the sea (7)
5. Imaginary half-woman with a fish's tail (7)
6. A shellfish with ten legs (4)
7. There are lots of these in the sea (4)
8. Large sea fish with lots of sharp teeth (5)
9. Moving ridges of water in the sea (5)
10. Large sea animal with eight tentacles (7)

# 15. TV Characters

1. Thomas the Tank Engine's pal (5)
2. He's also known as T.C. (3, 3)
3. This builder likes to fix things (3)
4. He's a big purple dinosaur (6)
5. This powerful man is very strong (5)
6. One of the Rugrats (5)
7. The name of the main tank engine (6)
8. ____ Bunny (4)
9. This crime-solving dog gets very scared (6, 3)
10. Dummy-sucking Simpsons character (6)

| N | B | O | B | F | I | X | W | T | S | A | H |
|---|---|---|---|---|---|---|---|---|---|---|---|
| P | A | S | H | L | T | C | H | J | U | F | I |
| L | C | U | B | O | Y | O | K | P | S | W | D |
| E | D | Y | M | A | M | F | T | B | E | N | L |
| I | K | M | Y | A | I | L | A | H | I | Y | P |
| G | Y | B | S | H | N | K | C | Y | B | E | I |
| G | N | X | P | A | S | M | P | F | S | N | U |
| A | S | L | M | Y | S | J | O | A | G | R | B |
| M | C | E | K | W | G | U | T | X | U | A | S |
| L | H | A | F | B | J | P | H | N | B | B | X |
| S | C | O | O | B | Y | D | O | O | C | Y | H |
| U | H | E | N | R | Y | A | N | L | A | W | G |

# 16. Family Fun

1. The man who brings you up (3)
2. Father of your mom or dad (7)
3. Mother of your mom or dad (7)
4. The child of your aunt or uncle (6)
5. Your brother or sister's daughter (5)
6. The woman who brings you up (3)
7. Daughter of the same parents as another person (6)
8. Sister or sister-in-law of your mom or dad (6)
9. Your brother or sister's son (6)
10. Son of the same parents as another person (7)

| B | E | C | E | I | N | U | I | F | K | E | M |
|---|---|---|---|---|---|---|---|---|---|---|---|
| H | R | X | A | L | C | J | I | H | Z | O | W |
| N | E | P | H | E | W | S | X | B | M | R | P |
| I | S | C | B | A | M | D | N | A | R | G | U |
| Z | F | O | H | I | F | G | E | M | C | E | I |
| E | A | U | J | R | D | L | A | W | N | L | O |
| I | R | S | N | E | P | A | S | H | D | H | W |
| T | M | I | R | T | I | U | D | P | K | A | U |
| N | C | N | S | S | J | H | O | N | D | K | D |
| U | O | A | M | I | H | Z | E | I | A | Y | X |
| A | B | L | X | S | D | N | P | F | W | R | K |
| R | B | R | O | T | H | E | R | R | U | E | G |

# 17. Clothes

1. Wear these to walk in (5)
2. An alternative to pants (5)
3. A top, often made of wool (6)
4. Wear these on your feet under shoes (5)
5. This top is shaped like a T (1, 5)
6. Wear these over your legs (5)
7. Wear these under your clothes (9)
8. This is a combined skirt and top (5)
9. This goes over your clothes when you go outside (4)
10. This long woolly item keeps your neck warm (5)

| G | S | E | O | H | S | Q | I | L | U | D | L |
|---|---|---|---|---|---|---|---|---|---|---|---|
| A | K | H | V | F | Y | R | B | G | M | R | F |
| U | M | X | R | I | E | N | R | U | O | E | A |
| I | N | A | O | P | F | U | N | V | K | S | T |
| H | C | L | M | H | Q | D | A | S | O | S | R |
| S | R | U | G | B | E | M | R | K | N | O | I |
| Y | J | E | K | R | H | E | H | H | I | M | H |
| N | U | V | W | L | S | Y | X | B | H | Q | S |
| F | Q | E | I | T | R | T | A | O | C | F | T |
| M | A | V | N | A | G | T | R | I | K | S | N |
| R | B | A | L | K | N | M | U | V | E | O | G |
| Y | P | R | I | U | S | O | C | K | S | Y | X |

# 18. In the Garden

1. Use this to dig (5)
2. These plants aren't wanted (5)
3. Grow plants in this building (10)
4. You cut the grass with it (9)
5. A small house for children to play in (9)
6. A ceramic or plastic object to put plants in (9)
7. A wheeled object that carries heavy things (11)
8. Paved area where people can sit (5)
9. A beautiful plant with petals (6)
10. A wooden structure to separate gardens (5)

| W | R | I | R | E | W | O | M | N | W | A | L |
|---|---|---|---|---|---|---|---|---|---|---|---|
| H | Y | J | T | A | L | P | A | T | I | O | B |
| E | F | D | K | O | T | R | B | L | G | N | D |
| E | L | E | L | N | P | E | T | Y | C | Z | S |
| L | O | A | C | B | Z | R | J | I | D | Q | D |
| B | W | G | W | N | D | H | E | U | C | U | E |
| A | E | R | Y | I | E | E | L | W | B | J | E |
| R | R | J | T | D | Q | F | B | K | O | L | W |
| R | K | T | A | B | K | N | G | T | I | L | K |
| O | U | P | D | W | Y | N | A | Q | U | Z | F |
| W | S | R | E | S | U | O | H | Y | A | L | P |
| J | K | G | R | E | E | N | H | O | U | S | E |

# 19. Space

1. Earth's only natural satellite (4)
2. Someone who goes into outer space (9)
3. Large body in space that revolves around the sun (6)
4. This explosive thing shoots into space (6)
5. Reusable spacecraft (7)
6. Bodies of gas that shine in the sky (5)
7. The moon has none of this force on it (7)
8. Includes the sun and eight planets (5, 6)
9. The planet we live on (5)
10. Heavenly body with a luminous "tail" (5)

| Q | C | H | G | T | E | K | C | O | R | I | V |
|---|---|---|---|---|---|---|---|---|---|---|---|
| B | O | M | R | L | D | Q | Z | B | A | H | O |
| R | M | E | A | U | W | M | G | T | S | K | L |
| D | E | T | V | V | B | O | E | N | T | O | G |
| H | T | S | I | K | L | N | X | S | R | K | E |
| M | Z | Y | T | G | A | R | D | G | O | S | L |
| O | B | S | Y | L | H | M | T | K | N | W | T |
| O | I | R | P | V | T | U | H | Y | A | X | T |
| N | U | A | T | Q | B | T | I | L | U | O | U |
| S | K | L | D | S | R | D | Z | D | T | R | H |
| Q | G | O | H | A | X | N | V | O | N | M | S |
| Z | R | S | E | L | S | R | A | T | S | X | D |

| F | O | T | R | A | E | H | S | T | U | A | R |
|---|---|---|---|---|---|---|---|---|---|---|---|
| T | C | Z | Q | H | K | E | O | D | A | E | H |
| E | R | L | A | T | U | L | M | Z | K | B | N |
| E | K | N | M | U | S | C | L | E | Q | F | V |
| F | D | F | C | S | Q | N | V | E | S | T | P |
| S | L | R | E | O | A | M | N | A | R | E | T |
| A | T | Y | U | S | N | O | B | C | L | E | N |
| C | E | P | Q | C | B | T | K | B | R | N | O |
| F | Z | U | K | R | L | F | A | T | Z | K | H |
| S | L | I | A | N | R | E | G | N | I | F | B |
| R | P | C | L | Q | N | O | V | R | S | H | L |
| K | N | O | T | T | U | B | Y | L | L | E | B |

# 20. The Body

1. You see with these (4)
2. Allows the leg to bend (4)
3. On top of your neck (4)
4. You walk on these (4)
5. You pick things up with these (5)
6. Tissue that allows us to move (6)
7. This pumps blood around the body (5)
8. This hard material part makes up the skeleton (4)
9. Also known as the navel (5, 6)
10. They are on the end of your fingers (11)

# 21. Opposites

1. The opposite of cold (3)
2. The opposite of thin (3)
3. The opposite of big (5)
4. The opposite of up (4)
5. The opposite of difficult (4)
6. The opposite of quiet (4)
7. The opposite of right (4)
8. The opposite of backward (7)
9. The opposite of quickly (6)
10. The opposite of smooth (5)

| Z | F | P | D | Y | L | W | O | L | S | P | E |
|---|---|---|---|---|---|---|---|---|---|---|---|
| O | R | E | S | Q | K | S | X | H | C | H | N |
| U | X | M | E | D | H | B | L | Y | S | A | E |
| D | N | K | K | T | R | D | O | X | N | K | T |
| N | B | T | F | U | Z | A | R | J | T | J | G |
| W | K | E | R | F | N | F | W | I | S | F | D |
| O | L | S | L | P | K | R | U | R | Q | L | S |
| D | X | T | D | B | O | M | G | T | O | C | M |
| Q | F | O | C | U | E | G | A | X | K | F | A |
| G | I | H | G | E | J | F | P | I | E | S | L |
| K | Z | H | D | N | O | F | T | K | Z | D | L |
| M | U | D | U | O | L | R | B | H | R | S | J |

## 22. Magic

1. The magic word (11)
2. A magician's helper (9)
3. Pull this out of a hat (6)
4. Someone who performs magic (8)
5. Magicians perform these (6)
6. Tricks sometimes involve a pack of these (5)
7. A magic black and white stick (4)
8. Harry who is a famous young magician (6)
9. Wave this around to conceal things (12)
10. "Hey _____" is the magic saying (6)

| | | | | | | | | | | | |
|---|---|---|---|---|---|---|---|---|---|---|---|
| F | E | I | H | C | R | E | K | D | N | A | H |
| A | B | R | A | C | A | D | A | B | R | A | M |
| O | H | N | F | D | H | S | E | S | W | Q | A |
| T | L | K | J | H | S | O | N | N | L | J | A |
| S | E | A | B | D | V | A | M | K | H | S | R |
| E | M | W | R | L | I | R | F | C | S | S | A |
| R | D | A | Q | C | E | H | D | I | V | X | B |
| P | C | K | I | T | N | N | S | N | Q | K | B |
| S | F | G | T | A | E | T | D | C | M | S | I |
| L | A | O | J | O | A | B | W | N | L | F | T |
| M | P | H | V | N | B | K | D | M | A | S | A |
| A | Q | M | T | R | I | C | K | S | J | W | Z |

## 23. The Beach

| | | | | | | | | | | |
|---|---|---|---|---|---|---|---|---|---|---|
| O | G | H | R | S | W | I | M | S | U | I | T |
| D | T | E | W | I | N | D | B | R | E | A | K |
| U | S | L | C | S | A | Y | W | Q | L | N | C |
| N | A | T | J | U | D | H | X | D | H | O | J |
| W | N | S | G | S | O | G | C | D | P | T | J |
| P | D | A | H | Y | C | T | R | K | G | J | X |
| L | W | C | D | Q | U | L | F | H | C | N | H |
| E | I | D | C | H | T | C | N | B | W | E | R |
| W | C | N | P | A | D | D | L | I | N | G | D |
| O | H | A | H | S | I | F | R | A | T | S | C |
| T | E | S | D | G | H | S | O | P | U | Q | Y |
| Y | S | L | I | F | E | G | U | A | R | D | T |

1. A chair you sit on on the beach (4, 5)
2. Splashing in the sea (8)
3. Dry yourself off with this (5)
4. A star-shaped sea creature (8)
5. Put this up to shelter you from wind (9)
6. These popular snacks can be eaten on the beach (10)
7. A little wooden shack on the beachfront (3)
8. A castle made with a bucket and spade (10)
9. Suit ladies wear (8)
10. Someone who watches swimmers in case they get into trouble (9)

## 24. Time

1. Ten years (6)
2. 60 seconds (6)
3. 60 minutes (4)
4. 365 days (4)
5. Wear this on your wrist to tell the time (5)
6. There are 60 of these in one minute (7)
7. Clock that beeps when it's time to get up (5)
8. There are twelve of these in a year (6)
9. There are seven of these each week (4)
10. A clock in a tall wooden case (11)

| | | | | | | | | | | |
|---|---|---|---|---|---|---|---|---|---|---|
| O | M | I | N | U | T | E | C | P | S | Y | T |
| A | D | M | U | E | V | W | F | R | N | X | F |
| B | S | H | C | T | A | W | G | E | M | O | B |
| S | D | N | O | C | E | S | D | H | W | B | G |
| D | O | T | N | S | N | D | R | T | E | A | P |
| R | P | X | Y | A | C | A | H | A | Y | L | X |
| U | W | E | F | D | E | N | N | F | S | A | G |
| O | G | V | D | Y | M | B | T | D | U | R | B |
| H | A | S | B | A | O | P | S | N | F | M | S |
| T | N | H | E | Y | C | D | U | A | V | D | Y |
| C | B | M | D | X | W | E | M | R | N | X | A |
| S | H | T | N | O | M | G | D | G | D | S | D |

## 25. Drinks

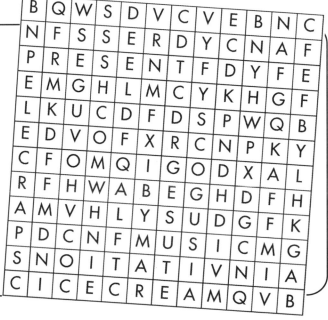

1. Made with bags or leaves (3)
2. Apple or orange (5)
3. Ginger ____ (4)
4. Free and pure (5)
5. This type of drink has bubbles in it (10)
6. Made from beans (6)
7. Made from grapes, alcoholic (4)
8. Add this flavoring to water to make a drink (7)
9. Drink you can pour over your cereal (4)
10. Sweet that can also be a hot drink (9)

| J | O | T | C | H | O | C | O | L | A | T | E |
|---|---|---|---|---|---|---|---|---|---|---|---|
| C | O | R | D | I | A | L | H | K | D | S | X |
| Y | C | B | E | D | A | Z | R | E | E | B | D |
| C | A | R | B | O | N | A | T | E | D | M | B |
| K | H | E | F | F | O | C | V | H | J | D |   |
| J | D | M | C | N | N | S | K | W | I | N | E |
| S | X | T | B | B | T | Y | O | N | L | H | K |
| S | E | B | H | I | Z | R | A | V | C | F | C |
| A | L | K | V | Z | B | J | R | E | T | A | W |
| W | N | M | I | Y | W | D | B | V | S | X | S |
| O | Z | D | F | M | I | L | K | N | A | O | L |
| I | A | S | N | M | C | J | U | I | C | E | Z |

## 26. The Playground

| G | L | Y | T | R | O | F | Y | S | E | E | K |
|---|---|---|---|---|---|---|---|---|---|---|---|
| K | E | L | N | I | J | D | S | I | O | Y | U |
| O | E | P | R | L | A | D | D | E | R | S | H |
| U | R | L | V | E | H | X | F | D | V | W | C |
| H | L | E | D | Z | C | D | F | K | U | G | T |
| B | K | I | C | A | S | C | P | X | I | M | O |
| E | F | N | W | E | R | G | O | J | N | R | C |
| L | D | Y | T | R | S | C | T | S | H | Y | S |
| L | S | H | T | A | G | S | S | X | D | F | P |
| I | J | I | K | V | F | I | M | T | K | F | O |
| G | N | I | P | P | I | K | S | E | A | N | H |
| P | F | N | X | Z | H | W | T | V | J | C | S |

1. A break between lessons when children play (6)
2. A game played with elastic (4, 6)
3. You have to touch another person in this game (3)
4. Hide and ____ (4)
5. A game where you kick a ball (6)
6. This rings to signal the end of break (4)
7. A hop, skip and jump game (9)
8. Stuck in the ___ (3)
9. Jumping with a rope (8)
10. Snakes and _____ (7)

## 27. Party Time

1. Dance to this (5)
2. Eat this at the party (4)
3. A gift for the host (7)
4. A present might be carried in this (3)
5. Hope you have a _____ birthday (5)
6. You might wear this to the party (5, 5)
7. Have this treat with jello (3, 5)
8. Pass this on to get a prize (6)
9. You need one of these to go to the party (10)
10. In musical _____ you should sit down when the music stops (6)

| B | Q | W | S | D | V | C | V | E | B | N | C |
|---|---|---|---|---|---|---|---|---|---|---|---|
| N | F | S | S | E | R | D | Y | C | N | A | F |
| P | R | E | S | E | N | T | F | D | Y | F | E |
| E | M | G | H | L | M | C | Y | K | H | G | F |
| L | K | U | C | D | F | D | S | P | W | Q | B |
| E | D | V | O | F | X | R | C | N | P | K | Y |
| C | F | O | M | Q | I | G | O | D | X | A | L |
| R | F | H | W | A | B | E | G | H | D | F | H |
| A | M | V | H | L | Y | S | U | D | G | F | K |
| P | D | C | N | F | M | U | S | I | C | M | G |
| S | N | O | I | T | A | T | I | V | N | I | A |
| C | I | C | E | C | R | E | A | M | Q | V | B |

# 28. Vacations

1. Send these to your friends (9)
2. Pack your clothes in this (8)
3. Where you catch the airplane from (7)
4. A building to stay in with lots of rooms (5)
5. Use this to find your way around (3)
6. A roll-up bag you sleep in (8, 3)
7. A mobile home you can stay in (7)
8. A material home held up with poles (4)
9. Don't forget this to clean your teeth with (10)
10. We hope the weather is like this (5)

| T | E | N | T | G | B | F | D | S | W | E | Q |
|---|---|---|---|---|---|---|---|---|---|---|---|
| A | M | E | K | B | R | E | L | I | A | R | T |
| S | L | E | E | P | I | N | G | B | A | G | F |
| L | P | H | S | U | R | B | H | T | O | O | T |
| N | O | F | J | R | H | U | Q | H | D | E | D |
| W | S | S | U | N | N | Y | F | G | F | S | N |
| G | T | B | E | M | L | D | V | A | B | A | L |
| Q | C | D | F | A | E | E | N | Q | R | C | W |
| K | A | S | D | J | H | W | T | B | U | T | K |
| E | R | B | P | A | M | G | E | O | D | I | J |
| N | D | L | F | R | M | S | H | Q | H | U | B |
| S | S | T | R | O | P | R | I | A | F | S | A |

# 29. Farmyard Animals

1. The male of this animal is called a gander (5)
2. The male of this animal is called a billy (4)
3. This bird lives on water and quacks (4)
4. A small furry domesticated animal (3)
5. A female chicken (3)
6. A male version of a cow (4)
7. A large bird that gobbles (6)
8. A baby sheep (4)
9. A baby dog (5)
10. A mammal found on South American farms (5)

| M | J | L | N | D | F | V | H | B | C | N | X |
|---|---|---|---|---|---|---|---|---|---|---|---|
| L | N | K | T | I | K | Q | N | E | H | H | K |
| L | G | O | O | S | E | U | E | D | V | I | Y |
| A | C | E | D | U | C | K | M | D | G | K | E |
| M | X | J | H | X | C | H | I | C | L | T | K |
| A | T | C | N | X | H | B | Y | V | B | V | R |
| D | A | B | K | G | N | E | J | P | N | M | U |
| F | O | L | V | T | D | C | B | G | P | U | T |
| G | G | I | K | Q | M | M | J | H | Q | U | X |
| V | X | E | B | U | A | F | X | D | T | L | P |
| B | U | L | L | L | F | N | K | K | I | C | J |
| C | J | M | Q | G | E | T | A | C | V | F | B |

# 30. Bedtime

1. A girl wears this to sleep in (7)
2. Something you rest your head on (6)
3. You may drink this before you go to bed (5)
4. Pictures that you see when you are asleep (6)
5. Mommy might come and ___ you into bed (4)
6. Turn this out before you go to sleep (5)
7. Read or listen to one at bedtime (5)
8. This toy may sleep with you (5)
9. Drink this warm before bed (4)
10. Have a hug and a ____ before bed (4)

| G | J | K | B | V | C | F | D | S | W | H | S |
|---|---|---|---|---|---|---|---|---|---|---|---|
| Q | E | I | T | H | G | I | N | R | T | Y | C |
| S | K | W | Z | C | U | I | K | L | I | M | I |
| K | W | I | Q | V | G | M | S | C | C | F | T |
| C | B | X | S | J | G | M | C | N | X | W | Q |
| U | T | H | R | S | A | F | W | K | A | G | J |
| T | E | D | Y | E | M | T | H | T | C | I | S |
| K | D | V | R | C | V | B | E | Z | V | H | T |
| G | D | D | W | U | Q | R | U | J | B | D | O |
| F | Y | C | H | R | X | K | C | F | S | W | R |
| S | B | Z | F | T | W | O | L | L | I | P | Y |
| X | T | H | G | I | L | Y | D | H | G | V | K |

# 31. The Desert

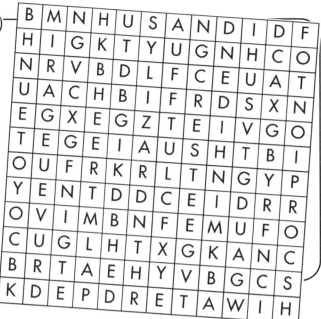

1. A prairie wolf (6)
2. The sun's warmth (4)
3. A pool of water in the desert (5)
4. This animal has one or two humps (5)
5. A reptile with four legs and a long tail (6)
6. A tree with large leaves and no branches (4, 4)
7. An optical illusion caused by the atmosphere (6)
8. Fine fragments of crushed rock (4)
9. Small creature with a sting in its long tail (8)
10. There isn't much of this drink in the desert (5)

| B | M | N | H | U | S | A | N | D | I | D | F |
|---|---|---|---|---|---|---|---|---|---|---|---|
| H | I | G | K | T | Y | U | G | N | H | C | O |
| N | R | V | B | D | L | F | C | E | U | A | T |
| U | A | C | H | B | I | F | R | D | S | X | N |
| E | G | X | E | G | Z | T | E | I | V | G | O |
| T | E | G | E | I | A | U | S | H | T | B | I |
| O | U | F | R | K | R | L | T | N | G | Y | P |
| Y | E | N | T | D | D | C | E | I | D | R | R |
| O | V | I | M | B | N | F | E | M | U | F | O |
| C | U | G | L | H | T | X | G | K | A | N | C |
| B | R | T | A | E | H | Y | V | B | G | C | S |
| K | D | E | P | D | R | E | T | A | W | I | H |

# 32. Flowers

| J | K | N | P | A | N | S | I | E | V | H | C |
|---|---|---|---|---|---|---|---|---|---|---|---|
| X | D | A | D | A | I | S | Y | R | F | O | J |
| H | R | T | N | Y | S | N | A | P | G | L | K |
| P | C | E | B | J | F | G | D | U | C | L | X |
| P | N | F | W | Z | F | K | G | C | N | Y | A |
| E | E | G | E | O | M | B | D | R | V | J | Y |
| T | V | F | N | E | L | A | M | E | N | T | L |
| A | K | H | S | S | X | F | P | T | Q | E | I |
| L | M | O | Z | B | D | R | N | T | N | S | L |
| J | R | D | E | P | A | T | S | U | H | G | K |
| X | A | T | E | U | Q | U | O | B | S | J | P |
| D | N | G | M | V | Q | N | G | F | A | E | L |

1. A funnel-shaped flower (4)
2. An arrangement of flowers (7)
3. A flower that is named after the sun (9)
4. A wild plant with yellow, cup-shaped flowers (9)
5. A small flower with white petals (5)
6. A colored outer part of a flower head (5)
7. A green, flat organ that grows from the stem (4)
8. Member of the violet family, with broad petals (5)
9. Rearrange the letters of "sore" to make this flower (4)
10. A prickly plant associated with Christmas (5)

# 33. The Letter 'W'

1. Opposite of man (5)
2. Opposite of black (5)
3. Wear this on your wrist (5)
4. Use a pen to do this (5)
5. It runs in streams (5)
6. Birds use them to fly (5)
7. Humpty Dumpty sat on one (4)
8. Do this to clean yourself (4)
9. Cats have them on their faces (8)
10. Spiders make these (3)

| W | V | H | F | W | A | T | E | R | F | D | S |
|---|---|---|---|---|---|---|---|---|---|---|---|
| A | D | C | E | D | W | R | I | T | E | W | R |
| L | R | T | E | S | X | W | Y | N | W | H | G |
| L | K | S | J | J | R | O | Y | R | E | I | S |
| W | N | D | F | S | H | E | R | I | A | T | W |
| G | F | T | G | C | I | P | K | D | K | E | C |
| D | X | N | A | F | S | H | R | S | G | S | V |
| Y | I | E | V | T | N | T | S | E | I | G | S |
| W | W | H | R | A | G | X | N | A | F | H | E |
| V | K | S | M | D | S | S | Y | C | W | T | W |
| T | F | O | G | A | W | A | T | C | H | T | F |
| S | W | W | E | B | S | E | T | E | E | A | S |

# 34. The Letter 'S'

1. You get one of these if you stay in the sun (6)
2. Wear these on your feet around the house (8)
3. The green supporting part of a plant (4)
4. A precious metal and a color (6)
5. Words and music make a ____ (4)
6. The number between six and eight (5)
7. Close your eyes and go to ____ (5)
8. A soft-bodied animal with a shell (5)
9. These twinkle in the night sky (5)
10. An apology (5)

| S | D | F | G | M | H | S | L | E | E | P | J |
|---|---|---|---|---|---|---|---|---|---|---|---|
| I | K | S | E | L | S | P | C | O | S | R | S |
| L | E | T | I | K | U | D | I | T | J | I | T |
| V | S | O | R | S | O | E | A | S | S | D | S |
| E | D | K | O | S | W | R | A | K | R | R | I |
| R | W | R | Z | O | S | N | F | G | E | L | D |
| F | R | L | C | D | A | D | E | S | P | O | N |
| Y | H | J | S | T | S | K | N | D | P | H | E |
| G | S | R | N | U | W | A | R | A | I | C | V |
| I | E | U | O | J | I | L | J | S | L | G | E |
| K | S | Z | X | L | D | T | R | K | S | F | S |
| R | U | S | Y | G | N | O | S | R | O | S | H |

# 35. Spies

1. Leaving something to be picked up later is called a dead ____ (4)
2. Spies carry important things in this (9)
3. Spies who are on a secret mission are said to have gone _____ (10)
4. To help you find your way (3)
5. Write your message in ____ to keep it secret (4)
6. Something which not many people know (6)
7. Spies wear this color to go unnoticed (5)
8. Spies wear these to cover their eyes (10)
9. Use this to get in touch with other spies (4, 5)
10. Spies use these to keep dry in the rain (8)

| K | O | S | U | N | G | L | A | S | S | E | S |
|---|---|---|---|---|---|---|---|---|---|---|---|
| L | R | E | V | O | C | R | E | D | N | U | K |
| A | E | N | O | H | P | L | L | E | C | O | M |
| R | E | D | O | C | V | J | E | A | E | R | I |
| S | O | T | L | A | K | F | L | T | S | L | O |
| J | E | W | I | P | N | L | G | B | A | A | J |
| F | R | A | O | N | E | T | E | R | C | E | S |
| K | V | R | K | R | J | J | P | W | F | N | O |
| C | D | A | B | T | S | R | I | S | E | B | K |
| A | M | M | G | P | K | L | O | E | I | P | V |
| L | U | E | J | F | A | V | A | M | R | K | J |
| B | S | I | O | W | N | M | A | T | B | G | R |

# 36. Birds

1. Powerful bird of prey (5)
2. A small brown-gray bird (7)
3. Nickname for the budgerigar (6)
4. A small bird with a red breast (5)
5. A brightly colored bird that talks (6)
6. A large blackbird with a harsh cry (4)
7. This bird lays its eggs in other birds' nests (6)
8. Large bird from Australia that doesn't fly (3)
9. A pink-feathered bird with long legs (8)
10. Can hover in the air, this bird's wings hum (11)

| N | R | O | B | I | N | F | C | H | S | T | U |
|---|---|---|---|---|---|---|---|---|---|---|---|
| D | I | K | X | E | O | O | K | C | U | C | Y |
| W | R | A | O | G | N | I | M | A | L | F | M |
| S | N | I | M | O | P | K | E | N | B | O | A |
| H | W | F | B | N | D | T | O | R | R | A | P |
| Y | O | T | E | G | C | I | R | C | U | V | F |
| M | R | U | A | E | N | E | B | Y | P | M | H |
| N | R | X | G | S | O | I | I | N | U | K | E |
| B | A | A | L | W | H | F | M | G | T | I | X |
| I | P | D | E | O | K | M | A | M | D | J | F |
| N | S | Y | T | R | C | P | F | E | U | U | C |
| M | E | F | B | C | U | N | W | X | S | H | B |

# 37. Creepy Crawlies

1. A flying insect which is black and yellow (3)
2. Rearrange the letters "WIGEAR" for this insect (6)
3. Small flying insect that carries disease (8)
4. Has a hard body and biting mouthparts (6)
5. A common small flying insect that buzzes (3)
6. It burrows in soil and has a long body (4)
7. A jumping insect that chirps loudly (7)
8. It has two pairs of wings, strong jaws and a sting (4)
9. An insect that can hop, walk and fly (11)
10. This catches other insects while flying (9)

| R | I | S | T | U | I | C | K | L | P | M | V |
|---|---|---|---|---|---|---|---|---|---|---|---|
| N | G | R | A | S | S | H | O | P | P | E | R |
| S | F | H | E | W | Q | R | G | B | B | I | W |
| E | M | Y | L | F | N | O | G | A | R | D | P |
| L | C | C | R | B | L | Z | S | K | G | L | S |
| R | R | K | E | E | B | R | E | C | T | G | A |
| W | I | T | S | U | H | I | L | F | V | K | W |
| O | C | I | P | E | C | N | T | K | M | H | Y |
| R | K | G | I | W | R | A | E | R | B | L | R |
| M | E | V | K | I | W | G | E | Q | F | I | N |
| U | T | H | R | F | T | P | B | S | Z | C | K |
| N | C | O | T | I | U | Q | S | O | M | U | E |

# 38. Jewelry

1. Wear this on your wrist (8)
2. Wear this round your neck (8)
3. The fastening on a chain (5)
4. Wear this round your ankle (6)
5. These go in your ears (8)
6. Lots of jewelry is made from this precious metal (4)
7. This intricate item is worn on your head (5)
8. Wear this when you get engaged or married (4)
9. This jewelry goes round your waist (10)
10. These gems are found in oysters (6)

| K | L | N | I | A | H | C | Y | L | L | E | B |
|---|---|---|---|---|---|---|---|---|---|---|---|
| D | P | E | A | R | L | S | V | X | U | E | R |
| R | J | E | C | A | L | K | C | E | N | N | S |
| S | N | W | O | B | L | R | Q | K | D | I | Z |
| G | A | U | J | R | W | C | L | A | S | P | R |
| N | N | B | E | A | D | L | N | W | S | L | J |
| I | K | V | J | C | Y | B | E | H | J | A | K |
| R | L | X | D | E | I | D | E | O | R | Q | S |
| R | E | O | W | L | L | S | B | A | R | F | D |
| L | T | K | Q | E | Z | U | I | D | W | B | L |
| N | E | S | R | T | O | T | J | V | J | I | O |
| L | S | G | N | I | R | R | A | E | W | X | G |

# 39. Boys' Names

1. Can be shortened to Andy (6)
2. The first man on Earth (4)
3. A shortened version of Robert (3)
4. Name that rhymes with "five" (5)
5. Little ____ who was a friend of Robin Hood (4)
6. The Prince of Wales, was married to Diana (7)
7. This piper picked a peck of pickled peppers (5)
8. Shortened version of Anthony (4)
9. Name that rhymes with "park" (4)
10. Bill is a shortened version of this name (7)

| S | D | K | O | M | A | R | K | P | V | W | Q |
|---|---|---|---|---|---|---|---|---|---|---|---|
| Y | U | C | L | I | V | E | B | R | D | L | Y |
| B | H | N | D | H | U | G | W | F | N | D | N |
| V | Q | S | P | Z | I | X | H | G | N | S | O |
| A | R | E | L | W | K | U | I | H | V | K | T |
| N | P | L | H | I | D | C | O | P | B | P | D |
| D | W | R | S | L | B | J | O | Y | R | U | H |
| R | F | A | D | L | G | G | Q | V | I | N | M |
| E | L | H | N | I | U | H | X | B | K | L | A |
| W | Y | C | Z | A | P | B | O | B | D | O | D |
| Q | D | K | G | M | F | R | P | Z | S | W | A |
| B | V | D | R | E | T | E | P | I | N | Y | C |

# 40. Countries

1. Country famous for chocolate and yodeling (11)
2. The president of this country lives in the White House (7)
3. This country is shaped a bit like a boot (5)
4. This country is associated with the Berlin Wall (7)
5. London is the capital of this country (7)
6. The warm land of flamenco dancing (5)
7. This country has a Great Wall (5)
8. Home to the Barrier Reef (9)
9. Associated with flat land and tulips (7)
10. Home of Paris and the Eiffel Tower (6)

| | | | | | | | | | | | |
|---|---|---|---|---|---|---|---|---|---|---|---|
| B | N | M | S | A | M | E | R | I | C | A | C |
| D | N | A | L | R | E | Z | T | I | W | S | M |
| K | C | E | A | I | N | F | L | C | U | S | A |
| M | Z | I | T | A | L | Y | B | E | G | G | U |
| F | H | L | W | K | A | H | R | E | D | K | S |
| K | O | E | S | T | I | G | R | U | N | N | T |
| A | L | C | U | C | E | M | T | A | A | S | R |
| I | L | N | B | N | A | Z | N | M | L | B | A |
| C | A | A | M | N | F | I | C | E | G | H | L |
| L | N | R | Y | S | H | K | L | N | N | W | I |
| F | D | F | E | C | A | U | H | F | E | S | A |
| W | B | Z | S | P | A | I | N | R | I | M | E |

# 41. Wild Animals

| | | | | | | | | | | | |
|---|---|---|---|---|---|---|---|---|---|---|---|
| L | O | E | L | L | E | Z | A | G | M | D | S |
| D | C | R | U | Y | W | U | T | V | B | D | N |
| M | L | H | C | K | B | A | B | O | O | N | D |
| H | W | V | I | D | X | E | K | A | N | S | R |
| U | T | L | N | M | D | M | A | Q | J | Y | N |
| S | S | E | A | L | P | U | S | O | G | R | O |
| K | U | S | R | Y | H | A | C | K | W | H | O |
| Y | R | O | V | H | Y | E | N | A | L | D | S |
| W | L | M | A | U | T | A | Q | Z | D | C | A |
| C | A | K | D | L | N | Y | W | V | E | M | B |
| R | W | X | R | A | U | G | A | J | O | E | T |
| A | T | L | E | O | P | A | R | D | S | U | N |

1. An African ape (10)
2. A slithering reptile with no legs (5)
3. A kind of large monkey (6)
4. A small antelope (7)
5. Sea animal with thick skin (4)
6. Arctic sledge-dog (5)
7. A big cat that cannot change its spots (7)
8. A large seal-like animal with long tusks (6)
9. Large meat-eating animal of the cat family (6)
10. An animal with a howl that sounds like laughter (5)

# 42. The Sea

1. A very big sea (5)
2. Vessel for traveling on water (4)
3. A very big sea mammal (5)
4. Sea creature with ten arms round its mouth (5)
5. A tower with a light to warn or guide ships (10)
6. A fierce tropical fish (7)
7. Sea creature with eight tentacles (7)
8. A vessel that can operate under water (9)
9. Someone who dives under water (5)
10. Someone who rescues swimmers from danger (9)

| | | | | | | | | | | | |
|---|---|---|---|---|---|---|---|---|---|---|---|
| O | J | K | O | C | T | O | P | U | S | O | N |
| I | E | L | V | D | X | Z | S | D | E | W | E |
| D | S | T | P | I | R | A | N | H | A | O | X |
| I | U | S | J | O | G | H | I | T | K | S | D |
| V | O | J | E | E | D | O | P | J | U | F | R |
| E | H | W | L | V | F | C | L | B | G | D | A |
| R | T | L | A | T | C | E | M | J | L | B | U |
| K | H | Z | H | S | T | A | I | B | O | C | G |
| I | G | J | W | B | R | N | G | A | E | Z | E |
| V | I | D | X | I | K | H | T | W | V | D | F |
| S | L | E | N | P | L | J | J | X | L | K | I |
| W | G | E | F | D | I | U | Q | S | O | H | L |

# 43. Weather

1. Wet drops that fall (4)
2. How hot or cold it is (11)
3. The light of the sun (8)
4. Wear these in the rain (5)
5. This can be forked or sheet (9)
6. Violent storm-wind (9)
7. Frozen white flakes (4)
8. A mass of watery vapor in the sky (5)
9. A description of the weather by an announcer (6)
10. Frozen dew or vapor (5)

| I | T | E | M | P | E | R | A | T | U | R | E |
|---|---|---|---|---|---|---|---|---|---|---|---|
| H | G | O | N | S | T | G | K | M | I | E | B |
| V | N | B | F | R | O | S | T | R | O | N | T |
| O | I | M | Q | Z | V | C | G | B | V | I | H |
| K | N | E | N | A | C | I | R | R | U | H | S |
| B | T | C | I | R | E | P | O | R | T | S | O |
| O | H | B | G | O | C | H | F | R | C | N | I |
| O | G | S | T | D | N | C | S | L | I | U | K |
| T | I | V | N | M | U | V | K | N | Q | S | M |
| S | L | R | I | H | Z | O | V | B | O | N | N |
| E | O | Q | A | I | G | V | L | T | G | W | M |
| S | N | K | R | L | K | J | H | C | H | S | Z |

# 44. Creepy Crawlies

1. A bug that walks on water (10)
2. A creature with eight legs (6)
3. This travels in armies and makes holes (3)
4. Also known as a daddy long-legs (10)
5. A beetle-like insect with a hard body (9)
6. A small, crawling insect with many legs (9)
7. Mollusk famous for being so slow (5)
8. A small, slimy animal (4)
9. A small, bloodsucking worm (5)
10. Larva of a kind of beetle that bores in wood (8)

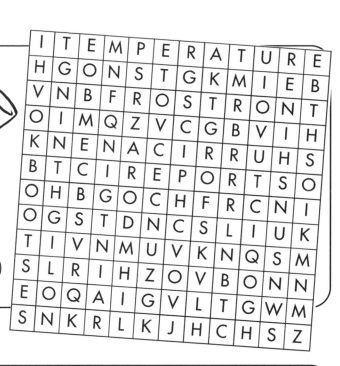

| H | A | R | V | E | S | T | M | A | N | R | C |
|---|---|---|---|---|---|---|---|---|---|---|---|
| N | R | H | T | Y | R | U | B | K | N | Y | W |
| T | E | Q | C | E | N | T | I | P | E | D | E |
| W | T | Z | O | D | I | K | G | J | S | H | I |
| O | A | R | C | H | G | J | S | G | D | H | U |
| O | K | L | K | B | W | L | N | H | C | T | F |
| D | S | S | R | Y | U | S | F | E | R | G | H |
| W | D | I | O | G | Z | S | E | E | D | H | G |
| O | N | N | A | T | K | L | D | I | U | Q | L |
| R | O | Y | C | B | H | I | N | L | T | B | O |
| M | P | N | H | D | P | G | T | W | U | N | J |
| K | S | R | L | S | N | A | I | L | T | Z | A |

# 45. Characters

1. Pumba's friend (6)
2. The cowboy from Toy Story (5)
3. The lovable deer (5)
4. Astronaut called Buzz (9)
5. He was friends with Tinkerbell (5, 3)
6. The female version of He-man (5)
7. Was the beauty to the beast (5)
8. The baby lion from The Lion King (5)
9. The lobster friend of Ariel (9)
10. The friendly giant in Harry Potter books (6)

| J | O | B | I | V | H | A | G | R | I | D | R |
|---|---|---|---|---|---|---|---|---|---|---|---|
| B | E | L | L | E | A | J | E | S | O | R | W |
| Y | C | J | Y | D | O | O | W | D | G | A | C |
| I | S | R | H | G | V | Y | C | K | J | E | N |
| O | H | E | W | J | N | J | M | X | C | Y | A |
| X | E | T | A | N | A | R | B | O | B | T | I |
| B | R | I | S | C | P | H | A | K | R | H | T |
| E | A | M | R | N | R | I | M | E | D | G | S |
| D | Y | O | C | V | E | O | B | N | C | I | A |
| S | V | N | I | E | T | W | I | A | X | L | B |
| N | J | E | H | N | E | S | C | V | J | V | E |
| S | I | M | B | A | P | B | C | O | Y | I | S |

# 46. Movies

1. Who stole Christmas? (6)
2. There were 101 of them (10)
3. Nanny who was actually a man, Mrs ____ (9)
4. This movie has Woody and Slinky in it (3, 5)
5. A strong man who goes green when angry (4)
6. Dog which was partner to Lady (5)
7. Ariel is this type of creature (7)
8. A film about a princess with ugly sisters (10)
9. Creature that Beauty falls in love with (5)
10. Simba the lion's dad, ____ of the jungle (4)

| G | B | L | M | E | R | M | A | I | D | L | D |
|---|---|---|---|---|---|---|---|---|---|---|---|
| N | C | A | S | F | E | T | X | H | N | O | G |
| I | O | L | B | E | A | S | T | R | U | I | S |
| K | N | L | H | D | M | W | E | B | L | B | N |
| F | G | E | R | I | H | Y | T | K | D | M | A |
| K | D | R | I | W | H | F | S | G | I | T | I |
| L | E | E | T | B | I | K | C | O | X | F | T |
| U | C | D | O | R | G | R | I | N | C | H | A |
| H | L | N | E | H | N | F | E | M | R | D | M |
| S | H | I | R | G | P | M | A | R | T | H | L |
| T | F | C | X | D | O | C | T | I | B | N | A |
| E | T | O | Y | S | T | O | R | Y | L | S | D |

# 47. Games

| I | L | M | N | R | S | T | U | W | C | B | P |
|---|---|---|---|---|---|---|---|---|---|---|---|
| H | Y | R | A | N | O | I | T | C | I | P | E |
| O | P | E | R | A | T | I | O | N | T | D | T |
| P | W | Y | B | I | E | K | Y | G | M | L | W |
| A | S | L | U | S | C | F | G | D | I | B | I |
| R | C | O | N | L | R | J | S | Y | N | H | S |
| T | R | P | M | P | T | E | E | H | T | D | T |
| E | A | O | I | R | E | D | D | N | E | P | E |
| S | B | N | H | D | L | B | K | D | G | W | R |
| U | B | O | S | D | R | A | C | U | A | A | C |
| O | L | M | U | P | M | T | I | N | E | L | T |
| M | E | S | C | L | U | E | D | O | R | L | H |

1. Hunt the mouse (9)
2. Buy houses and hotels to win (8)
3. Go up these and watch out for snakes (7)
4. Put your hands and feet on the colored dots (7)
5. Become a doctor with this game (9)
6. Draw pictures and guess the word (10)
7. Put letter tiles together to form words (8)
8. This pack of 52 provides many games (5)
9. Guess the murderer, place and weapon (4)
10. Remove the blocks without toppling the lot (5)

# 48. Royalty

1. Married to a king (5)
2. Home for royalty (6)
3. A special chair that royals sit on (6)
4. Eight kings of England have had this name (5)
5. Beautiful jewelery worn on the head (5)
6. Windsor C____, a British royal home (6)
7. Royalty have these people to do things for them (8)
8. The son of the king and queen (6)
9. A person who guards the royal family (9)
10. Prince Charles is the Prince of ____ (5)

| L | B | V | C | D | Y | N | W | E | X | Q | L |
|---|---|---|---|---|---|---|---|---|---|---|---|
| J | O | P | W | A | L | E | S | E | S | S | F |
| G | D | F | S | T | I | E | C | N | I | R | P |
| C | Y | N | S | E | R | V | A | N | T | S | E |
| A | G | C | E | D | O | Z | T | Y | N | J | G |
| S | U | V | T | Q | K | C | R | O | W | N | S |
| T | A | Y | L | H | J | F | D | S | E | V | N |
| L | R | R | Y | W | R | K | G | M | Z | N | E |
| E | D | N | P | I | N | O | V | T | I | L | E |
| Q | D | E | S | N | C | M | N | D | Y | E | U |
| L | T | H | F | E | Z | O | X | E | Q | W | Q |
| I | V | E | C | A | L | A | P | G | J | C | M |

# 49. The Letter 'P'

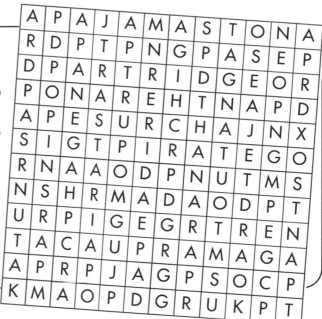

1. A yellow vegetable (7)
2. A talking bird (6)
3. Wear these on your legs (5)
4. A baby is pushed around in this (4)
5. A farmyard animal (3)
6. A bird commonly associated with a pear tree (9)
7. Wear these in bed (7)
8. An evil sailor who steals treasure (6)
9. A leopard (7)
10. Another word for a couple or two of something (4)

| A | P | A | J | A | M | A | S | T | O | N | A |
|---|---|---|---|---|---|---|---|---|---|---|---|
| R | D | P | T | P | N | G | P | A | S | E | P |
| D | P | A | R | T | R | I | D | G | E | O | R |
| P | O | N | A | R | E | H | T | N | A | P | D |
| A | P | E | S | U | R | C | H | A | J | N | X |
| S | I | G | T | P | I | R | A | T | E | G | O |
| R | N | A | A | O | D | P | N | U | T | M | S |
| N | S | H | R | M | A | D | A | O | D | P | T |
| U | R | P | I | G | E | G | R | T | R | E | N |
| T | A | C | A | U | P | R | A | M | A | G | A |
| A | P | R | P | J | A | G | P | S | O | C | P |
| K | M | A | O | P | D | G | R | U | K | P | T |

# 50. School

1. Eat this at school (6)
2. School's out! (8)
3. You may have to wear this at school (7)
4. Use this to draw straight lines (5)
5. The periods where you learn about the subjects (7)
6. Girls wear this for P.E. (8)
7. This person teaches you (7)
8. The teacher writes on this with chalk (10)
9. Work you have to do after school (8)
10. Written tests that may be longer than other tests (5)

| B | L | E | S | S | O | N | S | T | J | L | I |
|---|---|---|---|---|---|---|---|---|---|---|---|
| K | U | F | O | E | R | E | H | C | A | E | T |
| H | B | M | I | B | V | S | W | X | M | K | T |
| O | L | S | T | J | L | F | S | R | D | A | N |
| M | A | T | U | K | G | Q | O | A | G | O | X |
| E | C | R | S | U | F | F | D | M | I | U | Z |
| W | K | I | O | T | I | B | J | T | S | W | S |
| O | B | K | D | N | V | I | A | T | G | M | R |
| R | O | S | U | M | E | C | S | S | A | Q | E |
| K | A | M | K | U | A | X | O | X | L | B | L |
| S | R | Y | J | J | V | W | G | E | D | S | F | U |
| O | D | G | I | R | E | N | N | I | D | V | R |

# 51. Food

1. Menthol herb (4)
2. Part of a pig (5)
3. A beef patty in a bun with relish (6)
4. Roast dinner is usually eaten on this day (6)
5. This quick snack is made from potatoes (5)
6. Sauce made from cooked meat juices (5)
7. Sweet pudding that comes after dinner (7)
8. This round fruit grows on trees (5)
9. The inside part of a sandwich (7)
10. This fruit is often given to ill people (6)

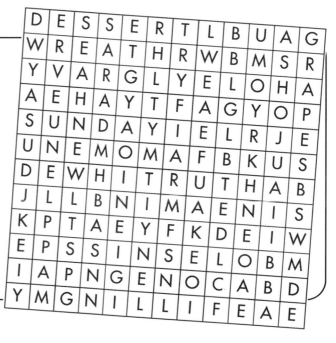

| D | E | S | S | E | R | T | L | B | U | A | G |
|---|---|---|---|---|---|---|---|---|---|---|---|
| W | R | E | A | T | H | R | W | B | M | S | R |
| Y | V | A | R | G | L | Y | E | L | O | H | A |
| A | E | H | A | Y | T | F | A | G | Y | O | P |
| S | U | N | D | A | Y | I | E | L | R | J | E |
| U | N | E | M | O | M | A | F | B | K | U | S |
| D | E | W | H | I | T | R | U | T | H | A | B |
| J | L | L | B | N | I | M | A | E | N | I | S |
| K | P | T | A | E | Y | F | K | D | E | I | W |
| E | P | S | S | I | N | S | E | L | O | B | M |
| I | A | P | N | G | E | N | O | C | A | B | D |
| Y | M | G | N | I | L | L | I | F | E | A | E |

# 52. Christmas

1. The kissing plant (9)
2. He has a carrot for a nose (7)
3. Hang this on the tree (6)
4. Rudolph is one (8)
5. Type of song sung at Christmas (5)
6. Another name for Father Christmas (5)
7. A festive arrangement of flowers (6)
8. Santa's reindeers pull this with presents on (6)
9. Drape this over the tree (6)
10. A heavenly being that goes on top of the tree (5)

| K | D | U | V | I | S | E | L | B | U | A | B |
|---|---|---|---|---|---|---|---|---|---|---|---|
| W | R | E | A | T | H | F | G | X | E | A | W |
| L | E | P | F | N | A | M | W | O | N | S | K |
| S | E | J | K | N | K | H | C | E | I | K | U |
| H | D | A | L | H | G | I | E | L | S | I | E |
| F | N | E | I | C | O | A | L | M | F | J | N |
| K | I | U | V | Y | T | K | H | O | N | A | F |
| D | E | G | W | N | S | D | E | E | R | L | Y |
| P | R | X | A | F | L | F | K | V | U | A | G |
| J | W | S | T | I | N | S | E | L | W | E | C |
| F | P | A | N | G | E | L | A | S | I | J | X |
| V | M | I | S | T | L | E | T | O | E | L | D |

# 53. Clothes

| C | A | P | R | I | E | D | C | U | R | E | R |
|---|---|---|---|---|---|---|---|---|---|---|---|
| T | O | C | Y | S | A | G | V | T | A | V | T |
| C | V | S | W | F | J | L | P | B | I | C | R |
| N | A | E | Z | T | U | O | I | X | N | T | I |
| J | R | M | S | Y | W | V | K | J | C | A | H |
| T | V | D | F | T | I | E | H | D | O | O | S |
| I | R | A | S | G | D | S | O | C | A | C | R |
| U | B | Q | G | F | C | S | W | E | T | I | E |
| E | A | S | F | A | J | R | U | I | S | T | D |
| W | C | X | E | F | V | T | F | Z | H | T | N |
| D | M | K | I | L | T | B | A | S | F | E | U |
| B | I | K | I | N | I | O | T | H | D | P | A |

1. A coat to wear when it rains (8)
2. Wear this on your head (3)
3. Waist-length sleeveless jacket (4)
4. Two-piece swimsuit (6)
5. Indian women wear this (4)
6. A skirt worn under your clothes (9)
7. Wear these to keep your hands warm (6)
8. Pants also known as pedal pushers (5)
9. Wear this under your top to stay warm (10)
10. Tartan skirt, part of traditional Scottish dress (4)

# 54. Nature

1. A large bee (9)
2. A freshwater fish (4)
3. A badger's burrow (4)
4. A red berry popular in summer (10)
5. A very young plant growing from a seed (8)
6. A pretend figure to scare birds away from crops (9)
7. Hanging flower of willow, hazel, etc. (6)
8. Large open-air fire (7)
9. Plant these to grow flowers and plants (5)
10. Black, bushy-tailed, smelly weasel-like animal (5)

| S | T | R | A | W | B | E | R | R | Y | N | L |
|---|---|---|---|---|---|---|---|---|---|---|---|
| M | P | K | A | O | L | D | W | N | F | B | P |
| E | I | N | T | E | K | L | Q | K | D | U | B |
| E | E | K | K | B | N | V | G | J | M | L | B |
| B | R | F | I | D | U | N | N | M | I | B | L |
| E | I | H | N | B | K | W | I | E | O | S | N |
| L | F | N | I | R | S | P | L | I | N | K | K |
| B | N | M | K | E | G | U | D | O | F | Q | P |
| M | O | L | W | O | R | C | E | R | A | C | S |
| U | B | O | L | K | F | H | E | S | K | N | K |
| B | W | N | F | T | T | E | S | B | D | M | F |
| C | A | R | P | P | Q | N | E | L | W | I | V |

# 55. Desserts

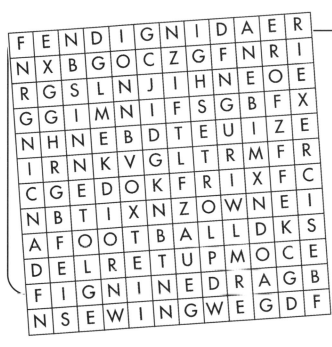

1. Used for pouring over cake (5)
2. An icy cold dessert (3, 5)
3. Mixed up pieces of fruit (5, 5)
4. Dessert of fruit with cake-like topping (7)
5. A baked dish of fruit (3)
6. Meringue cake containing cream and fruit (7)
7. Sponge cake, ice cream and meringue, Baked _____ (6)
8. Pastry with a cream filling and chocolate on top (6)
9. Pie or pastry flan with a sweet filling (4)
10. Baked sweet bread-like food (4)

| D | O | K | V | U | E | H | S | W | G | K | C |
|---|---|---|---|---|---|---|---|---|---|---|---|
| B | A | C | Q | P | A | V | L | O | V | A | Y |
| M | N | L | Y | T | B | R | D | G | N | H | S |
| A | R | K | A | D | F | E | F | R | U | B | O |
| E | S | H | W | S | V | P | I | E | I | R | T |
| R | O | E | V | K | T | R | W | T | Y | A | V |
| C | Q | G | B | Y | N | I | C | H | O | K | E |
| E | C | L | A | I | R | G | U | B | R | S | K |
| C | K | C | O | B | B | L | E | R | C | A | T |
| I | S | O | C | R | U | S | E | V | F | L | R |
| V | H | W | U | M | A | E | R | C | K | A | A |
| G | B | E | K | A | C | O | K | B | U | S | T |

# 56. Hobbies

| F | E | N | D | I | G | N | I | D | A | E | R |
|---|---|---|---|---|---|---|---|---|---|---|---|
| N | X | B | G | O | C | Z | G | F | N | R | I |
| R | G | S | L | N | J | I | H | N | E | O | E |
| G | G | I | M | N | I | F | S | G | B | F | X |
| N | H | N | E | B | D | T | E | U | I | Z | E |
| I | R | N | K | V | G | L | T | R | M | F | R |
| C | G | E | D | O | K | F | R | I | X | F | C |
| N | B | T | I | X | N | Z | O | W | N | E | I |
| A | F | O | O | T | B | A | L | L | D | K | S |
| D | E | L | R | E | T | U | P | M | O | C | E |
| F | I | G | N | I | N | E | D | R | A | G | B |
| N | S | E | W | I | N | G | W | E | G | D | F |

1. Sport with touchdowns (8)
2. People like to play games on this (8)
3. Ballet, modern, tap and more (7)
4. Planting and digging in the garden (9)
5. A love of books and magazines (7)
6. Walking is a form of _____ (8)
7. Hitting a ball over a net with rackets (6)
8. Passing a threaded needle through fabric (6)
9. Listening to this relaxes people (5)
10. Forming yarn into fabric of interlocking loops (8)

# 57. Girls' Names

1. Short for Victoria (5)
2. The cowgirl from Toy Story (6)
3. The first woman in space (9)
4. Short for Rosemary (5)
5. Popeye's girlfriend _____ Oyl (5)
6. A famous orphan with orange curls (5)
7. Princess who was married to Prince Charles (5)
8. An American pop star and actress (7)
9. A nun who helped poor people in Calcutta (6)
10. The same name as a coin (5)

| K | P | E | N | N | Y | L | I | O | R | S | T |
|---|---|---|---|---|---|---|---|---|---|---|---|
| U | K | T | A | S | E | R | E | T | H | H | J |
| O | I | J | K | H | F | T | E | I | S | O | R |
| A | N | N | I | E | J | D | U | W | X | K | S |
| F | R | L | W | B | S | P | C | X | R | D | P |
| H | I | A | N | I | T | N | E | L | A | V | I |
| E | N | N | K | T | J | D | I | T | B | S | V |
| V | D | A | U | O | F | E | F | J | K | F | I |
| I | S | I | J | H | L | K | S | G | U | H | C |
| L | X | D | W | F | R | P | D | S | H | W | K |
| O | T | P | B | U | K | R | C | X | I | K | Y |
| J | A | N | N | O | D | A | M | T | O | E | L |

# 58. The Letter 'M'

1. You need this when you're ill (8)
2. A two-wheeled motor vehicle (9)
3. Pour this on your cereal (4)
4. Vegetarians don't eat this (4)
5. Use this to find your way (3)
6. Cut the lawn (3)
7. The capital of Russia (6)
8. A planet in the solar system (4)
9. Everest is the world's highest (8)
10. Infectious disease causing red spots on the body (7)

| E | S | T | M | N | I | A | T | N | U | O | M |
|---|---|---|---|---|---|---|---|---|---|---|---|
| C | W | R | I | X | F | T | W | S | N | C | K |
| L | M | E | D | I | C | I | N | E | E | M | I |
| N | B | U | S | Z | M | O | S | C | O | W | U |
| M | C | S | K | E | S | V | B | T | R | F | M |
| V | W | T | X | I | E | H | G | P | A | M | N |
| U | O | F | T | K | L | M | E | C | L | D | T |
| K | M | R | A | W | S | N | M | S | X | K | S |
| I | Z | B | E | C | A | U | T | K | L | B | R |
| M | M | E | M | J | E | I | R | I | E | R | A |
| R | U | X | S | T | M | F | M | X | F | Z | M |
| L | E | K | I | B | R | O | T | O | M | C | E |

# 59. Flowers

| N | O | I | L | E | D | N | A | D | C | O | U |
|---|---|---|---|---|---|---|---|---|---|---|---|
| F | Y | J | I | R | D | G | R | F | W | C | Y |
| R | H | Y | A | C | I | N | T | H | P | A | E |
| I | D | I | H | C | R | O | L | C | S | R | D |
| P | B | F | Y | M | B | J | I | M | U | N | F |
| I | O | S | I | R | I | K | D | G | Y | A | O |
| L | W | C | U | F | T | S | O | E | R | T | C |
| U | R | D | G | E | U | R | F | Y | M | I | J |
| T | J | F | L | C | I | P | F | C | I | O | D |
| R | S | O | O | D | B | O | A | K | F | N | R |
| K | I | R | C | R | R | U | D | W | R | J | S |
| V | C | D | Y | M | P | O | L | L | E | N | I |

1. Deep purple flower (6)
2. A cup-shaped flower (5)
3. A yellow flower that blooms early in spring (8)
4. Colorful flower that lives in warm areas (6)
5. Weed with yellow flowers that turn into seeds (9)
6. Flower that can be white, pink or red (9)
7. Beautiful blue flower with long thin flat leaves (4)
8. Fertilizing powder from flowers (6)
9. A spring-flowering plant growing from a corm (6)
10. Plant with fragrant bell-shaped flowers (8)

# 60. Birds

1. Bird of the crow family (3)
2. A nighttime bird of prey (3)
3. A sea bird (7)
4. A very small bird (4)
5. Lays the biggest birds' eggs (7)
6. One of the fastest flying birds (6)
7. Small songbird that searches for insects (8)
8. Small migratory bird with a forked tail (7)
9. A bird of prey that eats the flesh of dead animals (7)
10. Large water bird with a long slender neck (4)

| H | I | N | E | R | W | A | C | N | O | C | Y |
|---|---|---|---|---|---|---|---|---|---|---|---|
| S | L | Y | V | J | B | E | F | W | R | B | G |
| W | E | O | G | W | D | I | L | Q | S | X | C |
| A | C | N | S | E | C | Y | V | J | H | F | E |
| L | V | I | H | T | F | S | A | E | L | A | R |
| L | U | L | T | N | R | D | B | J | Y | L | E |
| O | L | A | J | X | G | I | W | F | V | C | A |
| W | T | Q | H | R | T | Y | C | B | I | O | C |
| B | U | N | A | W | S | L | D | H | E | N | N |
| F | R | E | I | V | E | A | J | N | D | L | I |
| A | E | N | C | L | L | U | G | A | E | S | B |
| T | I | T | M | O | U | S | E | S | E | Q | Y |

# 61. Fairies

1. Fairies sit on these (10)
2. Fairies use these to fly (5)
3. Fairies use their wands to create this (5)
4. They sing these (5)
5. Area of trees where fairies are found (5)
6. They make up these to make magic (6)
7. Fairies can rarely be seen by who? (6)
8. Something fairies do in the air that people can't (3)
9. It's supposedly unlucky to step in this (4)
10. The leader of the fairies (5)

| M | R | I | N | G | B | V | D | O | K | F | I |
|---|---|---|---|---|---|---|---|---|---|---|---|
| H | A | Z | I | H | U | M | A | N | S | N | L |
| P | S | L | O | O | T | S | D | A | O | T | G |
| F | V | W | K | U | H | M | J | W | A | H | B |
| X | S | N | D | H | F | K | X | J | G | V | S |
| N | G | B | J | L | P | A | F | C | G | H | D |
| E | N | O | Y | I | Y | F | I | W | N | M | O |
| E | I | L | G | M | J | G | H | K | D | J | O |
| U | W | A | U | T | A | V | K | B | O | P | W |
| Q | P | H | N | M | J | N | A | Z | I | F | L |
| I | X | D | K | K | G | S | G | N | O | S | N |
| G | W | R | H | Y | M | E | S | B | M | U | O |

# 62. Space

1. A system of stars (6)
2. The ringed planet (6)
3. Planet nearest the Sun (7)
4. The name of a voyage to space (7)
5. Unmanned craft that explores space (5)
6. The study of stars and planets (9)
7. A planet in the solar system (6)
8. A meteor fallen to Earth (9)
9. A constellation of stars beginning with "O" (5)
10. Mixture of gases surrounding a planet (10)

| P | R | O | B | E | N | J | M | H | B | I | A |
|---|---|---|---|---|---|---|---|---|---|---|---|
| F | A | C | D | K | P | A | I | N | A | H | T |
| W | B | S | H | R | U | Q | S | D | S | E | M |
| N | V | Y | E | I | J | I | S | W | T | T | O |
| Y | U | R | A | N | U | S | I | F | R | I | S |
| X | D | C | F | R | J | K | O | K | O | R | P |
| A | P | J | I | E | F | R | N | S | N | O | H |
| L | M | E | R | C | U | R | Y | P | O | E | E |
| A | F | R | A | H | W | N | C | J | M | T | R |
| G | N | O | R | T | S | M | R | A | Y | E | E |
| N | B | I | N | O | I | R | O | D | F | M | N |
| A | J | K | S | A | T | U | R | N | G | I | L |

# 63. The Park

1. You can swing on these (6)
2. What you do in the playground (4)
3. Make sandcastles from this (4)
4. Run about on this soft surface (5)
5. Merry-go-_____ (5)
6. Water where ducks swim (4)
7. Go down this fast! (5)
8. Go to the water to feed these birds with bread (5)
9. A meal you can have outside (6)
10. Things such as soccer and tag (5)

| S | L | I | D | E | A | I | C | H | V | E | N |
|---|---|---|---|---|---|---|---|---|---|---|---|
| V | F | N | D | T | I | P | D | N | A | S | F |
| N | X | H | B | T | R | H | K | L | O | B | I |
| E | C | B | I | C | Y | C | I | N | C | I | P |
| O | R | O | U | N | D | X | B | O | U | T | H |
| D | F | V | L | H | W | V | C | D | E | V | C |
| A | S | W | I | N | G | S | U | F | L | D | A |
| T | B | M | N | O | E | C | M | S | S | Y | N |
| R | D | K | X | D | K | I | S | B | E | A | R |
| E | N | H | F | S | V | A | C | H | M | L | I |
| C | O | L | B | Y | R | A | T | V | A | P | X |
| O | P | W | E | G | M | D | N | E | G | F | K |

# 64. Landmarks

1. The famous tower in Paris (6)
2. One of the world's wonders found in Egypt (8)
3. Where in Australia is the Opera House? (6)
4. The famous bell in London, Big ___ (3)
5. The Leaning Tower is found in this Italian city (4)
6. The name of a famous British palace (10)
7. The Statue of _____ is in New York (7)
8. The Golden Gate in San Francisco is one (6)
9. The Arc de Triomphe is in this French city (5)
10. The Crown jewels are kept in the _____ of London (5)

| G | A | H | T | O | W | E | R | K | G | S | D |
|---|---|---|---|---|---|---|---|---|---|---|---|
| B | U | C | K | I | N | G | H | A | M | T | L |
| E | U | D | F | Y | E | N | D | Y | S | B | E |
| H | S | T | M | S | A | N | G | W | U | X | F |
| B | D | K | T | V | P | X | S | E | A | K | F |
| R | I | C | E | R | V | I | M | H | A | V | I |
| I | M | U | B | F | I | D | S | F | T | D | E |
| D | A | N | N | G | A | P | H | A | K | U | G |
| G | R | W | E | S | U | G | A | J | A | N | H |
| E | Y | G | B | X | H | T | K | R | B | E | S |
| K | P | A | D | F | F | V | E | M | I | M | L |
| E | T | L | I | B | E | R | T | Y | C | S | W |

| I | B | E | R | N | A | R | D | T | O | R | K |
|---|---|---|---|---|---|---|---|---|---|---|---|
| C | H | I | H | U | A | H | U | A | I | O | P |
| S | F | G | O | S | U | E | T | E | A | F | D |
| H | I | P | B | R | I | H | R | K | E | B | A |
| E | K | A | O | L | W | L | Q | T | L | G | L |
| P | S | T | L | F | E | Y | H | R | D | S | M |
| H | F | O | E | N | I | G | I | E | O | H | A |
| E | C | U | N | J | Y | O | T | X | O | K | T |
| R | G | E | U | Q | A | K | O | O | P | G | I |
| D | K | W | R | B | P | E | S | B | U | F | A |
| N | H | H | R | O | D | A | R | B | A | L | N |
| D | N | U | O | H | Y | E | R | G | I | T | K |

# 65. Dogs

1. A French dog (6)
2. A dog's home (6)
3. Large white dog with dark spots (9)
4. Retriever with a black or golden coat (8)
5. Rescue dog, St _____ (7)
6. Dog used to round up sheep (6)
7. Dog that has the same name as a type of fighter (5)
8. Very small Mexican dog (9)
9. Dog used by the police, German _____ (8)
10. Slender dog that is sometimes raced (9)

# 66. Spies

1. A loud bang (9)
2. A metal weapon spies use (3)
3. Someone who is not a friend (5)
4. This fast vehicle is used to escape (3)
5. Small mechanical device or tool (6)
6. Wear this so people won't know who you are (8)
7. Use these to see things far away (10)
8. A fictional spy with the number 007 (4)
9. Use this to photograph secret documents (6)
10. Someone who provides important information (8)

| E | U | F | O | E | G | R | S | R | A | C | T |
|---|---|---|---|---|---|---|---|---|---|---|---|
| N | B | D | K | B | W | N | X | V | K | H | J |
| E | I | Z | S | A | R | E | M | A | C | S | R |
| M | N | S | H | T | J | T | R | B | D | B | E |
| Y | O | F | H | L | K | D | G | N | F | Z | M |
| R | C | D | B | K | E | E | W | S | U | W | R |
| G | U | B | O | J | U | R | R | T | X | G | O |
| O | L | F | N | N | T | G | S | D | C | O | F |
| S | A | E | D | I | S | G | U | I | S | E | N |
| D | R | X | V | W | O | F | Z | K | B | U | I |
| K | S | G | A | D | G | E | T | T | E | G | N |
| J | H | N | O | I | S | O | L | P | X | E | D |

# 67. Hairstyles

1. An elegant hair twist (5)
2. Two ponytails on either side of your head (7)
3. Use this to hold your hair back (4)
4. Hair tied back with a band is called a _____ (8)
5. A plait that starts right at the top of your head (6, 5)
6. Use this device to make your hair wavy (7)
7. These make your hair curly (7)
8. These make your hair look longer (10)
9. These are a straightening tool (5)
10. This is a haircut and a boy's name (3)

| T | K | G | F | J | L | H | D | F | X | E | R |
|---|---|---|---|---|---|---|---|---|---|---|---|
| I | E | R | N | K | T | A | E | L | P | V | C |
| A | X | F | C | R | I | M | P | E | R | I | F |
| L | T | L | E | D | G | N | L | B | O | B | G |
| P | E | I | H | K | F | Z | W | T | R | U | K |
| H | N | A | L | S | E | H | C | N | U | B | V |
| C | S | T | J | D | I | D | G | X | E | X | Z |
| N | I | Y | M | S | S | R | E | L | R | U | C |
| E | O | N | H | N | V | K | E | H | P | J | I |
| R | N | O | X | O | L | R | F | I | L | F | D |
| F | S | P | F | R | D | N | L | W | G | D | S |
| E | N | H | L | I | C | C | V | Z | M | R | J |

# 68. Sports Equipment

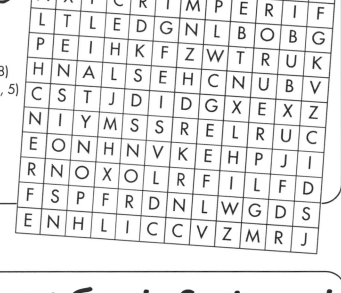

1. Wear these on your head to hold your hair back (5)
2. A round object you throw, catch, kick or hit (4)
3. Wear these on your feet when running around (8)
4. Jump over these in this athletics event (7)
5. Use this to hit a shuttlecock with (6)
6. Do judo or gymnastics on this (3)
7. Put sports equipment in this (3)
8. Wear these to kick a soccer ball (5)
9. These protect body parts (4)
10. Use this to hit a baseball (3)

| M | C | B | A | F | H | N | D | W | B | L | G |
|---|---|---|---|---|---|---|---|---|---|---|---|
| A | Z | U | R | T | E | K | C | A | R | S | X |
| T | S | B | Q | C | Y | I | P | S | T | V | J |
| R | V | T | P | A | D | S | V | O | H | A | S |
| A | G | F | N | C | F | R | O | I | Y | C | N |
| H | B | D | S | L | V | B | D | V | G | F | E |
| S | R | A | W | X | U | S | B | T | G | P | A |
| D | I | Y | T | C | V | A | A | R | A | J | K |
| N | J | P | Q | B | L | C | I | S | B | R | E |
| A | J | G | T | L | R | H | F | Z | D | L | R |
| B | G | S | E | L | D | R | U | H | U | Q | S |
| X | V | A | C | N | N | G | W | R | V | B | Y |

# 69. The Beach

1. Use this to dry yourself after a swim (5)
2. Women wear these to swim in (9)
3. Pictures of the beach you can send to people (9)
4. Men wear these to swim in (6)
5. You can see small sea creatures in this puddle (8)
6. Wooden construction that goes out over the sea (4)
7. Some beaches have these instead of sand (6)
8. Find pretty variations of these on the beach (6)
9. Flocks of these birds circle the beach (8)
10. Wear these to protect your eyes from the sun (10)

| M | S | H | L | R | K | T | O | W | E | L | P |
|---|---|---|---|---|---|---|---|---|---|---|---|
| S | L | D | U | C | W | J | H | V | U | I | S |
| K | L | T | O | F | G | G | X | Y | E | J | H |
| N | U | R | M | J | R | D | G | R | J | H | G |
| U | G | I | Z | S | L | L | E | H | S | K | L |
| R | A | S | E | S | S | A | L | G | N | U | S |
| T | E | R | G | H | D | F | D | G | X | U | S |
| J | S | K | M | T | D | H | G | I | B | D | E |
| U | P | O | S | T | C | A | R | D | S | W | N |
| B | S | I | V | W | X | L | G | Z | J | D | O |
| R | D | L | O | O | P | K | C | O | R | M | T |
| F | S | W | I | M | S | U | I | T | S | H | S |

# ANSWERS

## 1. Mother Nature

| | | | | | | | | | | | |
|--|--|--|--|--|--|--|--|--|--|--|--|
| B | Q | R | S | S | Q | U | I | R | R | E | L |
| T | H | E | D | G | E | H | O | G | U | T | S |
| L | M | E | J | P | Z | R | O | L | V | Q | R |
| Z | I | R | J | A | C | O | R | N | L | N | Z |
| O | L | T | K | M | D | A | B | S | T | M | A |
| E | N | P | Q | A | R | N | A | B | H | L | O |
| A | L | A | D | Y | B | U | G | D | L | L | O |
| R | A | L | E | A | V | E | S | P | K | A | W |
| T | S | Y | L | W | A | T | S | M | R | F | D |
| H | R | A | D | L | Q | P | R | V | O | J | I |
| B | O | T | N | D | J | O | K | S | M | J | Q |
| N | E | R | R | A | W | V | T | W | R | L | P |

## 2. Going Places

| | | | | | | | | | | | | | |
|--|--|--|--|--|--|--|--|--|--|--|--|--|--|
| D | L | H | O | S | P | I | T | A | L | F | N | | |
| T | U | O | G | E | T | T | H | A | O | I | A | | |
| I | R | W | U | O | Z | O | O | T | O | R | C | | |
| E | N | O | T | O | F | R | E | Y | P | E | U | | |
| H | T | L | P | H | E | S | O | O | G | S | L | | |
| L | A | E | M | P | C | O | U | J | N | T | O | | |
| O | E | L | Y | I | L | D | U | I | A | N | | | |
| O | O | V | I | F | S | A | S | T | M | T | O | | |
| H | L | Y | M | H | I | N | F | I | M | I | O | | |
| C | O | F | F | I | C | E | N | C | I | O | N | | |
| S | L | C | H | U | R | C | H | O | W | N | U | | |
| P | A | L | A | C | E | C | T | I | S | N | E | | |

## 3. Getting Around

| | | | | | | | | | | | | |
|--|--|--|--|--|--|--|--|--|--|--|--|--|
| N | M | C | E | B | O | A | T | M | S | T | S |
| V | O | D | A | F | D | R | O | R | H | U | E |
| H | T | O | L | Y | I | K | C | E | P | E | T |
| P | O | Z | G | D | S | R | S | T | N | Q | A |
| B | R | N | A | A | E | L | S | A | F | L | K |
| A | B | I | A | N | R | C | L | Z | G | S | S |
| T | A | M | A | N | P | T | O | E | R | R | |
| G | K | R | Y | A | R | O | R | B | E | O | E |
| W | E | T | N | I | A | C | U | H | K | T | L |
| S | L | R | A | Z | N | A | C | Y | A | L | |
| U | E | A | M | E | S | R | K | E | B | P | O |
| B | A | I | N | A | V | O | L | I | T | O | R |

## 4. Down on the Farm

| | | | | | | | | | | | | |
|--|--|--|--|--|--|--|--|--|--|--|--|--|
| S | R | A | B | B | I | T | U | N | T | Y | S |
| L | I | N | A | T | C | O | E | S | R | O | H |
| P | M | A | N | T | E | E | N | P | I | D | E |
| E | F | R | E | R | H | E | O | D | N | T | B |
| E | O | M | E | R | K | B | S | E | P | I | G |
| H | V | A | F | C | I | R | H | O | T | R | H |
| S | O | L | I | L | F | D | O | G | S | Z | G |
| T | E | H | Z | D | E | H | D | E | E | F | W |
| O | C | I | L | R | I | T | I | M | T | O | O |
| D | M | Q | T | A | O | G | T | E | H | T | C |
| I | G | T | O | N | M | A | N | N | O | I | |
| K | R | H | R | O | O | S | T | E | R | W | S |

## 5. Fantastic Food

| | | | | | | | | | | | | |
|--|--|--|--|--|--|--|--|--|--|--|--|--|
| L | A | E | R | E | C | A | Y | I | M | F | I |
| U | Y | A | S | E | R | D | T | O | A | S | T |
| T | O | R | W | Q | P | O | O | A | N | N | E |
| O | L | L | B | H | E | K | D | J | T | P | H |
| L | O | A | E | G | A | S | U | A | S | I | S |
| L | O | S | I | T | M | C | Y | H | X | Z | |
| E | H | E | P | O | T | A | T | O | B | S | F |
| J | P | I | N | E | A | P | P | L | E | H | A |
| O | R | Y | W | F | G | L | U | Y | I | K | N |
| T | C | A | K | E | G | U | S | O | U | T | S |
| K | T | O | E | G | V | C | H | P | E | A | S |
| L | A | T | E | R | U | A | P | L | S | E | A |

# 6. Cool Colors

```
L W R R Q I E G N A R O
G H M K E S T L R V T F
E I G G H V I W J R Z G
P T I K U S I Q I O R
E E N T E R U I Q N S E
L I D E R P H R S G E E
W G O L D T E U M G D N
O E L S V I C K C A L B
L R E W P D K H F P Z I
I G B R X D N Y L A N N
E W U E R D I N B S L S
Y P A V E R P O O A H T
```

# 9. At the Circus

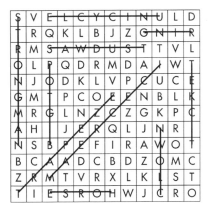

```
S V E L C Y C I N U L D
T R Q K L B J Z G N I R
R M S A W D U S T T V L
O L P Q D R M D A I W T
N J O D K L V P C U C E
G M T P C O E E N B L K
M R G L N Z C Z G K P C
A H   J E R Q L J N R
N S B P E F I R A W O T
B C A A D C B D Z O M C
Z R M T V R X L K L S T
T I E S R O H W J C R O
```

# 7. In the Home

```
J R V M E S A C K O O B
B T E L E V I S I O N B
E A B D H T B A T H T D
L F Y X C W G A Z N R R
B R E N A E L C M I A M
A L V E R S H J U D S S
T B T U R Q C T U L H K
A C N Y O K U P C K C E
R A A O T E O V A L A T
C T S I U R C T V B N T
S Z B P J Z D K P S T
S F I L M D E B R V Q E
```

# 11. At Work

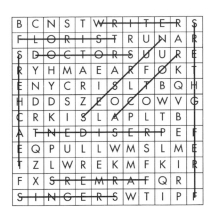

```
B C N S T W R I T E R S
F L O R I S T R U N A R
S D O C T O R S U U R E
R Y H M A E A R F O K T
E N Y C R I S L T B Q H
H D D S Z E O C O W V G
C R K I S L A P L T B
A T N E D I S E R P E F
E Q P U L L W M S L M E
T Z L W R E K M F K I R
F X S R E M R A F Q R
S I N G E R S W T I P F
```

# 12. Wild Animals

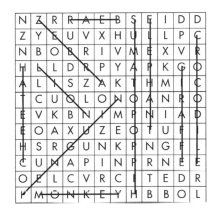

```
N Z R R A E B S E I D D
Z Y E U V X H U L L P C
N B O B R I V M E X V R
H L L D R P Y A P K G O
A L I S Z A K T H M I C
T C U O L O N O A N R O
E V K B N I M P N I A D
E O A X U Z E O T U F
H S R G U N K P N G F
C U N A P I N P R N E E
O E L C V R C I T E D R
P M O N K E Y H B B O L
```

# 10. Girls' Names

```
Z E L I Z A B E T H X Q
X M E I L N D Z O A W J
B J L N M A R Y B C T S
M D T E R A G R A M R P
K V R C I B Q J K Z O Y
U H S Y E N T I R B
K A O U S R O J P I H C
L R M K O C M A E P R A
D A B S T Q I V N F X R
N S E L D K G X A N M T
Z I V N W O B W B Z A S
A L M Z R J E N N Y R Z
```

# 8. Toy Store

```
B A R B I E F G Q D B R
S R O Z T W A S G I J L
S K I P J U M P R O P E
M N O I T A T S Y A L P
H E R A E B Y D D E T G
R O C K I N G H O R S E
Z Y X D V N H B K K F Z
Q N L M C A O A I O H I
O P U W K M B K J O J D
A C T I O N M A N B J O
C O L O R I N G K B B K
R T S E L B R A M F G L
```

# 13. Holidays

```
C Z C S A M T S I R H C
M M A N G E R O Y X S R
G P H B T C A R O L S E
N U R I D U A C U M F H
I D Z H M W R P A T N T
K D A T A V S K M O I A
C I M X L K L Z E K H F
O N P M E F K M S Y Z A
T G O E I B Q U D F W Q
S C R P O A X Y N W B
N T Y U L E L O G A Z X
Q S T N E S E R P L H H
```

# 14. Under the Sea

```
J Y X H U P W M J H F F
D C V N S H A R K Y D X
Y F U E K X E F J P N P
D O L P H I N U D E U
E Q H D S V L R C Q E
E M K U C F E H D A H S
W S W R J L K F M M R
A L A C S S U X E R V O
E B X B V Y E C H E P H
S F O K D M Y V K M E A
Y L E H S I F E A N Q E
O C T O P U S V H W J S
```

# 17. Clothes

```
G S E O H S Q I L U D L
A K H V F Y R B G M R F
U M X R I E N R U O E A
I N A O P F U N V K S T
H C L M H Q D A S O S R
S R U G B E M R K N O
Y J E K R H E H H I M H
N U V W L S Y X B H Q S
F Q E I T R T A O C F T
M A V N A G T R I K S N
R B A L K N M U V E O G
Y P R I U S O C K S Y X
```

# 15. TV Characters

```
N B O B F I X W T S A H
P A S H L T C H J U F I
L C U B O Y O K P S W D
E D Y M A M F T B E N L
K M Y A I L A H I Y P
G Y B S H N K C Y B E I
G N X P A S M F F S N U
A S L M Y S J O A G R B
M C F K W G U T X U A S
L H A F B J P H N B B X
S C O O B Y D O O C Y H
U H E N R Y A N L A W G
```

# 16. Family Fun

```
B E C E I N U I F K E M
H R X A L C J I H Z O W
N E P H E W S X B M R P
I S C B A M D N A R G U
Z F O H I F G E M C E I
E A U J R D L A W N L O
R S N E P A S H D H W
T M R T I U D P K A U
N C N S S J H O N D K D
U O A M H Z E I A Y X
A B L X S D N P F W R K
R B R O T H E R R U E G
```

# 18. In the Garden

```
W R I R E W O M N W A L
H Y J T A L P A T I O B
E F D K O T R B L G N D
E L E L N R E T Y C Z S
L O A C B Z R J I D Q D
B W G W N D H E U C U E
A E R Y I E E L W B J E
R R J T D Q F B K O L W
R K T A B K N G T I L K
O U P D W Y N A Q U Z F
W S R E S U O H Y A L P
J K G R E E N H O U S E
```

# 19. Space

```
Q G H G T E K C O R I V
B O M R L D Q Z B A H O
R M E A U W M G T S K L
D E T V V B O E N T O G
H T S K L N X S R K E
M Z Y G A R D G O S I
O B S Y L H M T K N W T
O I R P T U H Y A X T
N U A T Q B T I L U O U
S K L D S R D Z D T R H
Q G O H A X N V O N M S
Z R S E L S R A T S X D
```

# 20. The Body

```
F O T R A E H S T U A R
T C Z Q H K E O D A E H
E R L A T U L M Z K B N
E K N M U S C L E Q F V
F D F C S Q N V E S T P
S L R E O A M N A R E T
A T Y U S N O B C L E N
C E P Q C B T K B R N O
F Z U K R L F A T Z K H
S L I A N R E G N I F B
R P C L Q N O V R S H L
K N O T T U B Y L L E B
```

# 21. Opposites

```
Z F P D Y L W O L S P E
O R E S Q K S X H C H N
U X M E D H B L Y S A E
D N K K T R D O X N K T
N B T F U Z A R J T J G
W K E R F N F W I S F D
O L S L P K R U R Q L S
D X T D B O M G T O C M
Q F O C U E G A X K F A
G I H G E J F P I E S L
K Z H D N O F T K Z D E
M U D U O L R B H R S J
```

# 22. Magic

| F | E | I | H | C | R | E | K | D | N | A | H |
|---|---|---|---|---|---|---|---|---|---|---|---|
| A | B | R | A | C | A | D | A | B | R | A | M |
| O | H | N | F | D | H | S | E | S | W | Q | A |
| T | L | K | J | H | S | O | N | N | L | J | A |
| S | E | A | B | D | V | A | M | K | H | S | R |
| E | M | W | R | L | I | R | F | C | S | S | A |
| R | D | A | Q | C | E | H | D | I | V | X | B |
| P | C | K | I | T | N | N | S | N | Q | K | B |
| S | F | G | T | A | E | T | D | C | M | S |   |
| L | A | O | J | O | A | B | W | N | L | F | T |
| M | P | H | V | M | B | K | D | M | A | S | A |
| A | Q | M | F | T | R | I | C | K | S | J | W | Z |

# 23. The Beach

| O | G | H | R | S | W | I | M | S | U | I | T |
|---|---|---|---|---|---|---|---|---|---|---|---|
| D | T | E | W | I | N | D | B | R | E | A | K |
| U | S | L | C | S | A | Y | W | Q | L | N | C |
| N | A | I | J | U | D | H | X | D | H | O | J |
| W | N | S | G | S | O | G | C | D | P | T | J |
| P | D | A | H | Y | C | T | R | K | G | J | X |
| L | W | C | D | Q | U | L | F | H | C | N | H |
| E | I | D | C | H | T | C | N | B | W | E | R |
| W | C | N | P | A | D | D | L | I | N | G | D |
| O | H | A | H | S | I | F | R | A | T | S | C |
| T | E | S | D | G | H | S | O | P | U | Q | Y |
| Y | S | L | I | F | E | G | U | A | R | D | T |

# 24. Time

| O | M | I | N | U | T | E | C | P | S | Y | T |
|---|---|---|---|---|---|---|---|---|---|---|---|
| A | D | M | U | E | V | W | F | R | N | X | F |
| B | S | H | C | T | A | W | G | E | M | O | B |
| S | D | N | O | C | E | S | D | H | W | B | G |
| D | O | T | N | S | N | D | R | T | E | A | P |
| R | P | X | Y | A | C | A | H | A | Y | L | X |
| U | W | E | F | D | E | N | N | F | S | A | G |
| O | G | V | D | Y | M | B | T | D | U | R | B |
| H | A | S | B | A | O | P | S | N | F | M | S |
| T | N | H | E | Y | C | D | U | A | V | D | Y |
| C | B | M | D | X | W | E | M | R | N | X | A |
| S | H | T | N | O | M | G | D | G | D | S | D |

# 25. Drinks

| J | O | T | C | H | O | C | O | L | A | T | E |
|---|---|---|---|---|---|---|---|---|---|---|---|
| C | O | R | D | I | A | L | H | K | D | S | X |
| Y | C | B | E | D | A | Z | R | E | E | B | D |
| C | A | R | B | O | N | A | T | E | D | M | B |
| K | H | E | E | F | F | O | C | V | H | J | D |
| J | D | M | C | N | N | S | K | W | I | N | E |
| S | X | T | B | B | T | Y | O | N | L | H | K |
| S | E | B | H | I | Z | R | A | V | C | F | C |
| A | L | K | V | Z | B | J | R | E | T | A | W |
| W | N | M | I | Y | W | D | B | V | S | X | S |
| O | Z | D | F | M | I | L | K | N | A | O | L |
| I | A | S | N | M | C | J | U | I | C | E | Z |

# 26. The Playground

| G | L | Y | T | R | O | F | Y | S | F | F | K |
|---|---|---|---|---|---|---|---|---|---|---|---|
| K | E | L | N | I | J | D | S | I | O | Y | U |
| O | E | P | R | L | A | D | D | E | R | S | H |
| U | R | L | V | E | H | X | F | D | V | W | C |
| H | L | E | D | Z | C | D | F | K | U | G | T |
| B | K | I | C | A | S | C | P | X | I | M | O |
| E | F | N | W | E | R | G | O | J | N | R | C |
| L | D | Y | T | R | S | C | T | S | H | Y | S |
| L | S | H | T | A | G | S | S | X | D | F | P |
| I | J | I | K | V | F | I | M | T | K | F | O |
| G | N | I | P | P | I | K | S | E | A | N | H |
| P | F | N | X | Z | H | W | T | V | J | C | S |

# 27. Party Time

| B | Q | W | S | D | V | C | V | E | B | N | C |
|---|---|---|---|---|---|---|---|---|---|---|---|
| N | F | S | S | E | R | D | Y | C | N | A | F |
| P | R | E | S | E | N | T | F | D | Y | F | E |
| E | M | G | H | L | M | C | Y | K | H | G | F |
| L | K | U | C | D | F | D | S | P | W | Q | B |
| E | D | V | O | F | X | R | C | N | P | K | Y |
| C | F | O | M | Q | J | G | O | D | X | A | L |
| R | F | H | W | A | B | E | G | H | D | F | H |
| A | M | V | H | L | Y | S | U | D | G | F | K |
| P | D | C | N | F | M | U | S | I | C | M | G |
| S | N | O | I | T | A | T | I | V | N | I | A |
| C | I | C | E | C | R | E | A | M | Q | V | B |

# 28. Vacations

| T | E | N | T | G | B | F | D | S | W | E | Q |
|---|---|---|---|---|---|---|---|---|---|---|---|
| A | M | E | K | B | R | E | L | I | A | R | T |
| S | L | E | E | P | I | N | G | B | A | G | F |
| L | P | H | S | U | R | B | H | T | O | O | T |
| N | O | F | J | R | H | U | Q | H | D | E | D |
| W | S | S | U | N | N | Y | F | G | F | S | N |
| G | T | B | E | M | L | D | V | A | B | A | L |
| Q | C | D | F | A | E | E | N | Q | R | C | W |
| K | A | S | D | J | H | W | T | B | U | T | K |
| E | R | B | P | A | M | G | E | O | D | J | J |
| N | D | L | F | R | M | S | H | Q | N | U | B |
| S | S | T | R | O | P | R | I | A | F | S | A |

# 29. Farmyard Animals

| M | J | L | N | D | F | V | H | B | C | N | X |
|---|---|---|---|---|---|---|---|---|---|---|---|
| L | N | K | T | I | K | Q | N | E | H | H | K |
| I | G | O | O | S | E | U | E | D | V | I | Y |
| A | C | E | D | U | C | K | M | D | G | K | E |
| M | X | J | H | X | C | H | I | C | L | T | K |
| A | T | C | N | X | H | B | V | B | V | R | V |
| D | A | B | K | G | N | E | J | R | N | M | U |
| F | O | L | V | T | D | C | B | G | R | U | T |
| G | G | I | K | Q | M | M | J | H | Q | U | X |
| V | X | E | B | U | A | F | X | D | T | L | P |
| B | U | L | L | F | N | K | K | I | C | J |   |
| C | J | M | Q | G | E | T | A | C | V | F | B |

# 30. Bedtime

```
G J K B V C F D S W H S
Q E I T H G I N R T Y C
S K W Z C U I K L I M I
K W I Q V G M S C C F T
C B X S J G M C N X W Q
U T H R S A F W K A G J
T E D Y E M T H T C I S
K D V R C V B E Z V H I
G D D W U Q R U J B D O
F Y C H R X K C F S W R
S B Z F T W O L L I P Y
X T H G I L Y D H G V K
```

# 31. The Desert

```
B M N H U S A N D I D F
H I G K T Y U G N H C O
N R V B D L F C E U A T
U A C H B I F R D S X N
E G X E G Z T E I V G O
T E G E I A U S H T B
O U F R K R L T N G Y P
Y E N T D D C E I D R R
O V I M B N F E M U F O
C U G L H T X G K A N C
B R T A E H Y V B G C S
K D E P D R E T A W I H
```

# 32. Flowers

```
J K N P A N S I E V H C
X D A D A I S Y R F O J
H R T N Y S N A P G I K
P C E B J F G D U C L X
P N F W Z F K G C N Y A
E E G E O M B D R V J Y
T V F N E L A M E N T L
A K H S S X F P T Q E
L M O Z B D R N T N S L
J R D E P A T S U H G K
X A T E U Q U O B S J P
D N G M V Q N G F A E L
```

# 33. The Letter 'W'

```
W V H F W A T E R F D S
A D C E D W R I T E W R
L R T E S X W Y N W H G
L K S J J R O Y R E I S
W N D F S H E R I A T W
G F T G C I P K D K E C
D X N A F S H R S G S V
Y I E V T N T S E I G S
W W H R A G X N A F H E
V K S M D S S Y C W T W
T F O G A W A T C H T F
S W W E B S E T E E A S
```

# 34. The Letter 'S'

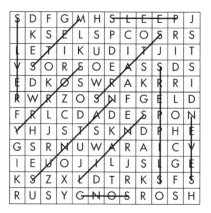

```
S D F G M H S L E E P J
K S E L S P C O S R S
L E T I K U D I T J I T
V S O R S O E A S S D S
E D K O S W R A K R R I
R W R Z O S N F G E L D
F R L C D A D E S P O N
Y H J S T S K N D P H E
G S R N U W A R A I C V
I E U O J L J S L G E
K S Z X L D T R K S F S
R U S Y G N O S R O S H
```

# 35. Spies

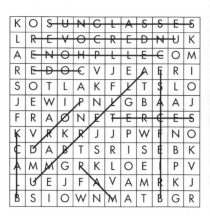

```
K O S U N G L A S S E S
L R E V O C R E D N U K
A E N O H P L L E C O M
R E D O C V J E A E R I
S O T L A K F L T S L O
J E W I P N L G B A A J
F R A O N E T E R C E S
K V R K R J J P W F N O
C D A B T S R I S E B K
A M M G R K L O E P V
L U E J F A V A M R K J
B S I O W N M A T B G R
```

# 36. Birds

```
N R O B I N F C H S T U
D I K X E G O K C U C Y
W R A G G N I M A L F M
S N I M O P K E N B O A
H W F B N D T O R R A P
Y O T E G C I R C U V F
M R U A E N E B Y P M H
N R X G S O I I N U K E
B A A L W H F M G T I X
I P D E O K M A M D J F
N S Y T R C P F E U U C
M E F B C U N W X S H B
```

# 37. Creepy Crawlies

```
R I S T U I C K L P M V
N G R A S S H O P P E R
S F H E W Q R G B B I W
E M Y L F N O G A R D P
L C C R B L Z S K G L S
R R K E E B R E C T G A
W I T S U H I L F V K W
O C I P E C N T K M H Y
R K G I W R A E R B L R
M E V K I W G E Q P I N
U T H R F T P B S Z C K
N C O T I U Q S O M U E
```

# 38. Jewelry

| K | L | N | I | A | H | C | Y | L | L | E | B |
|---|---|---|---|---|---|---|---|---|---|---|---|
| D | P | E | A | R | L | S | V | X | U | E | R |
| R | J | E | C | A | L | K | C | E | N | N | S |
| S | N | W | O | B | L | R | Q | K | D | I | Z |
| G | A | U | J | R | W | C | L | A | S | P | R |
| N | N | B | E | A | D | L | N | W | S | L | J |
| I | K | V | J | C | Y | B | E | H | J | A | K |
| R | L | X | D | E | I | D | E | O | R | Q | S |
| R | E | O | W | L | L | S | B | A | R | F | D |
| L | T | K | Q | E | Z | U | J | D | W | B | L |
| N | E | S | R | T | O | T | J | V | J | I | O |
| L | S | G | N | I | R | R | A | E | W | X | G |

# 39. Boys' Names

| S | D | K | O | M | A | R | K | P | V | W | Q |
|---|---|---|---|---|---|---|---|---|---|---|---|
| Y | U | C | L | I | V | E | B | R | D | L | Y |
| B | H | N | D | H | U | G | W | F | N | D | N |
| V | Q | S | P | Z | I | X | H | G | N | S | O |
| A | R | E | L | W | K | U | I | H | V | K | T |
| N | P | I | H | D | C | O | P | B | P | D | . |
| D | W | R | S | L | B | J | O | Y | R | U | H |
| R | F | A | D | L | G | G | Q | V | I | N | M |
| E | L | H | N | U | H | X | B | K | L | A | . |
| W | Y | C | Z | A | P | B | O | B | D | O | D |
| Q | D | K | G | M | F | R | P | Z | S | W | A |
| B | V | D | R | E | T | E | P | I | N | Y | C |

# 40. Countries

| B | N | M | S | A | M | E | R | I | C | A | C |
|---|---|---|---|---|---|---|---|---|---|---|---|
| D | N | A | L | R | E | Z | T | I | W | S | M |
| K | C | E | A | I | N | F | L | C | U | S | A |
| M | Z | I | T | A | L | Y | B | E | G | G | U |
| F | H | L | W | K | A | H | R | E | D | K | S |
| K | O | E | S | T | I | G | R | U | N | N | I |
| A | L | C | U | C | E | M | T | A | A | S | P |
| I | L | N | B | N | A | Z | M | M | L | B | A |
| C | A | A | M | N | F | I | C | E | G | H | L |
| L | N | R | Y | S | H | K | L | N | N | W | I |
| F | D | F | E | C | A | U | H | F | E | S | A |
| W | B | Z | S | P | A | I | N | R | I | M | E |

# 41. Wild Animals

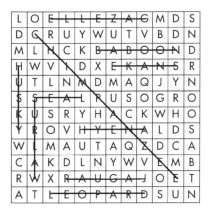

| L | O | E | L | L | E | Z | A | G | M | D | S |
|---|---|---|---|---|---|---|---|---|---|---|---|
| D | G | R | U | Y | W | U | T | V | B | D | N |
| M | L | H | C | K | B | A | B | O | O | N | D |
| H | W | V | I | D | X | E | K | A | N | S | R |
| U | T | L | N | M | D | M | A | Q | J | Y | N |
| S | S | E | A | L | P | U | S | O | G | R | O |
| K | U | S | R | Y | H | A | C | K | W | H | O |
| Y | R | O | V | H | Y | E | N | A | L | D | S |
| W | L | M | A | U | T | A | Q | Z | D | C | A |
| C | A | K | D | L | N | Y | W | V | E | M | B |
| R | W | X | R | A | U | G | A | J | O | E | T |
| A | T | L | E | O | P | A | R | D | S | U | N |

# 42. The Sea

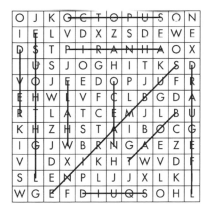

| O | J | K | O | C | T | O | P | U | S | O | N |
|---|---|---|---|---|---|---|---|---|---|---|---|
| I | E | L | V | D | X | Z | S | D | E | W | E |
| D | S | T | P | I | R | A | N | H | A | O | X |
| I | U | S | J | O | G | H | I | T | K | S | D |
| V | O | J | E | E | D | O | P | J | U | F | R |
| E | H | W | L | V | F | C | L | B | G | D | A |
| R | T | L | A | T | C | E | M | J | L | B | U |
| K | H | Z | H | S | T | I | B | O | C | G | . |
| I | G | J | W | B | R | N | G | A | E | Z | E |
| V | . | D | X | I | W | F | W | V | D | F | . |
| S | L | E | N | P | L | J | J | X | L | K | . |
| W | G | E | F | D | I | U | Q | S | O | H | L |

# 43. Weather

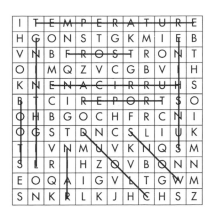

| I | T | E | M | P | E | R | A | T | U | R | E |
|---|---|---|---|---|---|---|---|---|---|---|---|
| H | G | O | N | S | T | G | K | M | I | E | B |
| V | N | B | F | R | O | S | T | R | O | N | T |
| O | K | M | Q | Z | V | C | G | B | V | H | . |
| K | N | E | N | A | C | I | R | R | U | H | S |
| B | T | C | I | R | E | P | O | R | T | S | O |
| O | H | B | G | O | C | H | F | R | C | N | I |
| O | G | S | T | R | N | C | S | L | I | U | K |
| T | . | V | N | M | U | V | K | N | Q | S | M |
| S | L | R | . | H | Z | O | V | B | O | N | N |
| E | O | Q | A | I | G | V | L | T | G | W | M |
| S | N | K | R | L | K | J | H | C | H | S | Z |

# 44. Creepy Crawlies

| H | A | R | V | E | S | T | M | A | N | R | C |
|---|---|---|---|---|---|---|---|---|---|---|---|
| N | R | H | T | Y | R | U | B | K | N | Y | W |
| T | E | Q | C | E | N | T | I | P | E | D | E |
| W | T | Z | O | D | I | K | G | J | S | H | I |
| O | A | R | C | H | G | J | S | G | D | H | U |
| O | K | L | K | B | W | L | N | H | C | T | F |
| D | S | S | R | Y | U | S | F | E | R | G | H |
| W | D | I | O | G | Z | S | E | E | D | H | G |
| O | N | N | A | T | K | L | D | I | U | Q | L |
| R | O | Y | C | B | H | I | N | L | T | B | O |
| M | P | N | H | D | P | G | T | W | U | N | J |
| K | S | R | L | S | N | A | I | L | T | Z | A |

# 45. Characters

| J | O | B | I | V | H | A | G | R | I | D | R |
|---|---|---|---|---|---|---|---|---|---|---|---|
| B | E | L | L | E | A | J | E | S | O | R | W |
| Y | C | J | Y | D | O | O | W | D | G | A | C |
| I | S | R | H | G | V | Y | C | K | J | E | N |
| O | H | E | W | J | N | J | M | X | C | Y | A |
| X | E | T | A | N | A | R | B | O | B | T | . |
| B | R | . | S | C | P | H | A | K | R | H | T |
| E | A | M | R | N | R | I | M | E | D | G | S |
| D | Y | O | C | V | E | O | B | N | C | . | A |
| S | V | N | I | E | T | W | I | A | X | L | B |
| N | J | E | H | N | E | S | C | V | J | V | E |
| S | I | M | B | A | P | B | C | O | Y | I | S |

# 46. Movies

| | | | | | | | | | | | |
|---|---|---|---|---|---|---|---|---|---|---|---|
| G | B | L | M | E | R | M | A | I | D | L | D |
| N | C | A | S | F | E | T | X | H | N | O | G |
| I | O | L | B | E | A | S | T | R | U | I | S |
| K | N | L | H | D | M | W | E | B | L | B | N |
| F | G | E | R | I | H | Y | T | K | D | M | A |
| K | D | R | I | W | H | F | S | G | I | T | C |
| L | E | E | T | B | I | K | C | O | X | F | |
| U | C | D | O | R | G | R | I | N | C | H | A |
| H | L | N | E | H | N | F | E | M | R | D | M |
| S | H | | R | G | P | M | A | R | T | H | L |
| T | F | C | X | D | O | C | T | I | B | N | A |
| E | T | O | Y | S | T | O | R | Y | L | S | D |

# 49. The Letter 'P'

| | | | | | | | | | | | |
|---|---|---|---|---|---|---|---|---|---|---|---|
| A | P | A | J | A | M | A | S | T | O | N | A |
| R | D | P | T | P | N | G | P | A | S | E | P |
| D | P | A | R | T | R | I | D | G | E | O | R |
| P | O | N | A | R | E | H | T | N | A | P | D |
| A | P | E | S | U | R | C | H | A | J | N | X |
| S | G | T | P | I | R | A | T | E | G | O | |
| R | N | A | A | O | D | P | N | U | T | M | S |
| N | S | H | R | M | A | D | A | O | D | P | T |
| U | R | P | G | E | G | R | T | R | E | N | |
| T | A | C | A | U | P | R | A | M | A | G | A |
| A | P | R | P | J | A | G | P | S | O | C | P |
| K | M | A | O | P | D | G | R | U | K | P | T |

# 47. Games

| | | | | | | | | | | | |
|---|---|---|---|---|---|---|---|---|---|---|---|
| I | L | M | N | R | S | T | U | W | C | B | P |
| H | Y | R | A | N | O | I | T | C | I | P | E |
| O | P | E | R | A | T | I | O | N | T | D | T |
| P | W | Y | B | I | E | K | Y | G | M | L | W |
| A | S | L | U | S | C | F | G | D | I | B | |
| R | C | O | N | L | R | I | S | Y | N | H | S |
| T | R | P | M | P | T | E | H | T | D | | |
| E | A | O | I | R | E | D | D | N | E | P | E |
| S | B | N | H | D | L | B | K | D | G | W | R |
| U | B | O | S | D | R | A | C | U | A | A | C |
| O | L | M | U | P | M | T | I | N | E | L | T |
| M | E | S | G | L | U | E | D | O | R | L | H |

# 48. Royalty

| | | | | | | | | | | | |
|---|---|---|---|---|---|---|---|---|---|---|---|
| L | B | V | C | D | Y | N | W | E | X | Q | L |
| J | O | P | W | A | L | E | S | E | S | S | F |
| G | D | F | S | T | I | E | C | N | I | R | P |
| C | Y | N | S | E | R | V | A | N | T | S | E |
| A | G | C | E | D | O | Z | T | Y | N | J | G |
| S | U | V | T | Q | K | C | R | O | W | N | S |
| T | A | Y | L | H | J | F | D | S | E | V | N |
| L | R | R | Y | W | R | K | G | M | Z | N | E |
| E | D | N | P | I | N | O | V | T | I | L | E |
| Q | D | E | S | N | C | M | N | D | Y | E | U |
| L | T | H | F | E | Z | O | X | E | Q | W | Q |
| I | V | E | C | A | L | A | P | G | J | C | M |

# 51. Food

| | | | | | | | | | | | |
|---|---|---|---|---|---|---|---|---|---|---|---|
| D | E | S | S | E | R | T | L | B | U | A | G |
| W | R | E | A | T | H | R | W | B | M | S | R |
| Y | V | A | R | G | L | Y | E | L | O | H | A |
| A | E | H | A | Y | T | F | A | G | Y | O | P |
| S | U | N | D | A | Y | I | E | L | R | J | E |
| U | N | E | M | O | M | A | F | B | K | U | S |
| D | E | W | H | I | T | R | U | T | H | A | B |
| J | L | L | B | N | I | M | A | E | N | I | S |
| K | P | T | A | E | Y | F | K | D | E | I | W |
| E | P | S | S | I | N | S | E | L | O | B | M |
| I | A | P | N | G | E | N | O | C | A | B | D |
| Y | M | G | N | I | L | L | I | F | E | A | E |

# 52. Christmas

| | | | | | | | | | | | |
|---|---|---|---|---|---|---|---|---|---|---|---|
| K | D | U | V | I | S | E | L | B | U | A | B |
| W | R | E | A | T | H | F | G | X | E | A | W |
| L | E | P | F | N | A | M | W | O | N | S | K |
| S | E | J | K | N | K | H | C | E | I | K | U |
| H | D | A | L | H | C | I | E | L | S | I | E |
| F | N | E | I | C | O | A | L | M | F | J | N |
| K | U | V | Y | T | K | H | O | N | A | F | |
| D | E | G | W | N | S | D | E | E | R | L | Y |
| P | R | X | A | F | L | F | K | V | U | A | G |
| J | W | S | T | I | N | S | E | L | W | E | C |
| F | P | A | N | G | E | L | A | S | I | J | X |
| V | M | I | S | T | L | E | T | O | E | L | D |

# 53. Clothes

| | | | | | | | | | | | |
|---|---|---|---|---|---|---|---|---|---|---|---|
| C | A | P | R | I | E | D | C | U | R | E | R |
| T | O | C | Y | S | A | G | V | T | A | V | T |
| C | V | S | W | F | J | L | P | B | I | C | R |
| N | A | E | Z | T | U | O | I | X | N | I | |
| J | R | M | S | Y | W | V | K | J | C | A | H |
| T | V | D | F | T | I | E | H | D | O | O | S |
| R | A | S | G | D | S | O | C | A | C | R | |
| U | B | Q | G | F | C | S | W | E | T | E | |
| E | A | S | F | A | J | R | U | I | S | T | D |
| W | C | X | E | F | V | T | F | Z | H | T | U |
| D | M | K | I | L | T | B | A | S | F | E | U |
| B | I | K | I | N | I | O | T | H | D | P | A |

## 54. Nature

| | | | | | | | | | | |
|---|---|---|---|---|---|---|---|---|---|---|
| S | T | R | A | W | B | E | R | R | Y | N | L |
| M | P | K | A | O | L | D | W | N | F | B | P |
| E | I | N | T | E | K | L | Q | K | D | U | B |
| E | E | K | K | B | N | V | G | J | M | L | B |
| B | R | F | D | U | N | N | M | I | B | L |
| E | H | N | B | K | W | E | O | S | N |
| L | F | N | I | R | S | P | L | I | N | K | K |
| B | N | M | K | E | G | U | D | O | F | Q | P |
| M | O | L | W | O | R | C | E | R | A | C | S |
| U | B | O | L | K | F | H | E | S | K | N | K |
| B | W | N | F | T | T | E | S | B | D | M | F |
| C | A | R | P | P | Q | N | E | L | W | I | V |

## 55. Desserts

| | | | | | | | | | | |
|---|---|---|---|---|---|---|---|---|---|---|
| R | O | K | V | U | E | H | S | W | G | K | C |
| B | A | C | Q | P | A | V | L | O | V | A | Y |
| M | N | L | Y | T | B | R | D | G | N | H | S |
| A | R | K | A | D | F | E | F | R | U | B | O |
| E | S | H | W | S | V | P | I | E | I | R | T |
| R | O | E | V | K | T | R | W | T | Y | A | V |
| C | Q | G | B | Y | N | I | C | H | O | K | E |
| E | C | L | A | I | R | G | U | B | R | S | K |
| C | K | C | O | B | B | L | E | R | C | A | T |
| I | S | O | C | R | U | S | E | V | F | L | R |
| V | H | W | U | M | A | E | R | C | K | A | A |
| G | B | E | K | A | C | O | K | B | U | S | T |

## 56. Hobbies

| | | | | | | | | | | |
|---|---|---|---|---|---|---|---|---|---|---|
| F | E | N | D | I | G | N | I | D | A | E | R |
| N | X | B | G | O | C | Z | G | F | N | R | I |
| R | G | S | L | N | J | J | H | N | E | O | E |
| G | G | M | N | I | F | S | G | B | F | X |
| N | H | N | E | B | D | T | E | U | I | Z | E |
| R | N | K | V | G | L | T | R | M | F |
| C | G | E | D | O | K | F | R | I | X | F | C |
| N | B | T | I | X | N | Z | O | W | N | E |
| A | F | O | O | T | B | A | L | L | D | K | S |
| D | E | L | R | E | T | U | P | M | O | C |
| F | I | G | N | I | N | E | D | R | A | G | B |
| N | S | E | W | I | N | G | W | E | G | D | F |

## 57. Girls' Names

| | | | | | | | | | | |
|---|---|---|---|---|---|---|---|---|---|---|
| K | P | E | N | N | Y | L | I | O | R | S | T |
| U | K | T | A | S | E | R | E | T | H | H | J |
| O | I | J | K | H | F | T | E | I | S | O | R |
| A | N | N | I | E | J | D | U | W | X | K | S |
| F | R | L | W | B | S | P | C | X | R | D | P |
| H | I | A | N | I | T | N | E | L | A | V | I |
| F | N | N | K | T | J | D | I | T | B | S | Y |
| Y | D | A | U | O | F | E | F | J | K | F |
| S | J | H | L | K | S | G | U | H | C |
| L | X | D | W | F | R | P | D | S | H | W | K |
| O | T | P | B | U | K | R | C | X | I | K | Y |
| J | A | N | N | O | D | A | M | T | O | E | L |

## 58. The Letter 'M'

| | | | | | | | | | | |
|---|---|---|---|---|---|---|---|---|---|---|
| E | S | T | M | N | I | A | T | N | U | O | M |
| C | W | R | I | X | F | T | W | S | N | C | K |
| L | M | E | D | I | C | I | N | E | E | M | I |
| N | B | U | S | Z | M | O | S | C | O | W | U |
| M | C | S | K | E | S | V | B | T | R | F | M |
| V | W | T | X | I | E | H | G | P | A | M | N |
| U | O | F | T | K | L | M | E | C | L | D | T |
| K | M | R | A | W | S | N | M | S | X | K | S |
| I | Z | B | E | C | A | U | T | K | L | B | R |
| M | M | E | M | J | E | I | R | E | R | A |
| R | U | X | S | T | M | F | M | X | F | Z | M |
| L | E | K | I | B | R | O | T | O | M | C | E |

## 59. Flowers

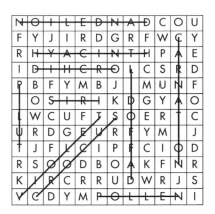

| | | | | | | | | | | |
|---|---|---|---|---|---|---|---|---|---|---|
| N | O | I | L | E | D | N | A | D | C | O | U |
| F | Y | J | I | R | D | G | R | F | W | C | Y |
| R | H | Y | A | C | I | N | T | H | P | A | E |
| I | D | I | H | C | R | O | L | C | S | R | D |
| P | B | F | Y | M | B | J | J | M | U | N | F |
| L | O | S | I | R | I | K | D | G | Y | A | O |
| U | W | C | U | F | J | S | O | E | R | T | C |
| T | J | F | L | C | I | P | F | C | I | O | D |
| R | S | O | O | D | B | O | A | K | F | N | R |
| K | J | R | C | R | R | U | D | W | R | J | S |
| V | C | D | Y | M | P | O | L | L | E | N | I |

## 60. Birds

| | | | | | | | | | | |
|---|---|---|---|---|---|---|---|---|---|---|
| H | I | N | E | R | W | A | C | N | O | C | Y |
| S | L | Y | V | J | B | E | F | W | R | B | G |
| W | E | Q | G | W | D | I | L | Q | S | X | C |
| A | C | N | S | E | C | Y | V | J | H | F | E |
| L | Y | I | H | T | F | S | A | E | L | A | R |
| L | U | L | T | N | R | D | B | Y | L | E |
| O | I | A | J | X | G | I | W | F | V | C | A |
| W | T | Q | H | R | T | Y | C | B | I | O | C |
| B | U | N | A | W | S | L | D | H | E | N | N |
| F | R | E | I | V | E | A | J | N | D | L | I |
| A | E | N | C | L | L | U | G | A | E | S | B |
| T | I | T | M | O | U | S | E | S | E | Q | Y |

## 61. Fairies

| | | | | | | | | | | |
|---|---|---|---|---|---|---|---|---|---|---|
| M | R | I | N | G | B | V | D | O | K | F | I |
| H | A | Z | I | H | U | M | A | N | S | N | L |
| P | S | L | O | O | T | S | D | A | O | T | G |
| F | V | W | K | U | H | M | J | W | A | H | B |
| X | S | N | D | H | F | K | X | J | G | V | S |
| N | G | B | J | L | P | A | F | C | G | H | D |
| E | N | O | Y | I | Y | F | W | N | M | O |
| U | I | L | G | M | J | G | H | K | D | J | O |
| U | W | A | U | T | A | V | K | B | O | P | W |
| Q | P | H | N | M | J | N | A | Z | I | F | L |
| I | X | D | K | K | G | S | G | N | O | S |
| G | W | R | H | Y | M | E | S | B | M | U | O |

## 62. Space

| | | | | | | | | | | | | |
|---|---|---|---|---|---|---|---|---|---|---|---|---|
| P | R | O | B | E | N | J | M | H | B | I | A |
| F | A | C | D | K | P | A | N | A | H | T |
| W | B | S | H | R | U | Q | S | D | S | E | M |
| N | V | Y | E | I | J | I | S | W | I | T | O |
| Y | U | R | A | N | U | S | F | R | I | S |
| X | D | C | F | R | J | K | O | K | O | R | P |
| A | P | J | I | E | F | R | N | S | N | O | H |
| L | M | E | R | C | U | R | Y | P | O | E | E |
| A | F | R | A | H | W | N | C | J | M | T | R |
| G | N | O | R | T | S | M | R | A | Y | E | E |
| N | B | I | N | O | I | R | O | D | F | M | N |
| A | J | K | S | A | T | U | R | N | G | I | L |

## 63. The Park

| | | | | | | | | | | | | |
|---|---|---|---|---|---|---|---|---|---|---|---|---|
| S | L | I | D | E | A | I | C | H | V | E | N |
| V | F | N | D | T | I | P | D | N | A | S | F |
| N | X | H | B | T | R | H | K | L | O | B | I |
| E | C | B | I | C | Y | C | I | N | C | I | P |
| O | R | O | U | N | D | X | B | O | U | T | H |
| D | F | V | L | H | W | V | C | D | E | V | C |
| A | S | W | I | N | G | S | U | F | L | D | A |
| T | B | M | N | O | E | C | M | S | S | Y | N |
| R | D | K | X | D | K | I | S | B | E | A | R |
| E | N | H | F | S | V | A | C | H | M | L | I |
| C | O | L | B | Y | R | A | T | V | A | P | X |
| O | P | W | E | G | M | D | N | E | G | F | K |

## 64. Landmarks

| | | | | | | | | | | | | |
|---|---|---|---|---|---|---|---|---|---|---|---|---|
| G | A | H | T | O | W | E | R | K | G | S | D |
| B | U | C | K | I | N | G | H | A | M | T | L |
| E | U | D | F | Y | E | N | D | Y | S | B | E |
| H | S | T | M | S | A | N | G | W | U | X | F |
| B | D | K | T | V | R | X | S | E | A | K | F |
| R | I | C | E | R | V | I | M | H | A | V |
| I | M | U | B | F | I | D | S | F | T | D | E |
| D | A | N | N | G | A | R | H | A | K | U | G |
| G | R | W | E | S | U | G | A | J | A | N | H |
| E | Y | G | B | X | H | T | K | R | B | E | S |
| K | P | A | D | F | F | V | E | M | I | M | L |
| E | T | L | I | B | E | R | T | Y | T | C | S | W |

## 65. Dogs

| | | | | | | | | | | | | |
|---|---|---|---|---|---|---|---|---|---|---|---|---|
| I | B | E | R | N | A | R | D | T | O | R | K |
| C | H | I | H | U | A | H | U | A | I | O | P |
| S | F | G | O | S | U | F | T | E | A | F | D |
| H | I | P | B | R | H | R | K | E | B | A |
| E | K | A | O | L | W | I | Q | T | L | G |
| P | S | T | L | F | E | Y | H | R | D | S | M |
| H | F | O | E | N | I | G | I | E | O | H | A |
| E | C | U | N | J | Y | O | T | X | O | K | T |
| R | G | E | U | Q | A | K | O | O | P | G |
| D | K | W | R | B | P | E | S | B | U | F | A |
| N | H | H | R | O | D | A | R | B | A | L |
| D | N | U | O | H | Y | E | R | G | I | T | K |

## 66. Spies

| | | | | | | | | | | | |
|---|---|---|---|---|---|---|---|---|---|---|---|
| E | U | F | O | E | G | R | S | R | A | C | T |
| N | B | D | K | B | W | N | X | V | K | H | J |
| E | I | Z | S | A | R | E | M | A | C | S |
| M | N | S | H | T | J | T | R | B | D | B | E |
| Y | O | F | H | L | K | D | G | N | F | Z | M |
| R | C | D | B | K | E | E | W | S | U | W | R |
| G | U | B | O | J | U | R | R | T | X | G | O |
| O | L | F | N | N | T | G | S | D | C | O | F |
| S | A | E | D | I | S | G | U | I | S | E | N |
| D | R | X | V | W | O | F | Z | K | B | U |
| K | S | G | A | D | G | E | T | T | E | G | N |
| J | H | N | O | I | S | O | L | P | X | E | D |

## 67. Hairstyles

| | | | | | | | | | | | | |
|---|---|---|---|---|---|---|---|---|---|---|---|---|
| T | K | G | F | J | L | H | D | F | X | E | R |
| T | E | R | N | K | T | A | E | L | P | V | C |
| A | X | F | C | R | I | M | P | E | R | I | F |
| L | T | L | E | D | G | N | L | B | O | B | G |
| P | E | H | K | F | Z | W | T | R | U | K |
| H | N | A | L | S | E | H | C | N | U | B | V |
| N | I | Y | M | S | S | R | E | L | R | U | C |
| E | O | N | H | N | V | K | E | H | P | J | I |
| R | N | O | X | O | L | R | F | I | L | F | D |
| P | S | P | F | R | D | N | L | W | G | D | S |
| E | N | H | L | I | C | C | V | Z | M | R | J |

## 68. Sports Equipment

| | | | | | | | | | | | | |
|---|---|---|---|---|---|---|---|---|---|---|---|---|
| M | C | B | A | F | H | N | D | W | B | L | G |
| A | Z | U | R | T | E | K | C | A | R | S | X |
| T | S | B | Q | C | Y | I | P | S | T | V | J |
| R | V | T | P | A | D | S | V | O | H | A | S |
| A | G | F | N | C | F | R | O | I | Y | C | N |
| H | B | D | S | L | V | B | D | V | G | F | E |
| S | R | A | W | X | U | S | B | T | G | P | A |
| D | I | Y | T | C | V | A | A | R | A | J | K |
| N | J | P | Q | B | L | C | I | S | B | R | E |
| A | J | G | T | L | R | H | F | Z | D | L | R |
| B | G | S | E | L | D | R | U | H | U | Q | S |
| X | V | A | C | N | N | G | W | R | V | B | Y |

## 69. The Beach

| | | | | | | | | | | | |
|---|---|---|---|---|---|---|---|---|---|---|---|
| M | S | H | L | R | K | T | O | W | E | L | P |
| S | L | D | U | C | W | J | H | V | U | S |
| K | L | T | O | F | G | G | X | Y | E | J | H |
| N | U | R | M | J | R | D | G | R | J | H | G |
| U | G | I | Z | S | L | L | E | H | S | K | L |
| R | A | S | E | S | S | A | L | G | N | U | S |
| T | E | R | G | H | D | F | D | G | X | U | S |
| J | S | K | M | T | D | H | G | I | B | D | E |
| U | P | O | S | T | C | A | R | D | S | W | N |
| B | S | I | V | W | X | L | G | Z | J | D | O |
| R | D | L | O | O | P | K | C | O | R | M | T |
| F | S | W | I | M | S | U | I | T | S | H | S |

# BRAIN STRAINING PUZZLES

# I. WINDOWS

Close all the windows on the screen as instructed. You will be left with four words that form the message.

|  | 1 | 2 | 3 | 4 |
|---|---|---|---|---|
| A | DO | PARTS | NOT | WORN |
| B | DEER | EATEN | EASTER | TRY |
| C | CHIME | READ | SPRAT | PUT |
| D | BRIBE | TRAPS | THIS | NUTS |

○ Close every window containing more than one letter E in row B.

○ Close every window in column 1 which has a vowel as its middle letter.

○ Close every window in columns 2 and 3 where a word uses all the same letters as in STRAP.

○ Close every window in column 4 where a word is made using letters in the second half of the alphabet.

# 2. ODD ONE OUT

Which is the odd one out, and why?

FACE

HANDS

SPRING

WINTER

# 3. CORNERED

The corner letters are in place. Use all the listed letters to complete the grid and form a word square in which words will read both across and down.

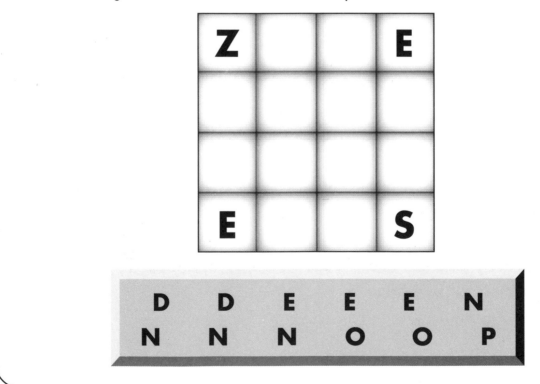

| Z |  |  | E |
|---|---|---|---|
|   |  |  |   |
|   |  |  |   |
| E |  |  | S |

D  D  E  E  E  N
N  N  N  O  O  P

# 4. LEVELER

All the tubes connected to glass Y should have liquid reaching the same level as in glass Y. All the tubes connected to glass Z should have liquid reaching the same level as in glass Z. Which tubes contain liquid at the wrong level?

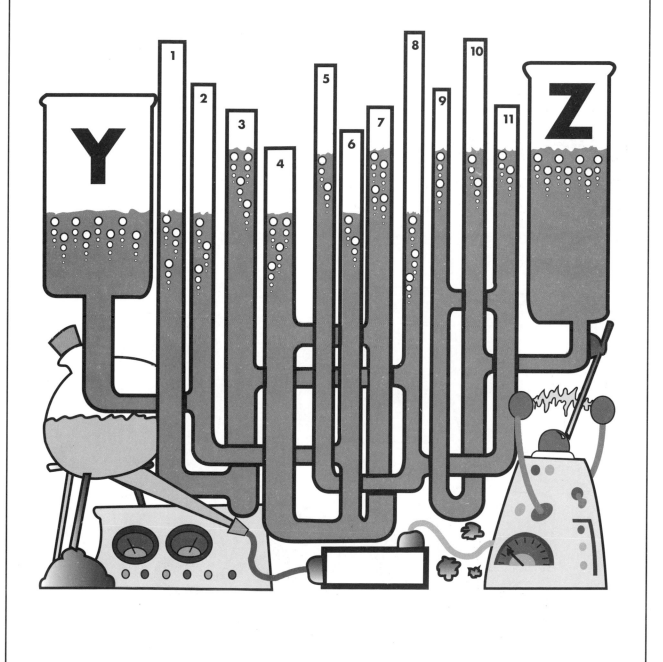

# 5. BACK WORDS

Solve the clues: the second answer is the first answer written backwards.

**FRIENDS** * **HIT**

* _ _ _ _ _     _ _ _

# 6. PICK A CARD

Here are eight cards, each with a number on. Add up the numbers on the gray cards and they total 19. Add up the numbers on the white cards and they total 20. Can you exchange one gray card with a white card, so that both groups of four cards add up to the same number?

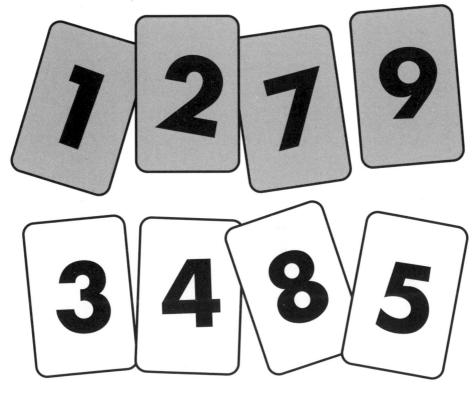

# 7. MIND THE GAP!

Which single three-letter word completes all of the following words?

T H _ _ _ _ E R

A R _ _ _ _

C _ _ _ _ D E D

D _ _ _ _ S Y

# 8. Snowbody There

oh yes there is! five polar bears are hiding in the snowscene. can you find them?

# 9. STEPS

Solve the clues and add or take away one letter of the previous word each time so that your solution will fit into the grid. You can change the order of the letters from the previous word.

1. Ocean
2. Secure
3. A large meal
4. Quicker
5. Signs of crying
6. Remainder
7. Collection

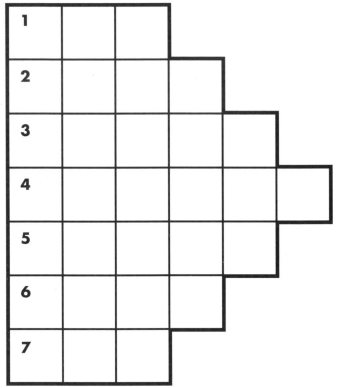

# 10. DOUBLE TROUBLE

Fill both pairs of blank spaces with the same two letters in the same order to make a word.

_ _ U R _ _

# 11. MOSAIC

Fit the letter tiles back into the frame. When the tiles fit together in the right order, the mosaic has five words reading across, and four words reading down.

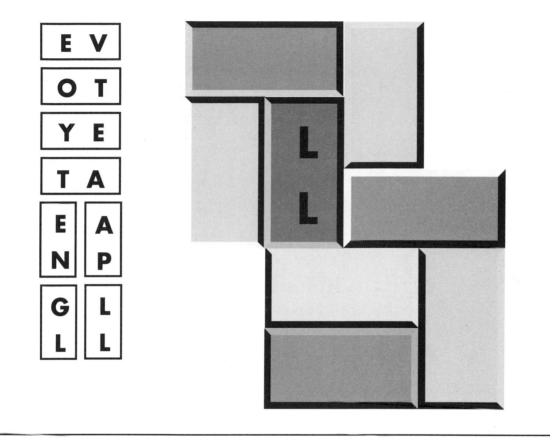

# 12. AFTER WORDS

Which word can go after all these words to make new words?

**B R U S H** _____

**F I R E** _____

**H O L L Y** _____

# 13. NUMBER NAMES

Each letter has a different numerical value between 1 and 6. The letter values are added together to make the total of each animal's name.

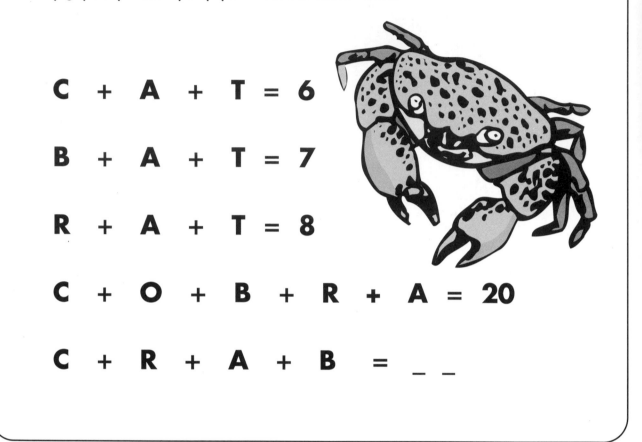

C + A + T = 6

B + A + T = 7

R + A + T = 8

C + O + B + R + A = 20

C + R + A + B = _ _

# 14. SPLITZER

This row of ten letters can be split into two five-letter words which are the names of two items of bedding. Words read from left to right and the letters are in the correct order. What are they?

Q S H U I E L T E T

/ _____

# 15. REVOLVER

Which of the entrances can you use to take a path to the middle of the maze?

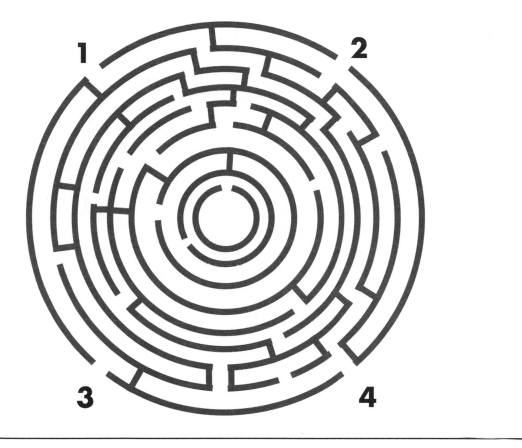

# 16. NUMBER-RING

Move around the circle. You have to write a number in the blank section that will continue the number pattern.

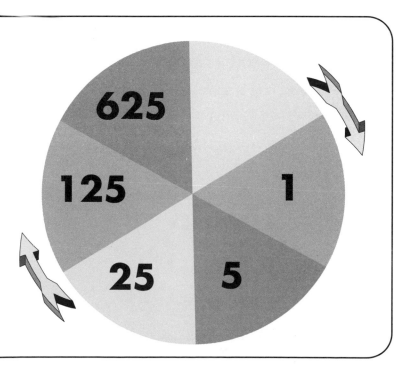

# 17. THROW A SIX

Start on the top line. Move from number to number down or sideways to reach the bottom line. You can only land on numbers which can be divided exactly by 6.

| 12 | 18 | 26 | 12 | 19 | 30 |
|----|----|----|----|----|----|
| 42 | 6  | 52 | 14 | 22 | 18 |
| 6  | 16 | 60 | 72 | 36 | 66 |
| 24 | 34 | 36 | 62 | 38 | 16 |
| 60 | 38 | 42 | 48 | 72 | 66 |
| 9  | 30 | 61 | 16 | 63 | 12 |

# 18. ALPHA-MUSIC

The groups of letters are arranged in alphabetical order. Move them around to spell out different types of music.

1. O P P _____

2. C D I O S _____

3. O L S U _____

4. A E E G G R _____

# 19. FIRST CHANGE

Each clue has two answers. The two answer words are spelt the same except that the first letter of the second answer has changed in the alphabet. So, for example, if answer one was BAT the second answer would be CAT.

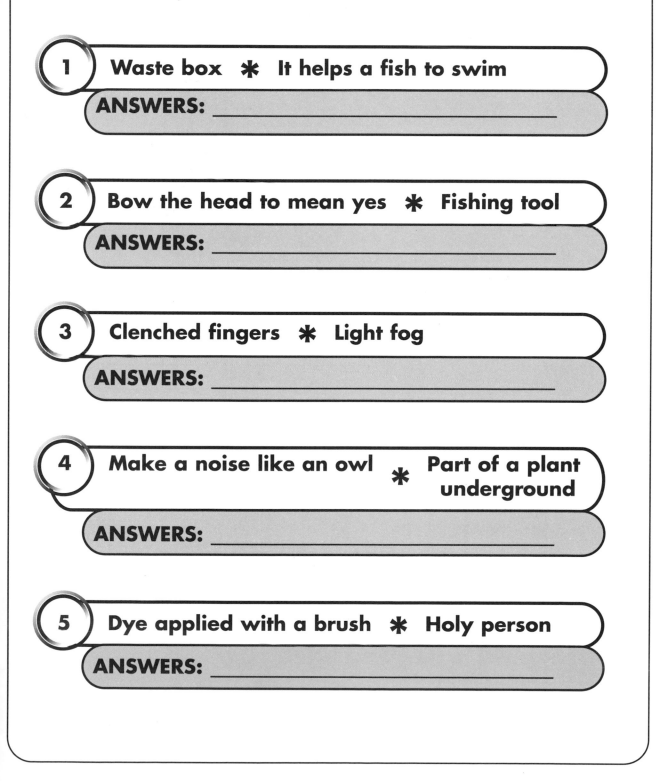

**1** Waste box ✱ It helps a fish to swim

ANSWERS: _____

**2** Bow the head to mean yes ✱ Fishing tool

ANSWERS: _____

**3** Clenched fingers ✱ Light fog

ANSWERS: _____

**4** Make a noise like an owl ✱ Part of a plant underground

ANSWERS: _____

**5** Dye applied with a brush ✱ Holy person

ANSWERS: _____

# 20. LIFT OFF

How many triangles can you count in the picture of the rocket?

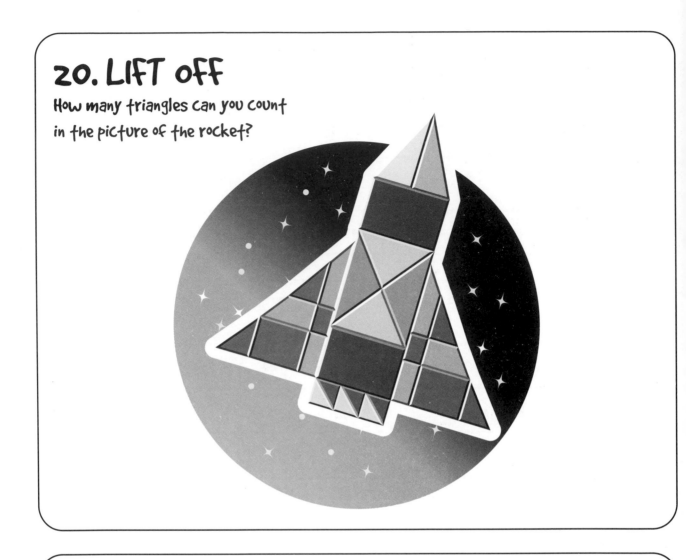

# 21. MIND THE GAP

Which single three-letter word completes all of the following words?

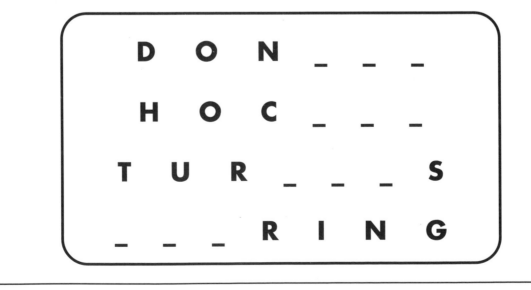

D O N _ _ _

H O C _ _ _

T U R _ _ _ S

_ _ _ _ R I N G

# 22. ON THE MOVE

The name of a means of transport is hidden in each of the sentences below. Find them by joining words or parts of words together.

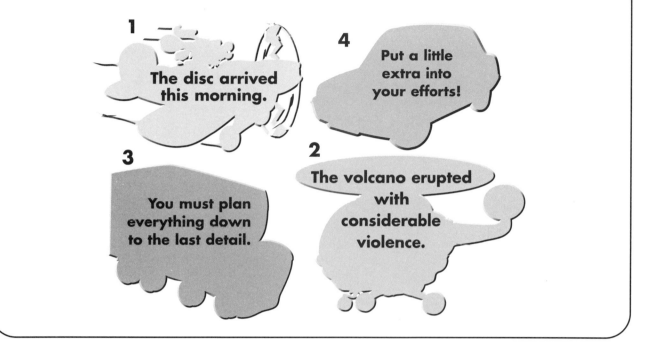

**1** The disc arrived this morning.

**4** Put a little extra into your efforts!

**3** You must plan everything down to the last detail.

**2** The volcano erupted with considerable violence.

# 23. PATTERN PLAY

Work out the pattern of numbers and then fill in the blanks.

| 5 | 3 | 2 | 1 |
|---|---|---|---|
| 8 | 5 | 3 | 2 |
| 11 | 7 | 4 | 3 |
|  | 9 |  | 4 |

# 24. GAME ON

The aim of the computer game is to round up monsters. Each player has captured five monsters. Which monsters did each player capture?

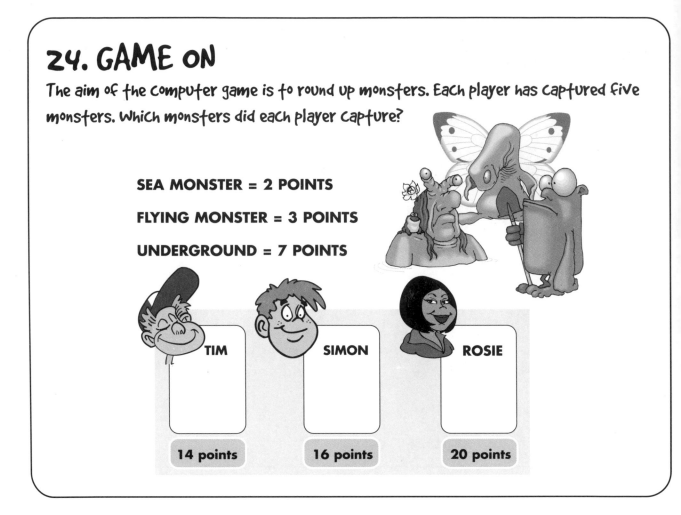

**SEA MONSTER = 2 POINTS**

**FLYING MONSTER = 3 POINTS**

**UNDERGROUND = 7 POINTS**

TIM

SIMON

ROSIE

14 points

16 points

20 points

# 25. ROBOT RACERS

The robot races are about to start. Both mechanical creatures move at exactly the same pace. Which one will finish first?

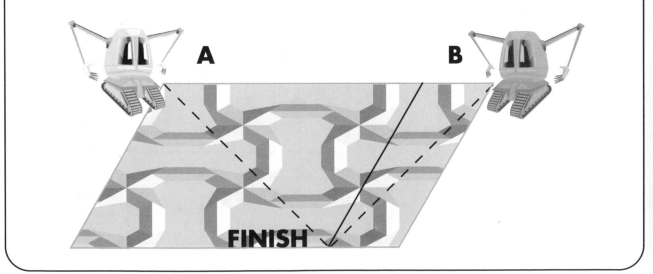

A

B

FINISH

# 26. CLOCKWISE

Solve the clues and write each eight-letter answer clockwise around the appropriate number 1-8. The first letter of each answer is already in place.

1. Daughter of a king and queen
2. Describes something that is the first of its type
3. Creature that has a shell on its back
4. Needlework woven on canvas
5. Person buying goods
6. Chosen
7. Ten hundreds
8. Blown up

## 27. FACE FACTS

Use the letters that make up the face to make a name.

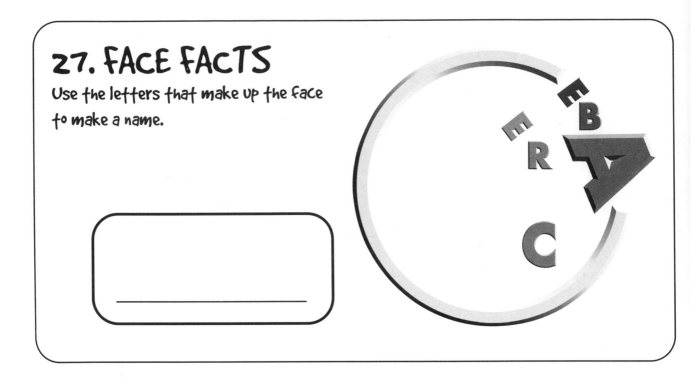

## 28. MENU BAR

Can you unscramble the groups of letters to spell out computing commands?

| File | Edit | Commands | Object | Type | Filter | View |
|------|------|----------|--------|------|--------|------|

N o p e ...   ▶ _____

V a s e ...   ▶ _____

T r i n p ...   ▶ _____

T u i q ...   ▶ _____

E l e d e t ...   ▶ _____

# 29. SYMBOL SHAPES

Shapes and signs have been used to take the place of letters of the alphabet. Can you work out what the words are? They are all shapes and the first word is TRIANGLE.

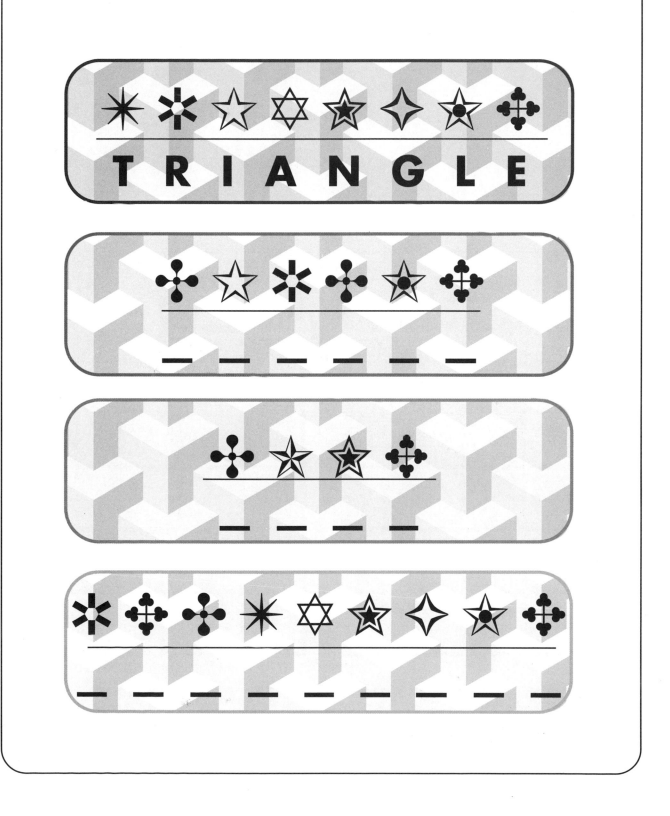

T R I A N G L E

# 30. WHAT'S NEXT?
What is the next letter to go in the space?

# 31. CAT CALLS
Use the words below to make two word squares. Each square must contain the word CATS.

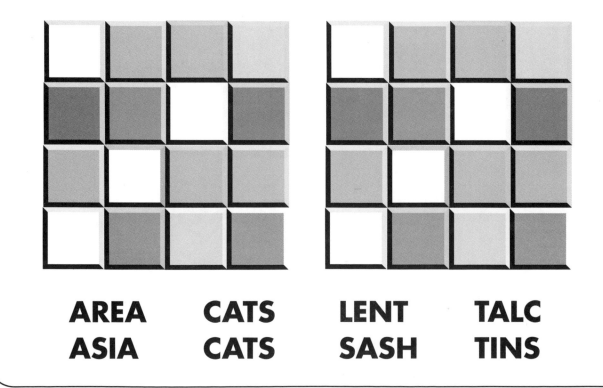

**AREA**      **CATS**      **LENT**      **TALC**
**ASIA**      **CATS**      **SASH**      **TINS**

# 32. WORTH IT!

In the names below, each letter has been given a numerical value from 1 to 3. The total value of each name is reached by adding up the individual letter values in the name. No two different alphabetical letters can have the same number.

A N N = 7

A N N A = 8

A L A N = 7

What is each letter worth?

# 33. COMPUTER CLASS

Mr Bright has eight children working on a computer project. A brand new state-of-the-art computer has just been delivered and everyone wants to work on it. Only four children can use it at any one time. Mr Bright decides to split the eight children into two groups of four, so everyone gets a chance to use the new machine. The teacher puts Emma, Joe, Liam and Madge into one group. Suzy, Roy, Tony and Troy form the other group. Mr Bright has a very logical reason for this. What is it?

_____

## 34. BACK WORDS

Solve the clues: the second answer is the first answer written backwards.

**METAL COOKING ROD** * **HANDY HINTS**

_ _ _ _ _ * _ _ _ _ _

## 35. LADDERS

Turn the top word into the bottom one by altering one letter with each step, forming a new word each time.

CHORD

_ _ _ _ _

_ _ _ _ _

_ _ _ _ _

_ _ _ _ _

LEASE

# 36. SECRET SEVEN

Rearrange the letters in the word below to make another word of seven letters.

R U F F I A N

_ _ _ _ _ _ _

CLUE

Think BIG WHEEL

# 37. PET PUZZLE

Four friends each have a different type of pet. All the pets have different names. Use the clues to decide what type of pet each person owns, along with the name of the animal.

## 38. LINKS
Which word will go after the first word and before the second word?

R A I N ( _ _ _ _ _ _ ) F I R E

## 39. SKYSCRAPER
A skyscraper is 200 meters high plus half of its own height.
How high is it?

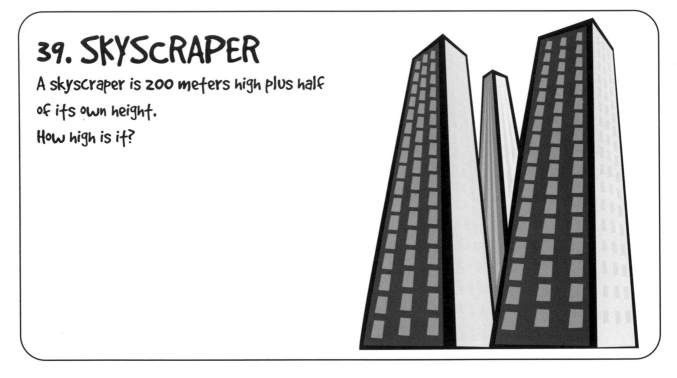

## 40. ADDER
Using other words with the same meaning, can you create a new word from two separate ones?

**NOT IN**    __ __ __

**+ GET THE RIGHT SIZE** __ __ __

**= SET OF CLOTHES**    __ __ __ __ __ __

# 41. NUMBER FIT

fit all the numbers back into the frame.

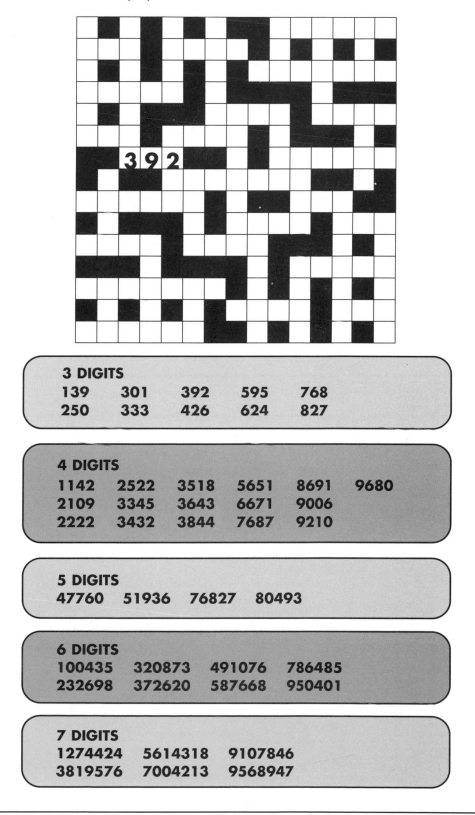

**3 DIGITS**

| 139 | 301 | 392 | 595 | 768 |
|-----|-----|-----|-----|-----|
| 250 | 333 | 426 | 624 | 827 |

**4 DIGITS**

| 1142 | 2522 | 3518 | 5651 | 8691 | 9680 |
|------|------|------|------|------|------|
| 2109 | 3345 | 3643 | 6671 | 9006 | |
| 2222 | 3432 | 3844 | 7687 | 9210 | |

**5 DIGITS**

47760   51936   76827   80493

**6 DIGITS**

| 100435 | 320873 | 491076 | 786485 |
|--------|--------|--------|--------|
| 232698 | 372620 | 587668 | 950401 |

**7 DIGITS**

| 1274424 | 5614318 | 9107846 |
|---------|---------|---------|
| 3819576 | 7004213 | 9568947 |

# 42. SEARCH PARTY

Here's a jumble of letters of the alphabet. Each letter appears once, except for some letters which do not appear at all. Work out the missing letters, making a note of them as you go. Now arrange them to spell out the name of a place to go for a day out.

U F N R D S I M G Y P
W O T K J V X Q L Z

**Missing Letters:**
_____

**Place name:**
_____

# 43. TOP TEN

complete the word by filling the spaces with a whole number between ONE and TEN.

1
6 4
COL _ _ _ L
2 5

# 44. RHYMER

My first is in van – But isn't in name.
My second's in time – But isn't in tame.
My third is in dart – But isn't in tray.
My fourth is in see – But isn't in say.
My fifth is in hot, – But isn't in three.
For a clue think of tape – And a link with TV.

# 45. ON ROUTE

Here's a signpost on the route from Westville to Eastville. You are heading from Westville to Eastville.

The road is absolutely straight. The next signpost has the same numbers but they have changed position as you are closer to Eastville.

What is the distance between the signposts?

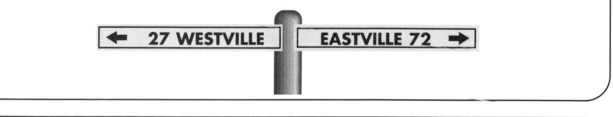

← 27 WESTVILLE     EASTVILLE 72 →

# 46. MEAL-WHEEL

Solve each clue and write the answers into the spaces in the grid. All answers have four letters. Put the first letter in the outer circle, then move towards the center. only ONE letter changes between answers, and answer 8 will be only one letter different from answer 1.

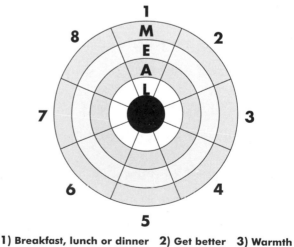

1) Breakfast, lunch or dinner   2) Get better   3) Warmth
4) Be able to listen to something   5) Be scared of something
6) Not too far away   7) Expensive
8) Give out cards to players in a game

# QUICK-FIRE PUZZLES

47. Which word, if pronounced right, is wrong, but if pronounced wrong is right?

48. What is so fragile that when its name is spoken, it's broken?

49. What demands an answer but asks no question?

50. A man was driving a black truck. His lights were not on. The moon was not out. A lady was crossing the street. How did the man see her?

51. If six children and two dogs were under an umbrella, how come none of them got wet?

52. What belongs to you, but is used more by others?

53. What has two hands but no arms?

54. What happens when you throw a green rock in the Red Sea?

55. A man and a dog were going down the street. The man rode, yet walked. What was the dog's name?

56. If an electric train travels 90 miles an hour in a westerly direction and the wind is blowing from the north, in which direction is the smoke blowing?

57. Where can you always find health, wealth and happiness?

58. At this moment everyone in the world is doing the same thing. What is it?

59. A doctor and a boy were fishing. The boy was the doctor's son, but the doctor was not the boy's father. Who was the doctor?

60. A frog fell into a well 12 feet deep. He could jump 3 feet, but every time he jumped 3 feet, he fell back 2 feet. How many times did he have to jump to get out of the well?

61. A man started to town with a fox, a goose and a sack of corn. He came to a stream which he had to cross in a tiny boat. He could only take one across at a time. He could not leave the fox alone with the goose or the goose alone with the corn. How did he get them all safely over the stream?

# ANSWERS

## 1. WINDOWS
Do not read this.

## 2. ODD ONE OUT
Winter. The others can be parts of a clock.

## 3. CORNERED

## 4. LEVELER
1, 7 and 8.

## 5. BACK WORDS
Pals * Slap.

## 6. PICK A CARD
Exchange the 8 and 9, but turn the 9 upside down to read as a 6.
Both rows now total 18.

## 7. MIND THE GAP
Row.

## 8. SNOWBODY THERE

# 9. STEPS

1. Sea 2. Safe 3. Feast 4. Faster 5. Tears 6. Rest 7. Set.

# 10. DOUBLE TROUBLE

Church.

# 11. MOSAIC

# 12. AFTER WORDS

Wood.

# 13. NUMBER NAMES

C+R+A+B =14. T = 1, A = 2, C = 3, B = 4, R = 5, O = 6.

# 14. SPLITZER

Quilt/Sheet.

# 15. REVOLVER

Only entrance 4 leads to the middle of the maze.

# 16. NUMBER-RING

3125. Multiply by 5 at each move.

# 17. THROW A SIX

| 12 | 18 | 26 | 12 | 19 | 30 |
|----|----|----|----|----|----|
| 42 | 6  | 52 | 14 | 22 | 18 |
| 6  | 16 | 60 | 72 | 36 | 66 |
| 24 | 34 | 36 | 62 | 38 | 16 |
| 60 | 38 | 42 | 48 | 72 | 66 |
| 9  | 30 | 61 | 16 | 63 | 12 |

# 41. NUMBER FIT

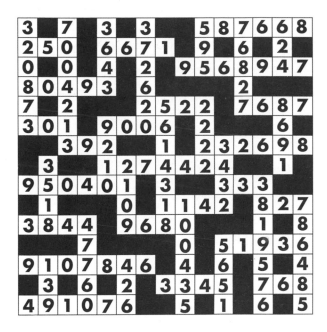

# 42. SEARCH PARTY

Beach.

# 43. TOP TEN

one. This completes the word colonel.

# 44. RHYMER

Video.

# 45. ON ROUTE

45 miles.

# 46. MEAL-WHEEL

1. Meal
2. Heal
3. Heat
4. Hear
5. Fear
6. Near
7. Dear
8. Deal.

# QUICK-FIRE PUZZLES

47. Wrong

48. Silence

49. A telephone

50. It was a bright sunny day.

51. Because it wasn't raining.

52. Your name.

53. A clock.

54. The rock gets wet.

55. Yet.

56. There is no smoke from an electric train!

57. In the dictionary.

58. Getting older.

59. His mother.

60. On the tenth jump he reached 13 feet and was out.

61. He took the goose over first and came back. Then he took the fox across and brought the goose back. Next he took the corn over. He came back alone and took the goose.

## 33. COMPUTER CLASS

The names in one group are made up of letters from the first half of the alphabet. The other group have names made up with letters from the second half of the alphabet.

## 34. BACK WORDS

Spit * Tips.

## 35. LADDERS

Chord, Chore, Chose, Chase, Cease, Lease.

## 36. SECRET SEVEN

Funfair.

## 37. PET PUZZLE

Lucy has a dog called Shula.
Martin has a cat called Ripley.
Peter has a snake called Monty.
Tina has a parrot called Horatio.

## 38. LINKS

Forest.

## 39. SKYSCRAPER

400 meters. If you are adding half of the height, the number you started with must also be equal to half the full height. 200 x 2 = 400.

## 40. ADDER

Out + fit = outfit.

# 26. CLOCKWISE

1. Princess 2. Original
3. Tortoise 4. Tapestry
5. Customer 6. Selected
7. Thousand 8. Exploded.

# 27. FACE FACTS

Rebecca.

# 28. MENU BAR

1. Open 2. Save 3. Print 4. Quit 5. Delete.

# 29. SYMBOL SHAPES

1. Triangle 2. Circle 3. Cone 4. Rectangle.

# 30. WHAT'S NEXT?

T. Letters are in alphabetical order. In each case the right half of each letter mirrors the left half.

# 31. CAT CALLS

# 32. WORTH IT!

A = 1. L = 2. N = 3.

# 18. ALPHA-MUSIC
1. Pop  2. Disco  3. Soul  4. Reggae.

# 19. FIRST CHANGE
1. Bin Fin  2. Nod Rod  3. Fist Mist  4. Hoot Root  5. Paint Saint.

# 20. LIFT OFF
23.

# 21. MIND THE GAP
Key.

# 22. ON THE MOVE
1. Car  2. Canoe  3. Plane  4. Train.

# 23. PATTERN PLAY
The missing numbers are 14 and 5.

Starting at the left, take away the second number from the first and it will give the third number. (14 – 9 = 5). The third number taken from the second gives the fourth number. (9 – 5 = 4).

# 24. GAME ON
Rosie captured  two underground monsters and three sea monsters.

(7 + 7 + 2 + 2 + 2 = 20 )

Simon captured one underground monster, one flying monster and three sea monsters.

(7 + 3 + 2 + 2 + 2 = 16)

Tim captured four flying monsters and one sea monster.

(3 + 3 + 3 + 3 + 2 = 14 )

# 25. ROBOT RACERS
Both will finish at the same time. The distance is equal.

# 1. PAINT BOX

Fill in the boxes using the letters R, G, Y and B. Each row across, each column down and each diagonal from corner to corner must contain a R, G, Y and B square.

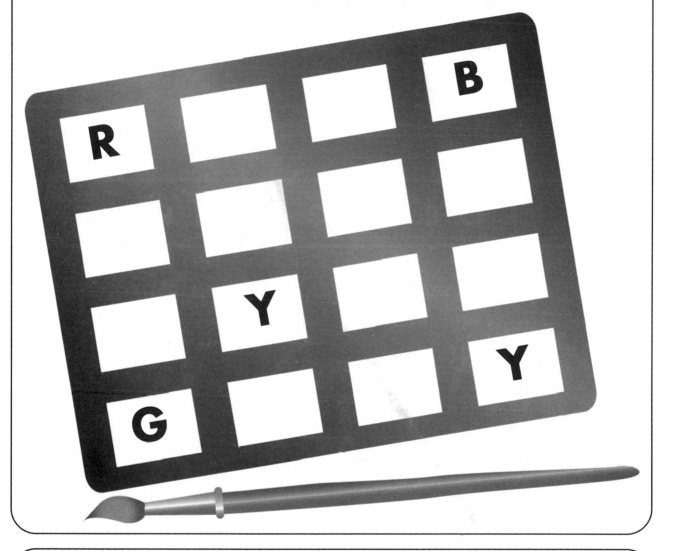

# 2. LINKS

Which word will go after the first word and before the second word?

QUICK(____)CASTLE

# 3. CLOCKWORK

If the big and small hands changed positions, which clock would show the latest time in the same twelve hour period?

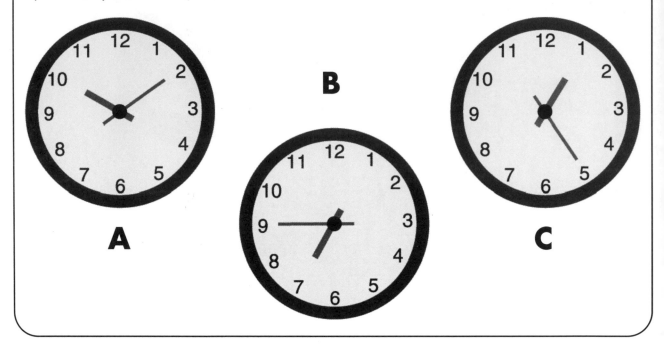

B

A

C

# 4. CREATURE CODE

Letters have been replaced by shapes. The first group spells out the word BEAR. Using the symbols from the first word, can you crack the code and work out what the other symbols are?

| 1 | ✝ ✜ ✡ ✳ | **B E A R** |
| 2 | ✺ ✜ ✝ ✳ ✡ | _____ |
| 3 | ✳ ✡ ✝ ✝ ☆ ✳ | _____ |
| 4 | ✳ ☆ ◆ ✜ ✳ | _____ |

# 5. SAIL AWAY

Which of the sails shown on yachts 1, 2 and 3 carries on the pattern made by A, B and C?

# 6. TOP TEN

Complete the word by filling the spaces with a whole number between ONE and TEN.

H _ _ _ ST

# 7. ADDER

Using other words with the same meaning, can you create a new word from two separate ones.

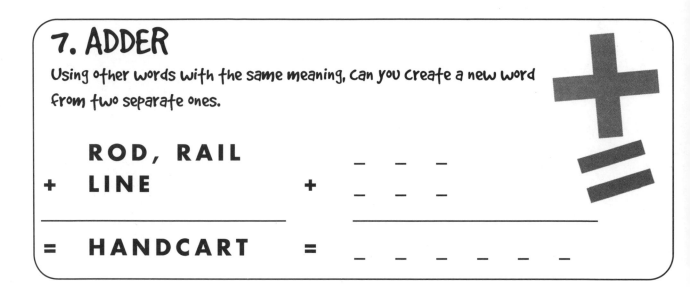

```
    ROD, RAIL                    _  _  _
+   LINE             +           _  _  _
_____      _____
=   HANDCART         =   _  _  _  _  _  _
```

# 8. UNWANTED

You have to fill the frame using the words in the list, starting from TIP which is in place at the top of the frame. All words contain THREE letters, and there is only one way possible to fill the frame. When the grid is complete there is ONE word that has not been used. What is the unwanted word?

| | |
|---|---|
| AIR | PAW |
| COW | ROW |
| CRY | SAD |
| DIP | SKI |
| EYE | TAR |
| FEW | TIP |
| FOG | WAS |
| GUN | WIN |
| IMP | YES |
| MOO | YOU |
| OAK | |

# 9. PIC-TRICK
Which single three-letter word completes all of the words below?

```
_ _ _ R O V E
  S H R _ _ _
  L _ _ _ I N G
_ _ _ _ L Y I N G
```

# 10. SECRET SEVEN
Rearrange the letters in the word below to make another word of seven letters.

C A S T E R S

_ _ _ _ _ _ _

**CLUE**

Think MOVIE STAR

# 11. CASUALTY!

These four people have all had accidents and visited the hospital. Can you name each one and work out the order in which they called at the hospital?

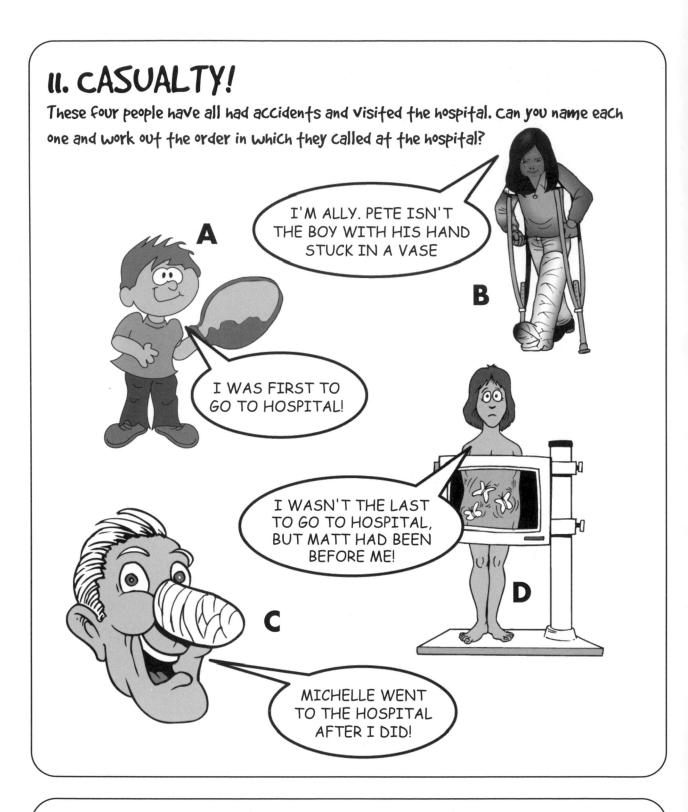

# 12. MORE OR LESS

Which is the higher number, the number of days in April or the number of months in two and a half years?

# 13. EYE CHART

Write your answers reading across the rows. Each answer is made by rearranging letters of the line above with one extra letter added.

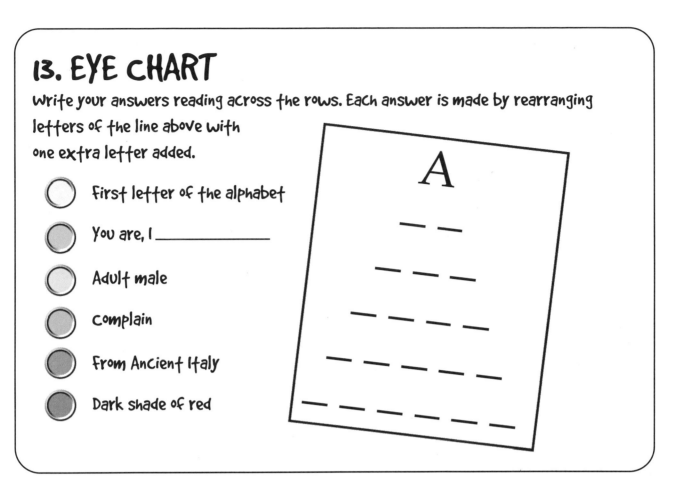

- First letter of the alphabet
- You are, I _____
- Adult male
- Complain
- From Ancient Italy
- Dark shade of red

# 14. LINK LETTERS

Put a letter in each of the sets of brackets which can be added to the end of the first word and the start of the second word. The first one uses the letter P, to make CRAMP and PINK. The five letters in order will spell out another word.

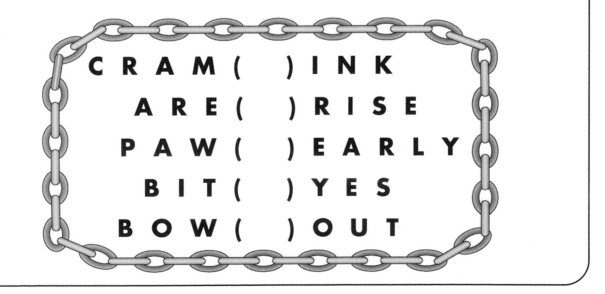

C R A M (   ) I N K
A R E (   ) R I S E
P A W (   ) E A R L Y
B I T (   ) Y E S
B O W (   ) O U T

## 15. SPLITZER

Split this row of ten letters into two five-letter words which are the names of musical instruments. The words read from left to right and the letters are in the correct order.

F O L R U G T A E N

## 16. STAR GAZING

Which other telescope contains the same nine stars as seen in the telescope?
Look out, the stars are NOT in the same positions in the pattern!

# 17. AFTER WORDS

Which word can go after all these words to make new words?

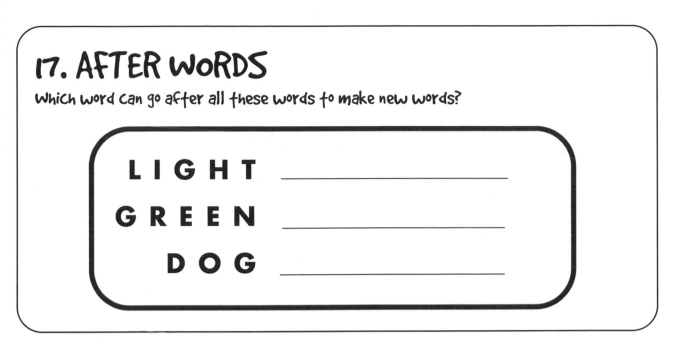

L I G H T  _____

G R E E N  _____

D O G  _____

# 18. JUST THE JOB

Start at the letter N, top left. Move from letter to letter, going in any direction, except diagonally, and spell out the names of five different jobs. You will use every letter once.

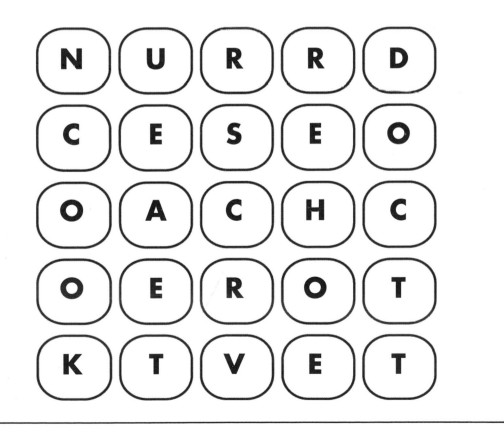

| N | U | R | R | D |
|---|---|---|---|---|
| C | E | S | E | O |
| O | A | C | H | C |
| O | E | R | O | T |
| K | T | V | E | T |

# 19. FACE IT

What is the total of all the numbers that make up the face?

# 20. SECRET SEVEN

Rearrange the letters below to make a seven-lettered word.

E A D H R E D

_ _ _ _ _ _ _

**CLUE**

**Think HAIR COLOR**

## 21. LINKS

Which word will go after the first word and before the second word?

TABLE ( _ _ _ _ _ _ ) RACKET

## 22. TRI-TANGLE

How many complete triangles can you count in the pattern?

## 23. TOP TEN

Complete the word by filling the spaces with a whole number between one and ten.

CON _ _ _ _ T

# 24. FIRST CHANGE

Each clue has two answers. The two answer words are spelt the same, except that the first letter of the second answer has moved forward one place in the alphabet. So for example, if the first answer was BAT the second answer would be CAT.

THE THING HIT IN TENNIS * SHOUT OUT OR YELL

ANSWERS: _____ /_____

CUT A LAWN * THIS INSTANT!

ANSWERS: _____ /_____

BEING WELL KNOWN * SPORTING CONTEST

ANSWERS: _____ /_____

A STYLE OF DANCING * BELONGING TO ME!

ANSWERS: _____ /_____

THE SHAPE OF A CIRCLE * NOISE

ANSWERS: _____ /_____

# 25. TWO TIMER

All the listed time-linked words are hidden in a letter grid. Each appears in a straight line that can go in any direction. One word appears twice in the grid. Which word is it?

**THE LIST**

AFTERNOON
DAY
MORNING
MINUTE
NIGHT
NOON
SECOND
TIME
WEEK

| M | T | N | O | O | N | D | B | U |
|---|---|---|---|---|---|---|---|---|
| N | O | A | L | A | W | H | A | D |
| O | V | R | A | D | O | E | O | Y |
| O | M | I | N | U | T | E | E | P |
| N | S | L | R | I | L | N | M | K |
| R | B | E | M | X | N | I | E | P |
| E | T | E | C | U | L | G | G | R |
| T | H | I | H | O | E | H | O | E |
| F | O | W | M | L | N | T | R | A |
| A | Z | E | B | E | P | D | X | L |

# 26. ADDER

Using other words with the same meaning, can you create a new word from two separate ones.

LIMB  _ _ _
+ OTHERWISE  _ _
———————————
= PROTECTIVE CLOTHING  _ _ _ _ _

# 27. MAZE CRAZE

To read the message, move through the maze from START to FINISH. You have to take a path that calls at every letter and you cannot go to the same letter more than once. There are four words in this piece of sound advice!

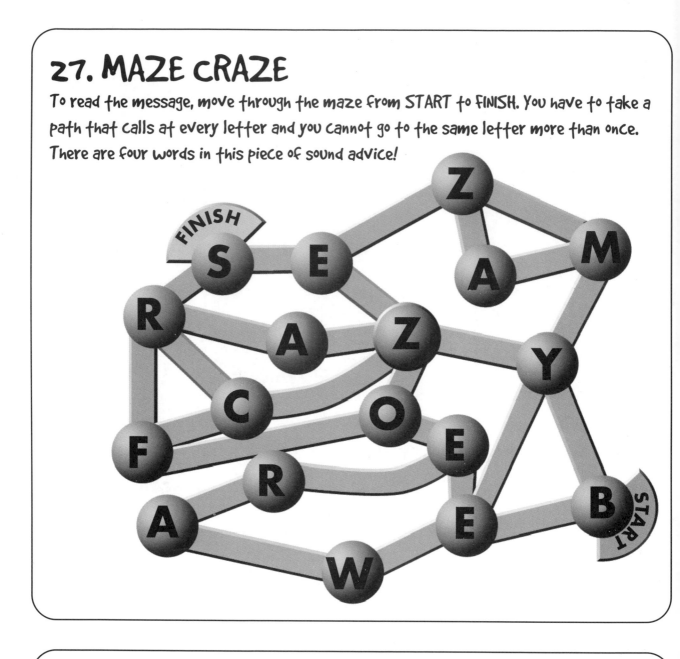

# 28. BACK WORDS

Solve the clues: the second answer is the first answer written backwards.

STICKY HAIR FIXER   *   LIMB

_ _ _   *   _ _ _ _

# 29. CUBED

A word square reads the same whether you look at it across or down. Use the listed words to make two different word squares. Use every word once with CUBE appearing in each word square.

| ABLE | BLUE | CUBE | CUBE |
|------|------|------|------|
| EYES | REEK | SCAR | UGLY |

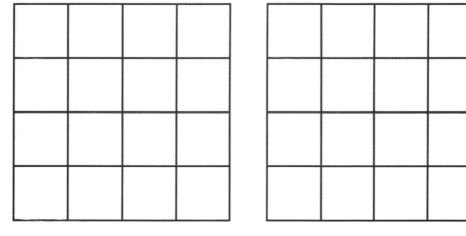

# 30. REALLY WILD!

The names of these wild animals have had the letters rearranged.
Can you sort them out?

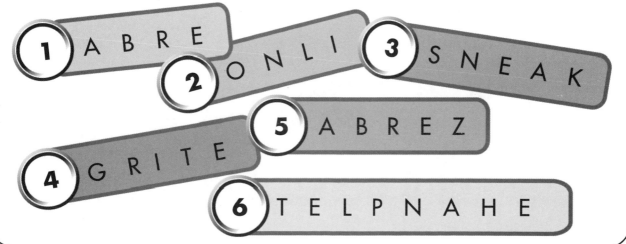

1. A B R E
2. O N L I
3. S N E A K
4. G R I T E
5. A B R E Z
6. T E L P N A H E

# 31. WHAT AM I?

My first is in slam
But isn't in lamp.

My second is in made
But isn't in damp.

My third is in pace
But isn't in pale.

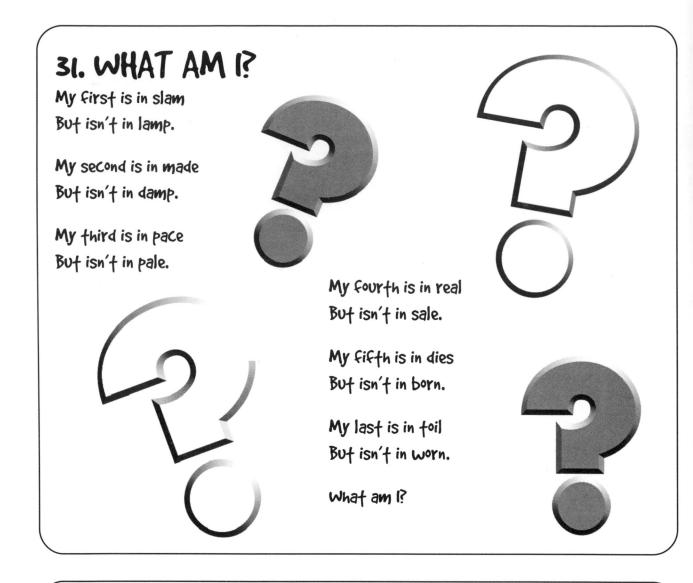

My fourth is in real
But isn't in sale.

My fifth is in dies
But isn't in born.

My last is in toil
But isn't in worn.

What am I?

# 32. LINE-NINE

The nine lines are arranged in a pattern containing three triangles. By moving the position of just three lines, can you form a pattern that contains five triangles?

# 33. MIND THE GAP

Which single three-letter word completes all of the following words?

H _ _ _ E R

T R _ _ _ S

R E P _ _ _ E D

C H _ _ _ I N G

# 34. HIT LIST

Noah Lott has set up his own information website. He's been up and running for five days. The first day was pretty quiet, but there's been more activity as the week has gone on. In fact, each day he has had 6 more hits than on the previous day. By the end of day five a total of 100 people have visited the site. How many had called at the end of the first day?

## 35. AFTER WORDS

Which word can go after all these words to make new words?

**B A L L** _____

**B A T H** _____

**B E D** _____

## 36. BRUSHSTROKES

Pick up these seven paintbrushes, labeled A–G, one at a time. You can only move the brush that is on top of the pile at each go.

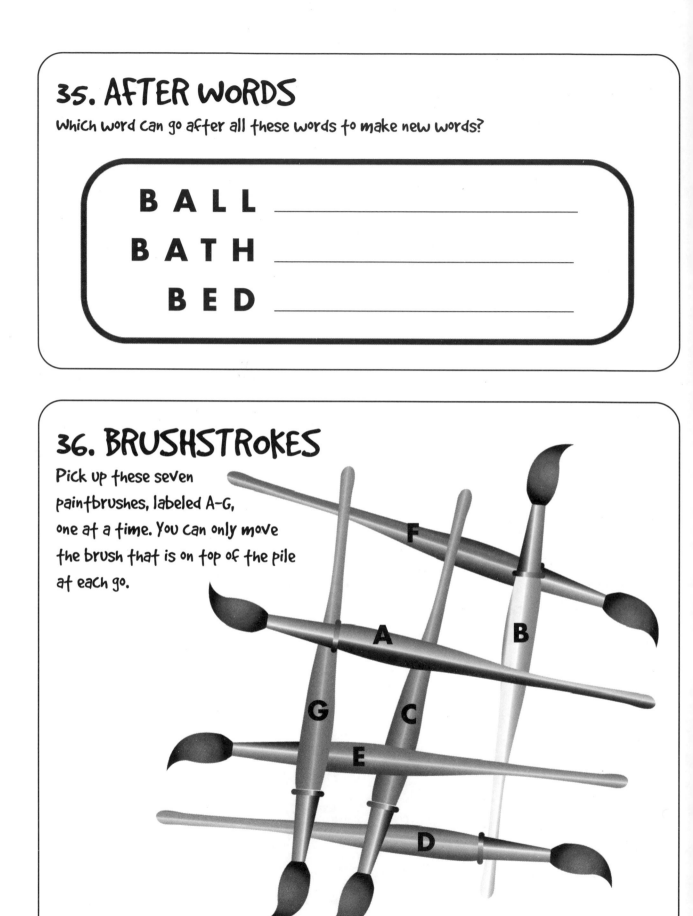

## 37. SECRET SEVEN

Rearrange the letters in the word below to make another of seven letters.

A D M I R E R
_ _ _ _ _ _ _

CLUE

Think
HUSBAND AND WIFE

## 38. HALF TIME

Each answer is a word containing four letters. The last two letters of one word are the same as the first two letters of the next word.

1   Middle of an apple

2   A short break

3   Mix in with a spoon

4   Part of the eye

5   Island

6   Go in front in a race

7   Eve's partner in the Garden of Eden

| 1 | | | |
|---|---|---|---|
| 2 | | | |
| 3 | | | |
| 4 | | | |
| 5 | | | |
| 6 | | | |
| 7 | | | |

# 39. HONEYCOMB

Each answer contains six letters and is written in the six spaces that link together around a number. Answers always go in a clockwise direction and every first letter is in place. When the honeycomb is complete the inner ring of six letters will spell out a star sign.

1 Old fashioned sea bandit.

2 People protecting or watching over a place.

3 Rough and tough.

4 Unlawful killing.

5 Season of the year.

6 Metal fastening bolts.

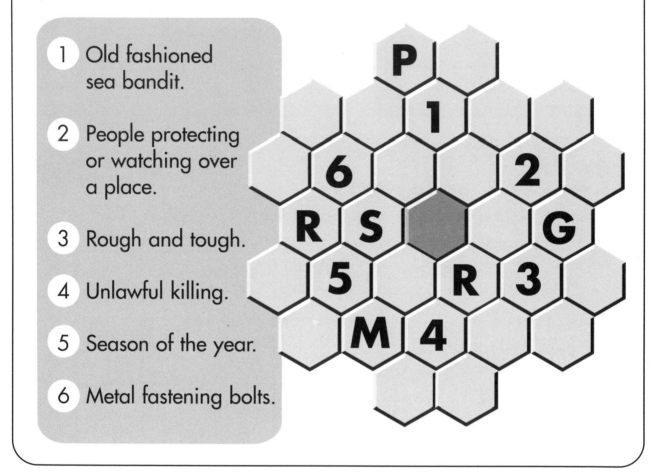

# 40. LINKS

Which word will go after the first word and before the second word?

BASE(_ _ _ _)GOWN

# 41. LOCKER ROOM

Forgetful Fran's forgotten the number on her locker. Can you work out which one it is?

- ○  It is directly above a locker that has a black door.

- ○  It is directly below a locker that has a black handle.

- ○  Fran's locker has a white handle.

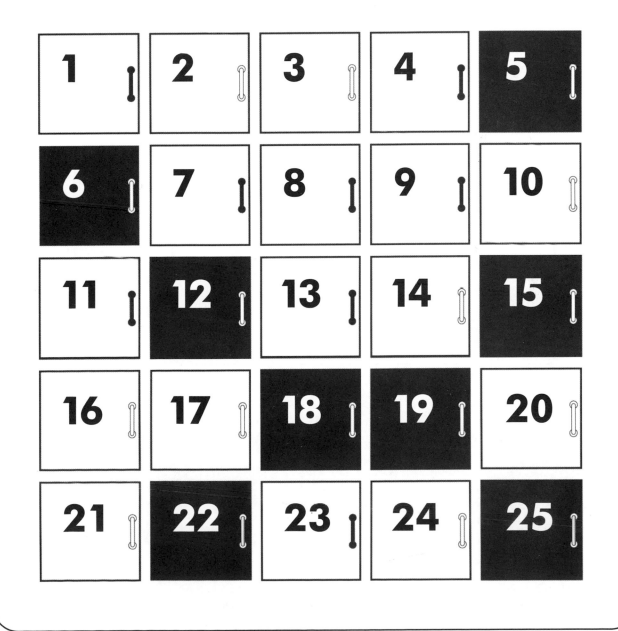

# 42. SPLIT UP

The words below have been split in half and the ends moved around. Can you repair the splits?

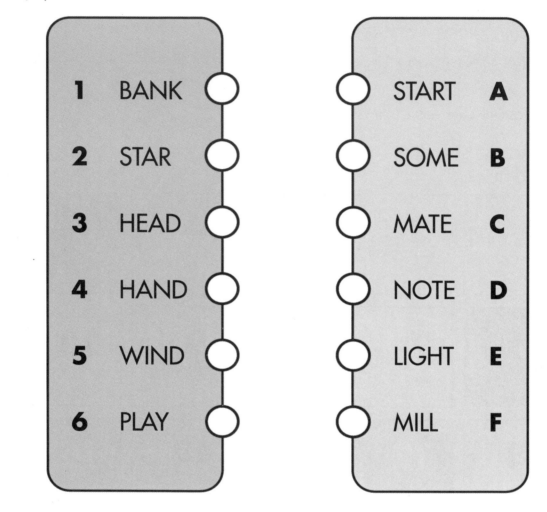

| | | | |
|---|---|---|---|
| 1 | BANK | ○ ○ | START | A |
| 2 | STAR | ○ ○ | SOME | B |
| 3 | HEAD | ○ ○ | MATE | C |
| 4 | HAND | ○ ○ | NOTE | D |
| 5 | WIND | ○ ○ | LIGHT | E |
| 6 | PLAY | ○ ○ | MILL | F |

# 43. BACK WORDS

Solve the clues: the second answer is the first answer written backwards.

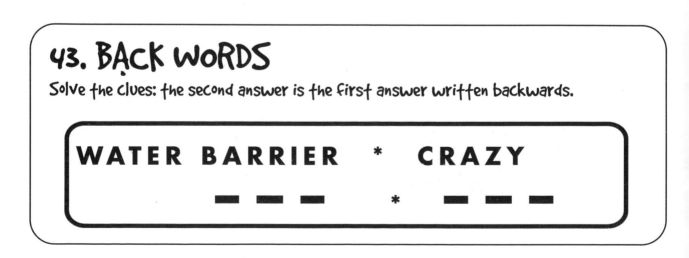

WATER BARRIER    *    CRAZY

— — —    *    — — —

# 44. FRUIT MACHINE

With each spin this fruit machine always shows a banana, cherries and a bunch of grapes. There's only one more combination to those shown here. What is it?

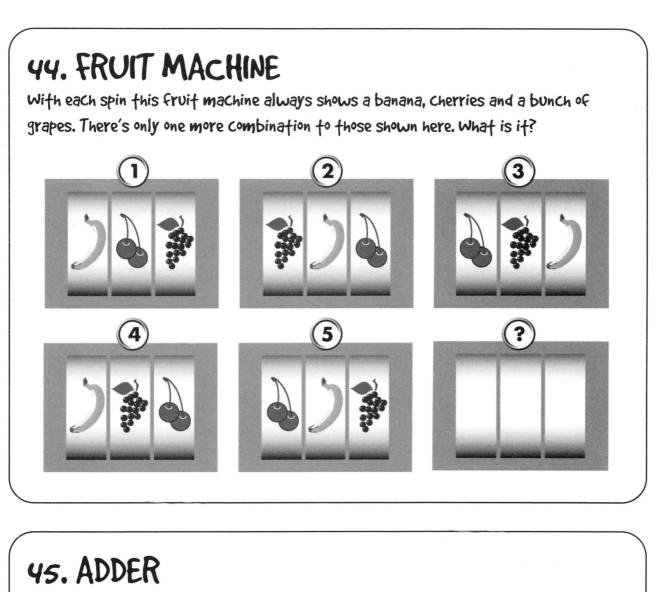

# 45. ADDER

Using other words with the same meaning, can you create a new word from two separate ones?

**CRAWLING INSECT**    _ _ _
**+ EDGE OF A SKIRT**    _ _ _
_____
**= HYMN**    _ _ _ _ _ _

# 46. VOWEL PLAY

The vowels – A, E, I, O and U – have been taken from the names of these capital cities. Can you work out the names?

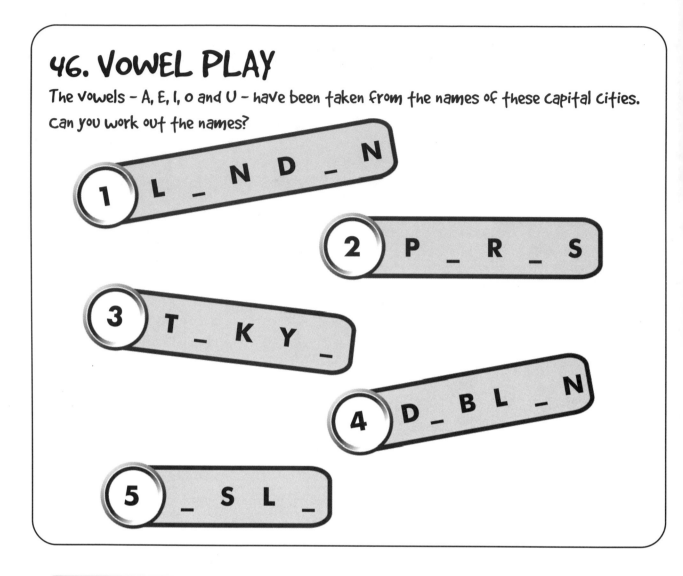

**1** L _ N D _ N

**2** P _ R _ S

**3** T _ K Y _

**4** D _ B L _ N

**5** _ S L _

# 47. SIDEWAYS

Which is greater, the number of sides in 16 triangles, or the number of sides in 12 squares?

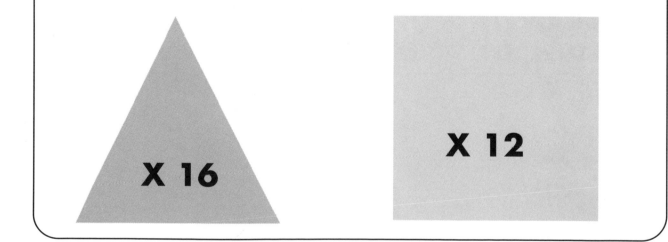

X 16

X 12

## 1. PAINT BOX

## 2. LINKS

Sand.

## 3. CLOCKWORK

Clock B. The time would be 8.35.

## 4. CREATURE CODE

1. Bear   2. Zebra   3. Rabbit   4. Tiger.

## 5. SAIL AWAY

Sails on yacht 3. Each section of pattern moves one position round the sails in a clockwise direction.

## 6. TOP TEN

one. This completes the word honest.

# 7. ADDER

Bar + Row = Barrow.

# 8. UNWANTED

The unused word is YOU.

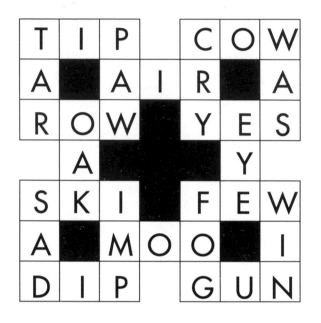

# 9. PIC-TRICK

Imp.

# 10. SECRET SEVEN

Actress.

# 11. CASUALTY!

A. Matt first
B. Ally last
C. Pete second
D. Michelle third.

# 12. MORE OR LESS

They are both the same – 30.

# 13. EYE CHART

1. A
2. Am
3. Man
4. Moan
5. Roman
6. Maroon

# 14. LINK LETTERS

The missing letters spell PANEL.

# 15. SPLITZER

Flute, organ.

# 16. STAR GAZING

Star group 1.

# 17. AFTER WORDS

House.

# 18. JUST THE JOB

Nurse, Cook, Teacher, Doctor, Vet.

# 19. FACE IT

The total is 26:
Face = 0,
Eyes = 8,
Nose = 2,
Eyebrows = 3,
Mouth = 1,
Ears = 6 (x2).

## 20. SECRET SEVEN

Redhead.

## 21. LINKS

Tennis.

## 22. TRI-TANGLE

16.

## 23. TOP TEN

Ten. This completes the word content.

## 24. FIRST CHANGE

1. Ball/call   2. Mow/Now   3. Fame/Game   4. Line/Mine   5. Round/Sound.

## 25. TWO TIMER

Time is hidden twice.

## 26. ADDER

Arm + or = Armor.

## 27. MAZE CRAZE

Beware of crazy mazes!

## 28. BACK WORDS

Gel * Leg.

## 29. CUBED

| C | U | B | E |
|---|---|---|---|
| U | G | L | Y |
| B | L | U | E |
| E | Y | E | S |

| S | C | A | R |
|---|---|---|---|
| C | U | B | E |
| A | B | L | E |
| R | E | E | K |

## 30. REALLY WILD!

1. Bear
2. Lion
3. Snake
4. Tiger
5. Zebra
6. Elephant.

## 31. WHAT AM I?

Secret.

## 32. LINE-NINE

Move the lines as shown. There are now four triangles of the same size and the outer lines of the pattern form a further triangle.

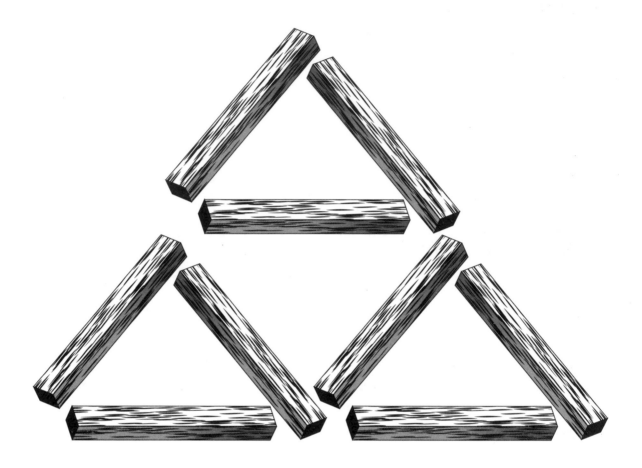

## 33. MIND THE GAP

Eat.

## 34. HIT LIST

8 hits on day one. 14 on day two.
20 on day three. 26 on day four. 32 on day five.

# 35. AFTER WORDS
Room.

# 36 .BRUSHSTROKES
A, G, E, C, D, B, F.

# 37. SECRET SEVEN
Married.

# 38. HALF TIME
1. Core
2. Rest
3. Stir
4. Iris
5. Isle
6. Lead
7. Adam.

# 39. HONEYCOMB
1. Pirate  2. Guards  3. Rugged  4. Murder  5. Summer  6. Rivets.
The inner circle spells TAURUS.

# 40. LINKS
Ball.

# 41. LOCKER ROOM
Locker number 14.

# 42. SPLIT UP

1. d
2. e
3. a
4. b
5. f
6. c.

# 43. BACK WORDS

Dam * Mad.

# 44. FRUIT MACHINE

Grapes,

Cherries,

Banana.

# 45. ADDER

Ant + Hem = Anthem.

# 46. VOWEL PLAY

1. London
2. Paris
3. Tokyo
4. Dublin
5. Oslo.

# 47. SIDEWAYS

Both equal 48.

# BRAIN
# WORKOUT
# PUZZLES

# 1. Shadow Shark

Which shadow belongs to the shark?

# 2. Beware of the Werewolf

Which shadow matches the werewolf?

# 3. Splatman

Which shadow matches Splatman?

## 4. Maze Race

Quick! How do you get out of the maze?

## 5. Sneaky Sandwich

Who took a sneaky bite out of the sea monster's sandwich? Follow the crumb trails to find out.

## 6. Shadow Match

Draw a line to join each item to its matching shadow.

## 7. Fast Fly

What's the quickest route for the fly to take to reach the flowers?

## 8. Growly Grizzly

Which growly grizzly silhouette matches the real one?

## 9. Oops!

There are ten differences between these pictures. Can you spot them?

## 10. Farm Fun

How many animals can you see in the picture?

## 11. Wrong Way

One creature in every row is pointing in the opposite direction. Circle the odd one out in each row.

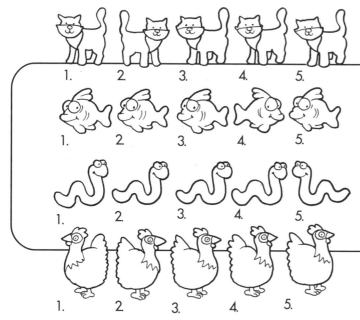

1.  2.  3.  4.  5.

1.  2.  3.  4.  5.

1.  2.  3.  4.  5.

1.  2.  3.  4.  5.

## 12. Teddy Bears

How many teddy bears are there in this picture?

# 13. Snowflakes

Two of these snowflake pictures match. Which two?

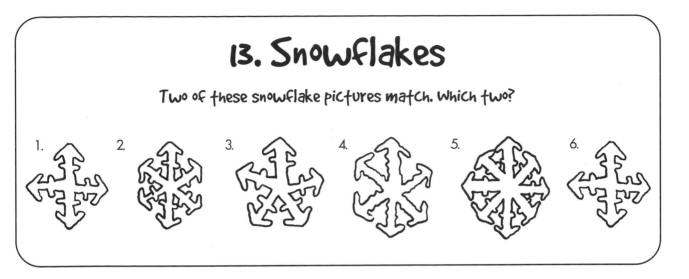

1.  2.  3.  4.  5.  6.

# 14. Fruity Split

Draw two straight lines (which can cross each other) to divide the box into four parts. Each part must contain one banana, one apple and one pear.

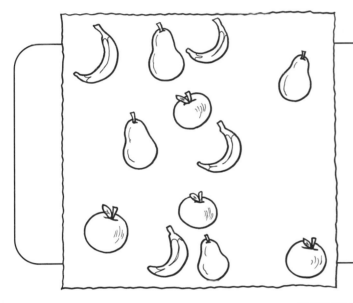

# 15. Squeaky Floorboards

Shh! Keep quiet! What is the only way to get out of the maze without stepping on the squeaky floorboards?

# 16. Vulture Trouble

Which vulture is the odd one out?

# 17. Kitty Tree

How many cats are hiding up and around the tree?

# 18. Ancient Book

What is the secret message written in the book? Use the letter code to find out.

□ = a
ᴍ = b
△ = e
Ϡ = g
▽ = k
⩘ = l
Ŋ = o
@ = p
♡ = r
▱ = s
○ = t
⨮ = u
✳ = z

## 19. Busy Bees

Draw lines to join each pair of bees.

## 20. Squid's Hid

Shade in the parts that have a dot to reveal the hidden image.

## 21. Rocket Science

Which cord leads to the space rocket?

# 22. Bathtime Tiger

There are ten differences between these two pictures. Can you spot them?

# 23. Private Detective

1.
2.
3.

Which trail leads to the secret footprints?

# 24. Find the fairies

Seven little fairies are hiding in the woods. Can you find them?

# 25. Lion Match

Two of these lions are the same. Which two?

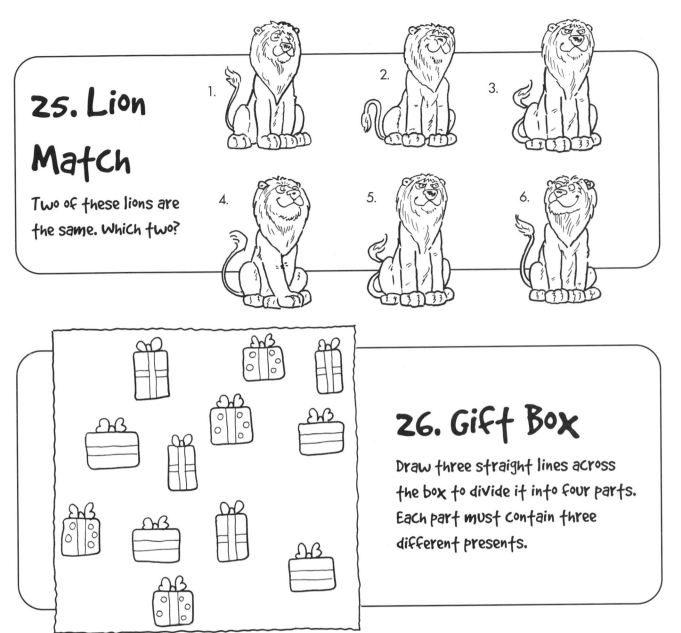

1.
2.
3.
4.
5.
6.

# 26. Gift Box

Draw three straight lines across the box to divide it into four parts. Each part must contain three different presents.

# 27. Zany Zebras

How many zebras are there in the picture?

## 28. DUCK!

Which pond contains the most ducks?

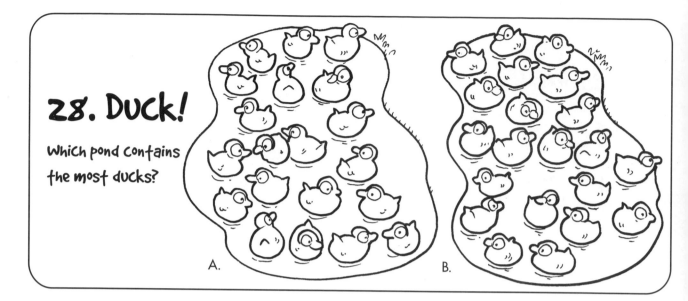

A.

B.

## 29. Fall Leaves

Follow the leaf trail and look at the leaf pattern. Which leaf comes next?

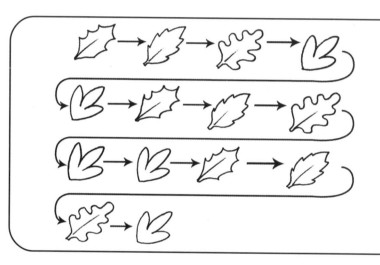

## 30. Secret Agent

Can you help the secret agent out of the maze?

# 31. Which Witch?

Which witch does this shadow belong to?

1.

2.

3.

4.

5.

# 32. Halloween Party

How many ghosts, skeletons, cats and pumpkins can you see at the Halloween party?

## 33. Building Split

This row of ten letters can be split into two five-letter words which are the names of two things used to make buildings. Words read from left to right and the letters are in the correct order. What are they?

B R S I T O C K N E

RED
E more.
E more.
E more.
E more.

## 34. Visual Aid

Guess the saying from the visual aid.

## 35. Ridiculous Riddle

What goes up and down the stairs without moving?

## 36. Snakes Alive

The name of a type of snake is hidden in each of the sentences below. Find them by joining words or parts of words together.

**1.** How sad Derek looks.
**2.** They stayed all night at the disco, bravely in my opinion.
**3.** The jumbo arrived on time.

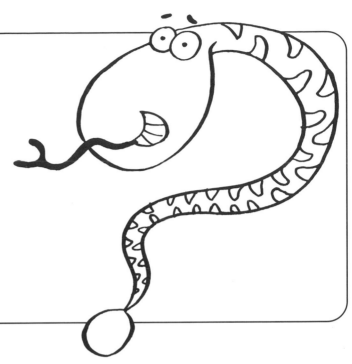

## 37. Flower Power

Here are the names of four flowers with the vowels removed. Can you name them?

DSY   BTTRCP   DFFDL   SNFLWR

## 38. Hunt The Word

The letters missing from this box make up the name of an animal. Can you name it?

## 39. Happy Birthday

Sally was eight the day before yesterday.

Next year she will be ten.

What is the date of Sally's birthday, and on which date would the first two things have been true?

## 40. Tennis Trouble

Two men were playing tennis. They played five sets and each man won three sets. How can this be possible?

## 41. Spoon Puzzle

Reposition six of the spoons in the pattern below to make six equal-sized diamond shapes in a star pattern.

## 42. What's Next?

What's the next letter in the series?

# B, C, D, E, G

## 43. What Is It?

Guess the phrase from the picture.

**Me right**

## 44. Tall Tale

Before Mount Everest was discovered, what was the tallest mountain in the world?

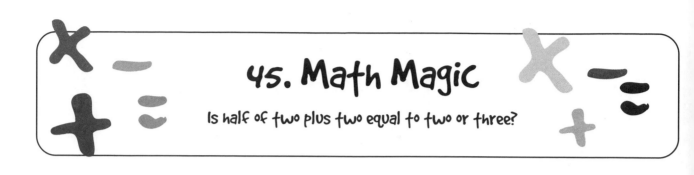

# 45. Math Magic

Is half of two plus two equal to two or three?

# 46. Give Me Five

Solve the clues, so that each answer contains five letters. Write all the answers in place and the shaded squares reading down will reveal the name of a musical instrument.

1. Opposite of last.
2. Outer covering of an egg.
3. Sailing boat.
4. Bad weather.
5. Light you can carry.
6. Push this to power a bicycle.
7. Meadow.
8. Number in a trio.

1. _ _ _ _ _
2. _ _ _ _ _
3. _ _ _ _ _
4. _ _ _ _ _
5. _ _ _ _ _
6. _ _ _ _ _
7. _ _ _ _ _
8. _ _ _ _ _

# 47. Word Mix

Rearrange the letters of GROW NO LINSEED to spell one single word.

GROW NO LINSEED

# 48. Word Ladder

Change NOSE into FAST by changing one letter at a time.

1. Misplace.
2. Opposite of found.
3. At the back.

NOSE

_ _ _ _

_ _ _ _

_ _ _ _

FAST

# 49. Big Is Best

Who is bigger? Mr Bigger, Mrs Bigger, or their baby?

# 50. The Hole Truth

If it takes three people to dig a hole, how many people does it take to dig half a hole?

# 51. Mathematical Equation

If five thousand, five hundred and five dollars is written as $5,505, how should twelve thousand, twelve hundred and twelve dollars be written?

# 52. Matchstick Marvel

Reposition four matches from this pattern to form five triangles.

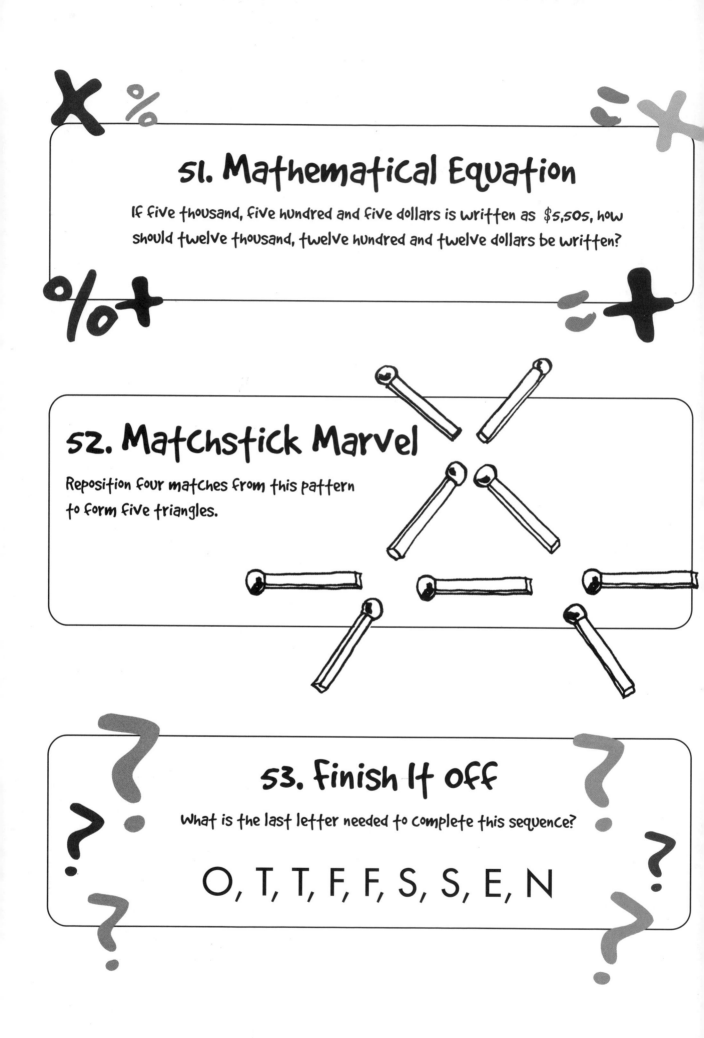

# 53. Finish It Off

What is the last letter needed to complete this sequence?

O, T, T, F, F, S, S, E, N

## 54. How Confusing

What starts with a T, ends with a T
and has T in it?

## 55. What Am I?

My first is in chair
But isn't in chain

My second is in pale
And also in pain

My third is in edge
But isn't in green

My fourth is in lime
But isn't in mean

My fifth's in cone
And also in round

Do you know what I am?
I'm connected with sound!

## 56. Hot or cold?

What moves faster,
heat or cold?

# 57. Math Trick

When can you add two to eleven and get one?

# 58. Word Scramble

Rearrange these letters to give the names of some animals you might find at the zoo.

DANAP

KNOMEY

NAHPETLE

FEIRAGF

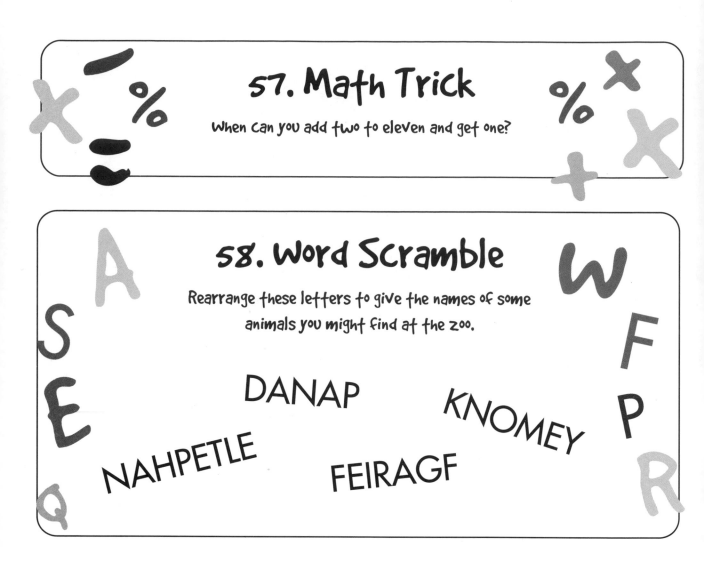

# 59. Work It Out

If two hours ago, it was exactly as long after one o'clock in the afternoon as it was before one o'clock in the morning, what time would it be now?

## 60. Animal Tracks

Make tracks and find seven different animals in the grid. Start at the letter in the top left square and move in any direction except diagonally. Every letter is used once.

```
C A M E A R
L L E B L E
I A R D E P
O P E G I H
N O R E T A
L E A P T N
```

## 61. Take Away

What is it that, when you take away the whole, you still have some left over?

## 62. Perplexing Puzzle

What is in the middle of nowhere?

# 63. Bowling

Four friends go bowling together. They decide that they will each play each other once. How many games will they play?

# 64. Fitting In

What is the only other letter that fits in the following series?

B, C, D, E, I, K, O, X

# 65. Key Words

There's a problem on the keyboard of Clare's computer. She types in letters but the screen only shows numbers! In each case the letter links to a number below it.

So, for example, I can stand for a Q, an A or a Z.

The number 9 could be an O or an L.

Can you work out what Clare was trying to say?

1 2 3 4 5 6 7 8 9 0
Q W E R T Y U I O P
A S D F G H J K L
Z X C V B N M

8 2165 5682 7136863
59 53 43018433

# 66. Secret Sevens

Rearrange the letters in the word below to make another word of seven letters.

## A D V E R T S

_ _ _ _ _ _ _

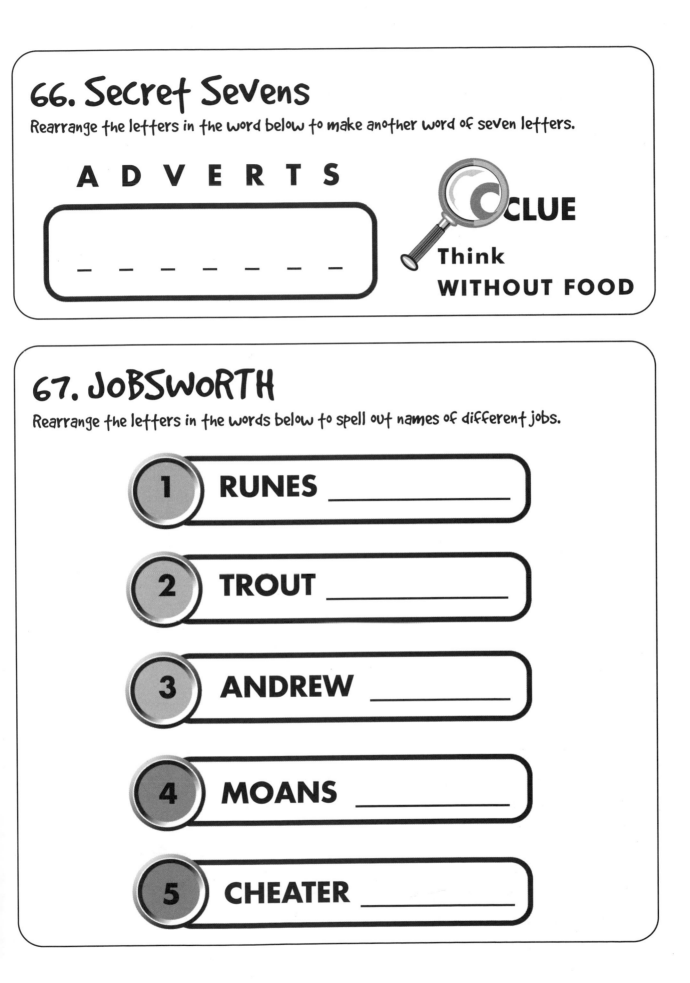

**CLUE**

Think
**WITHOUT FOOD**

# 67. JOBSWORTH

Rearrange the letters in the words below to spell out names of different jobs.

**1** RUNES _____

**2** TROUT _____

**3** ANDREW _____

**4** MOANS _____

**5** CHEATER _____

# 68. Rows and Arrows

Move from one square at a time to get from start to finish. You must move in the direction the arrow is pointing. If the arrow points in two ways then you can go in either direction.

**Start**

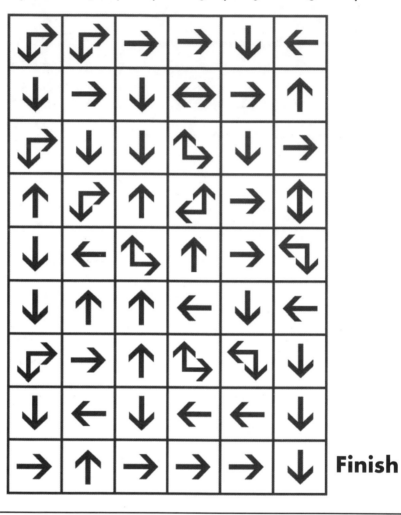

**Finish**

# 69. Splitzer

Split this row of ten letters into two five-letter words which are the names of animals. The words read from left to right and the letters are in the correct order.

P T A N I G D E A R

# ANSWERS

## 1. Shadow Shark

Shadow 4

## 2 Beware of the Werewolf

Shadow 4

## 3. Splatman

Shadow 3

## 4. Maze Race

## 5. Sneaky Sandwich

Trail C, lobster

## 6. Shadow Match

## 7. Fast Fly

Route 1

## 8. Growly Grizzly

Growly grizzly number 1

## 9. oops!

## 10. Farm Fun

20 animals

## 11. Wrong Way

| | |
|---|---|
| Cat 2 | Fish 4 |
| Worm 5 | Chicken 1 |

## 12. Teddy Bears

18 teddy bears

## 13. Snowflakes

Pictures 1 and 6

## 14. Fruity Split

## 15. Squeaky Floorboards

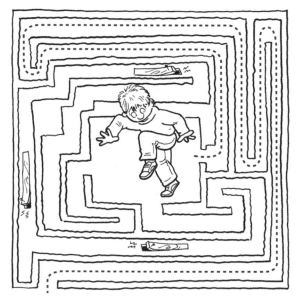

## 16. Vulture Trouble

Vulture 4

## 17. Kitty Tree

14 cats

## 18. Ancient Book

puzzle
books
are
great

## 19. Busy Bees

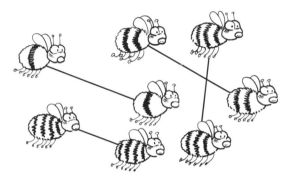

## 20. Squid's Hid

## 21. Rocket Science

Cord 1

## 22. Bathtime Tiger

## 23. Private Detective

Trail 2

## 24. Find the Fairies

## 25. Lion Match

Lions 3 and 5

## 26. Gift Box

## 27. Zany Zebra

16 zebras

## 28. Duck!

Pond A has 20 ducks but pond B has 21.

## 29. fall Leaves

## 30. Secret Agent

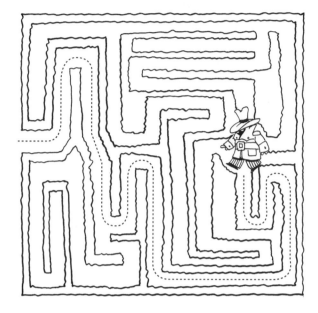

## 31. Which Witch?

Witch number 5

## 32. Halloween Party

11 ghosts
4 skeletons
8 pumpkins
2 cats

## 33. Building Split

Brick and Stone

## 34. Visual Aid

Ready for more.

## 35. Ridiculous Riddle

A carpet

## 36. Snakes Alive

1. Adder
2. Cobra
3. Boa

## 37. Flower Power

1. Daisy
2. Buttercup
3. Daffodil
4. Sunflower

## 38. Hunt The Word

Bear

## 39. Happy Birthday

Sally's birthday is December 31. The information would have been true on January 1.

## 40. Tennis Trouble

The two men were partners playing doubles.

## 41. Spoon Puzzle

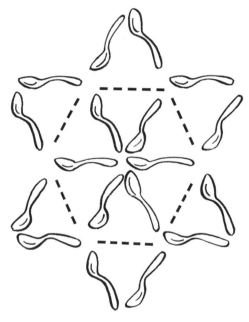

## 42. What's Next?

P—they all rhyme.

## 43. What Is It?

Right beside me

## 44. Tall Tale

Mount Everest—it was the tallest
mountain even before it was discovered!

## 45. Math Magic

Three

## 46. Give Me Five

1. First
2. Shell
3. Yacht
4. Storm
5. Torch
6. Pedal
7. Field
8. Three

The musical instrument made
is a RECORDER

## 47. Word Mix

ONE SINGLE WORD

## 48. Word Ladder

1. Lose
2. Lost
3. Last

## 49. Big Is Best

The baby, because he's a
little bigger!

## 50. The Hole Truth

You can't dig half a hole!

## 51. Mathematical Equation

$13,212

# 52. Matchstick Marvel

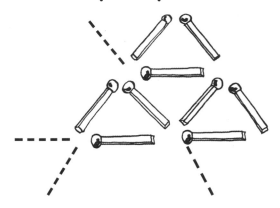

# 53. Finish It Off

T—the letters are the initials of the numbers one to ten.

# 54. How Confusing

A teapot

# 55. What Am I?

Radio

# 56. Hot or Cold

Heat—everyone can catch a cold!

# 57. Math Trick

When you add two hours to eleven o'clock you get one o'clock.

# 58. Word Scramble

Elephant
Panda
Giraffe
Monkey

# 59. Work It Out

Nine o'clock—since there are twelve hours between the two times, and half of that time equals six, then the halfway mark would have to be seven o'clock.
If it were seven o'clock, two hours ago, then the time would now be nine o'clock.

# 60. Animal Tracks

1. Camel
2. Lion
3. Leopard
4. Bear
5. Elephant
6. Tiger
7. Ape

# 61. Take Away

The word "wholesome".

# 62. Perplexing Puzzle

The Letter "H".

# 63. Bowling

There are six games.

# 64. Fitting In

H—all of the letters in the series flipped vertically look the same.

# 65. Key Words

I WANT THIS MACHINE TO BE REPAIRED.

# 66. Secret Seven

Starved.

# 67. Jobsworth

1. Nurse
2. Tutor
3. Warden
4. Mason
5. Teacher.

# 68. Rows and Arrows

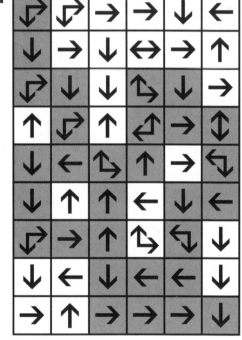

# 69. Splitzer

Panda, Tiger.

# BRAIN CRUNCHING PUZZLES

# 1. CUBED

Here are different views of the same cube. Each of the six sides has a different number. What number is the side that is opposite to number 5?

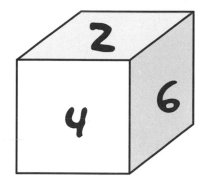
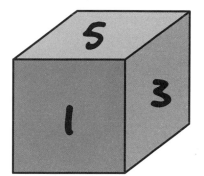
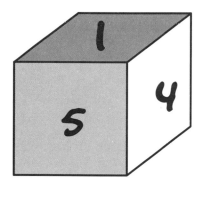
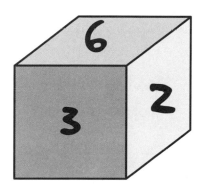

# 2. CLOTHES LINE

This line of ten letters can be split into two five-letter words which are the names of two items of clothing. Words read from left to right and the letters are in the correct order. What are they?

J E S A H I N R S T

_____ / _____

# 3. JIGSAW

Four toddlers have completed a jigsaw. Each child put one piece in place. From the clues, work out which piece each one put in and the order in which they inserted them.

- The boys put in the bottom pieces.
  Neither of them put in the last piece.

- Rosie's piece touches all the other pieces.

- Danny's piece is not directly below Rosie's piece.

- Tessa put her piece in place before Tim.

- The bottom left corner piece was the first to go in place.

# 4. AFTER-WORDS
Which word can go after all these words to make new words?

C H E C K _____

K N O C K _____

P U L L _____

# 5. CREATURE CODE
In this code, shapes and signs have been used to take the place of letters of the alphabet. The first group makes ELEPHANT. Which creature is in code in the second group?

E L E P H A N T

# 6. CONNECTIONS

Find a route along the connections to get from the top left circle to the middle circle in the bottom row. The circular areas can spin around to allow you to connect them to another circuit, but you have to have landed on a circular area before that can happen.

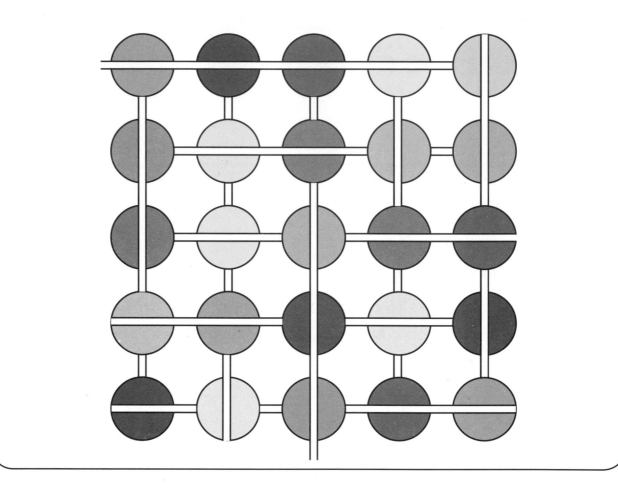

# 7. SECRET SEVEN

Rearrange the letters below to make a seven-letter word.

E L A P S E D

_ _ _ _ _ _ _

CLUE

Think HAPPY

# 8. TOP TEN

complete the word by filling the spaces with a whole number between one and ten.

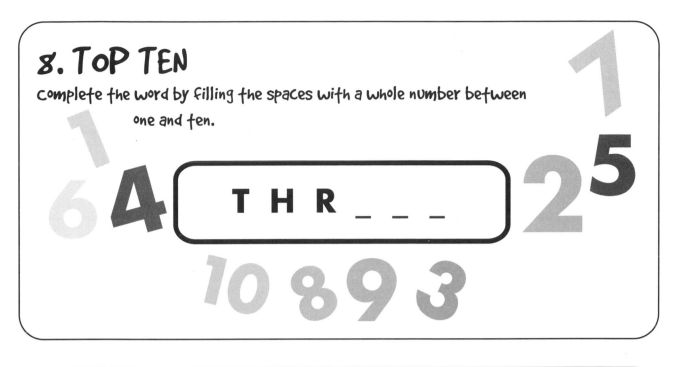

T H R _ _ _

# 9. SPACE TREK

which of the space portals logs on to a flight path that leads to a safe landing?

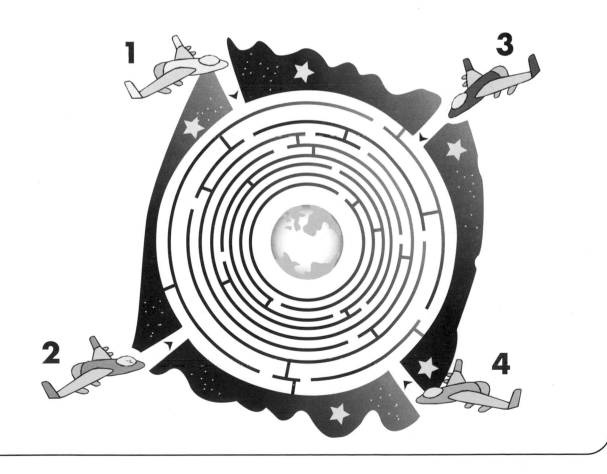

## 10. LINKS
Which word will go after the first word and before the second word?

S H O P P I N G ( _ _ _ _ _ _ ) B A L L

## 11. BACK WORDS
Solve the clues: the second answer is the first answer written backwards.

**TURN ROUND AND ROUND ∗ PINCHES**

_ _ _ _ ∗ _ _ _ _

## 12. ADDER
Using other words with the same meaning, can you create a new word from two separate ones?

**NOT IN**      _ _ _

**+ WEEP**      + _ _ _ _

**= PROTEST**   = _ _ _ _ _ _ _

# 13. ACT 3

With the word ACT in place, can you fit the words below containing three letters back into the frame?

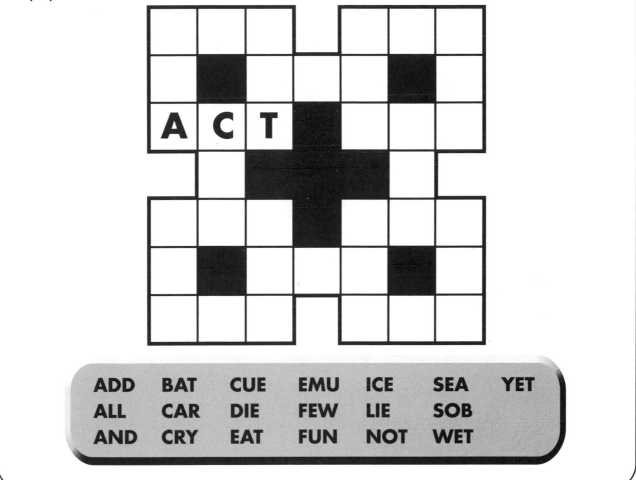

| ADD | BAT | CUE | EMU | ICE | SEA | YET |
| ALL | CAR | DIE | FEW | LIE | SOB |     |
| AND | CRY | EAT | FUN | NOT | WET |     |

# 14. FRUIT SPLIT

The name of a fruit is hidden in the sentence below. Find it by joining words or parts of words together.

**The sporting hero ran generously for charity.**

_____

# 15. SPIKE LIKES...

- Spike likes peas but he hates spinach.

- Spike likes eyes but he hates ears.

- Spike likes ewes but he hates rams.

- Why does Spike like these things?

# 16. FACE FACTS

Use the letters that make up the face to make a name.

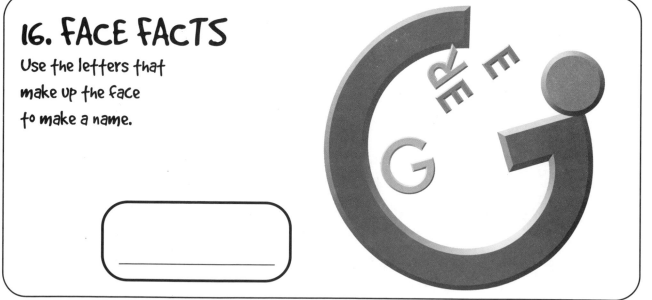

# 17. CRAZY CREATURES

Rearrange the letters in the words below to spell out the names of animals.

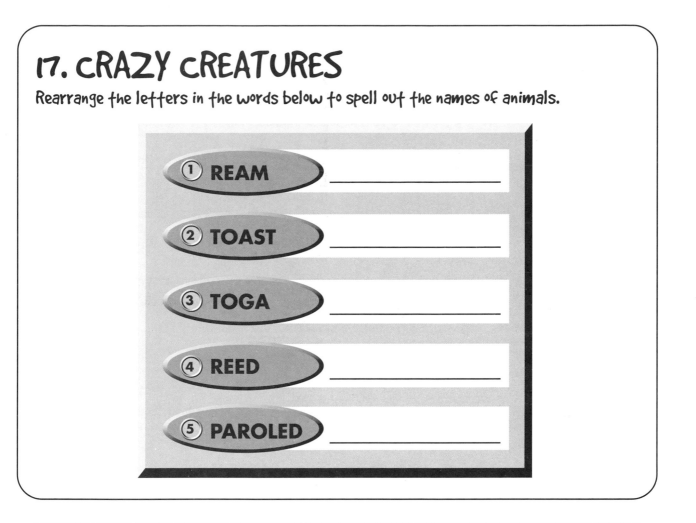

1. **REAM** _____
2. **TOAST** _____
3. **TOGA** _____
4. **REED** _____
5. **PAROLED** _____

# 18. GOING BATS

A word square reads the same across and down. Use the listed words to make two word squares. Each square must contain the word BATS.

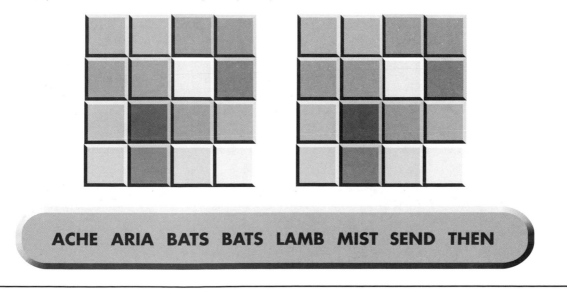

ACHE   ARIA   BATS   BATS   LAMB   MIST   SEND   THEN

# 19. FLY THE FLAG

Each flag stands for a letter of the alphabet. The first group of flags stands for SPAIN. Using the same code, can you work out which capital city the second group of flags spells?

S    P    A    I    N

\_\_\_    \_\_\_    \_\_\_    \_\_\_    \_\_\_

A B C D E F G H I J K L M
N O P Q R S T U V W X Y Z

# 20. SILHOUETTE

Which silhouette matches the outline shape?

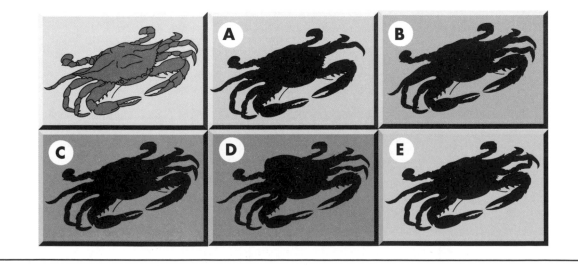

## 21. MIND THE GAP

Which single three-letter word completes all of the following words?

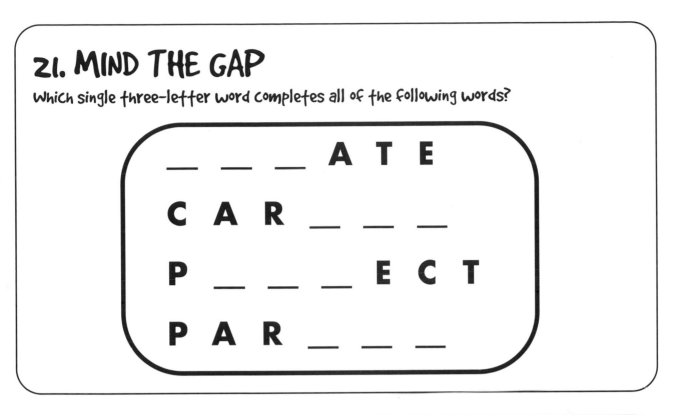

_ _ _ A T E

C A R _ _ _

P _ _ _ E C T

P A R _ _ _

## 22. COUNTER

How many triangles are there in this pattern?

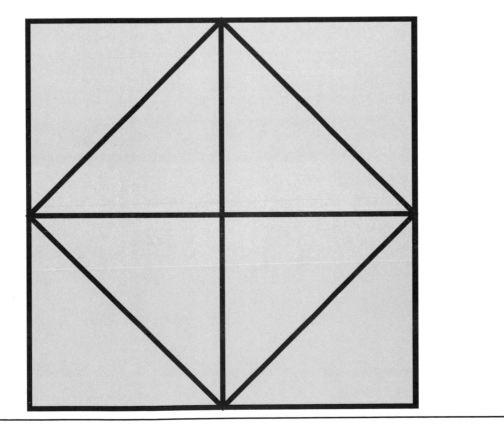

## 23. SECRET SEVEN

Rearrange the letters in the word below to make another word of seven letters.

**U N P A S T E**

_ _ _ _ _ _ _

CLUE

Think
SALTY SNACK

## 24. TRICKY SIGNS

If the first group of shapes makes the word car, what does the next group stand for, which describes a group of people traveling across a desert?

C A R

_ _ _ _ _ _ _

# 25. WHAT'S NEXT?

What is the next letter to go in the space?

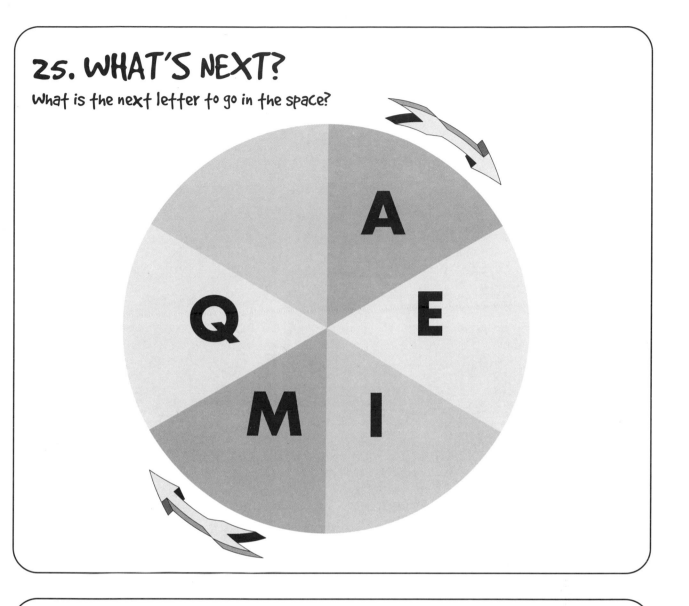

# 26. AFTER-WORDS

Which word can go after all these words to make new words?

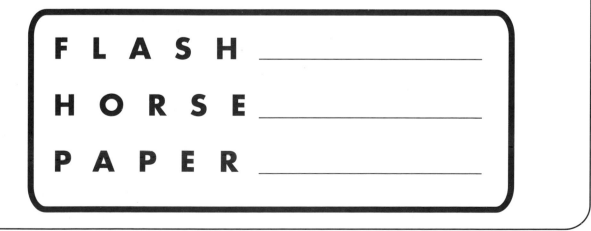

F L A S H _____

H O R S E _____

P A P E R _____

# 27. STARGAZER

All answers contain four letters and follow the direction shown by the arrows.

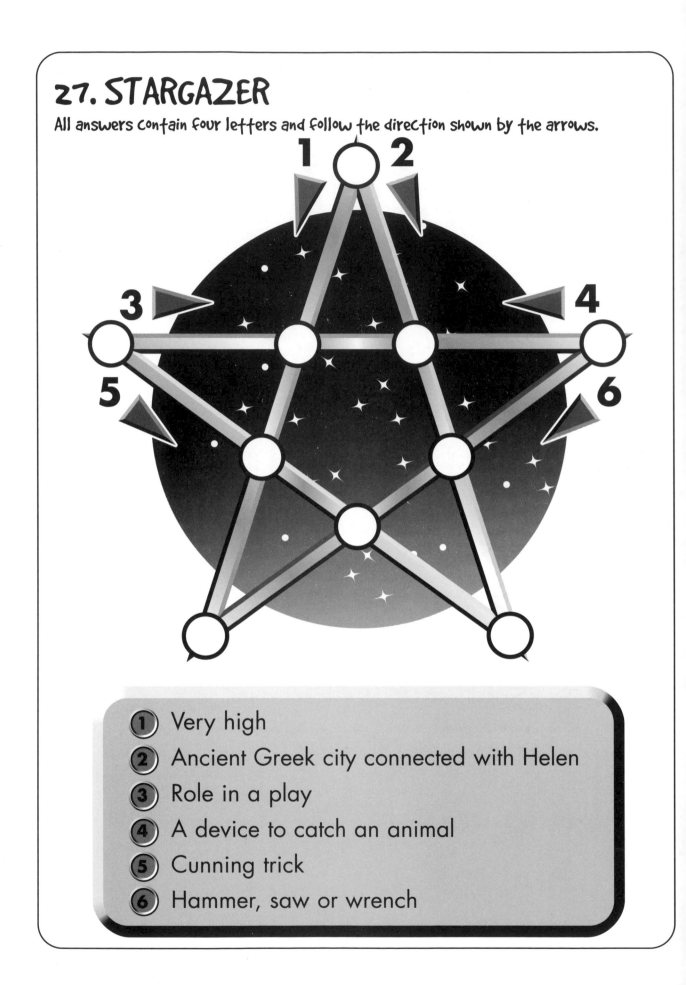

1. Very high
2. Ancient Greek city connected with Helen
3. Role in a play
4. A device to catch an animal
5. Cunning trick
6. Hammer, saw or wrench

# 28. NUMBER FIT

Fit all the numbers back into the frame.

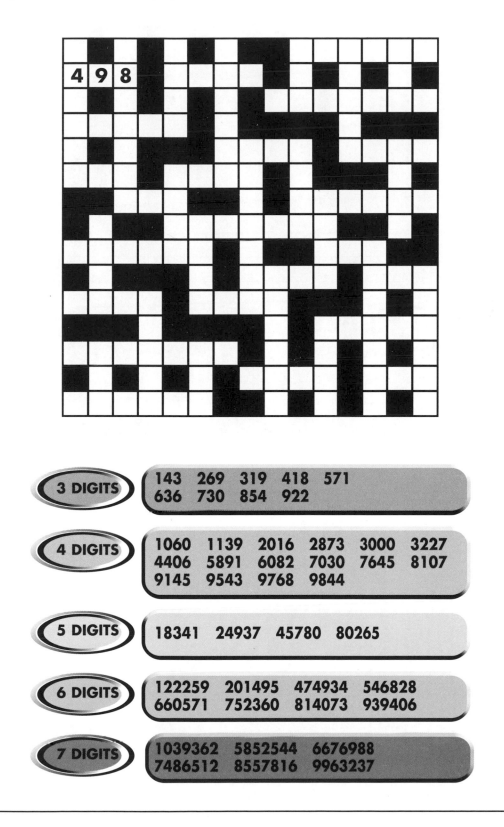

**3 DIGITS**
143  269  319  418  571
636  730  854  922

**4 DIGITS**
1060  1139  2016  2873  3000  3227
4406  5891  6082  7030  7645  8107
9145  9543  9768  9844

**5 DIGITS**
18341  24937  45780  80265

**6 DIGITS**
122259  201495  474934  546828
660571  752360  814073  939406

**7 DIGITS**
1039362  5852544  6676988
7486512  8557816  9963237

# 29. ON LINE

one line from each letter is missing. can you fill the gaps to make another word for glue?

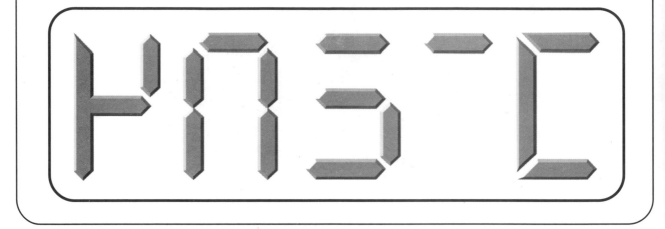

# 30. SECRET PLACES

The name of a country is hidden in each of the sentences below.
Find them by joining words or parts of words together.

**1** We visited the spa in November.

**2** That's the dress which I least like.

**3** Can a date be decided upon for the party?

# 31. PATTERN PLAY

Find the remaining pattern from the given shapes.

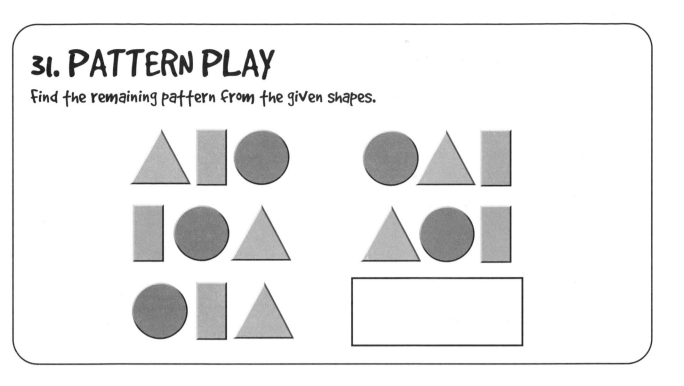

# 32. BACK WORDS

Solve the clues: the second answer is the first answer written backwards.

AMAZE ✳ CASHEWS, PECANS, PISTACHIOS ETC

＿ ＿ ＿ ＿ ＿ ✳ ＿ ＿ ＿ ＿ ＿

# 33. SPLITZER

This row of ten letters can be split into two five-letter words which are the names of two metals. Words read from left to right and the letters are in the correct order. What are they?

B S R A T S E S E L

/

## 34. MIDDLE MOVES

Each clue has two answers. Both answers are spelt the same except for the middle letter which is different.

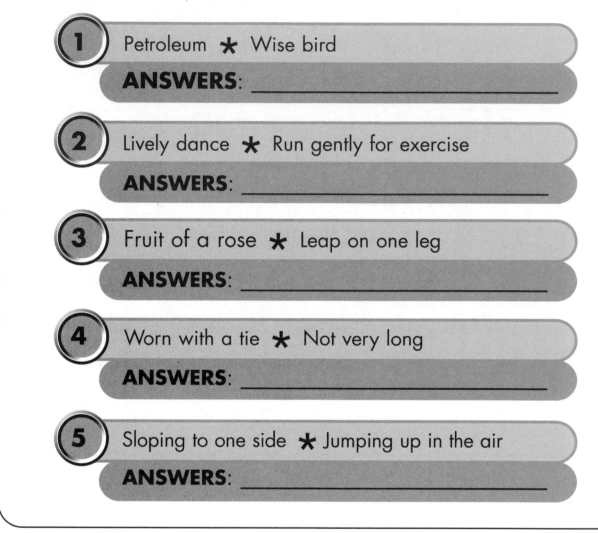

**1** Petroleum ✱ Wise bird

**ANSWERS**: _____

**2** Lively dance ✱ Run gently for exercise

**ANSWERS**: _____

**3** Fruit of a rose ✱ Leap on one leg

**ANSWERS**: _____

**4** Worn with a tie ✱ Not very long

**ANSWERS**: _____

**5** Sloping to one side ✱ Jumping up in the air

**ANSWERS**: _____

## 35. MORE OR LESS?

What is more, the number of hours in a week or the number of days in any six months?

_____

# 36. JUST JUICE

You are in a supermarket. Going down an aisle, the fruit juice is on your right.

You count ten different makes of fruit juice,

and there are ten cartons of each make.

You get to the end of the aisle, realize you have forgotten something and turn back.

This time looking to your left you see ten different makes of fruit juice, and there are ten cartons of each make. How many cartons of juice have you seen altogether?

# 37. NAME GAME

Each face stands for a letter in the alphabet. The first group makes IRENE. The second group makes JAN. Which name is formed by the third group?

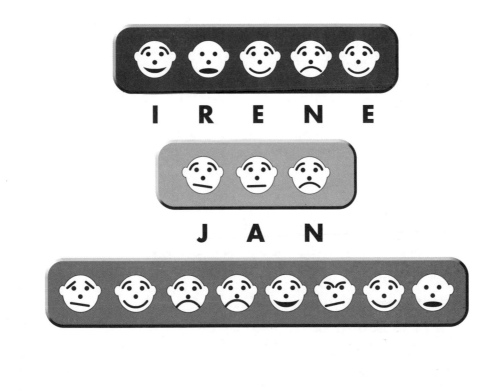

I    R    E    N    E

J    A    N

___  ___  ___  ___  ___  ___  ___  ___

# 38. NEWS ROUND

Solve each clue and write the answers into the spaces in the grid. All answers have four letters. Put the first letter in the outer circle, then move towards the center. Only one letter changes between answers, and answer 8 will be only one letter different from answer 1.

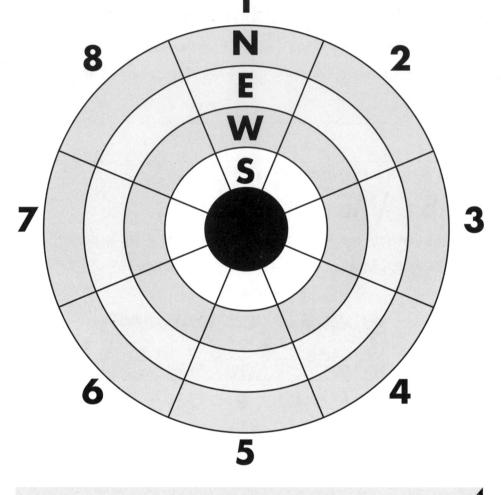

① Up to date information
② Mesh in a hockey or soccer goal
③ Hamsters, cats and dogs can be these
④ Green vegetables
⑤ The sound of ringing of bells
⑥ Sea creature
⑦ Oceans
⑧ Uses needle and thread

# 39. ALPHA-SEARCH

In this puzzle you have to search out the things that aren't there! Here's a jumble of letters of the alphabet. Each letter appears once, except for some letters which do not appear at all. First, work out the missing letters then arrange them to spell out the name of a fruit. You need to discover five letters.

Z F W R K N S
Y T U R X Q
L O G M V D J B I

# 40. TWINS

Which two faces are exactly alike?

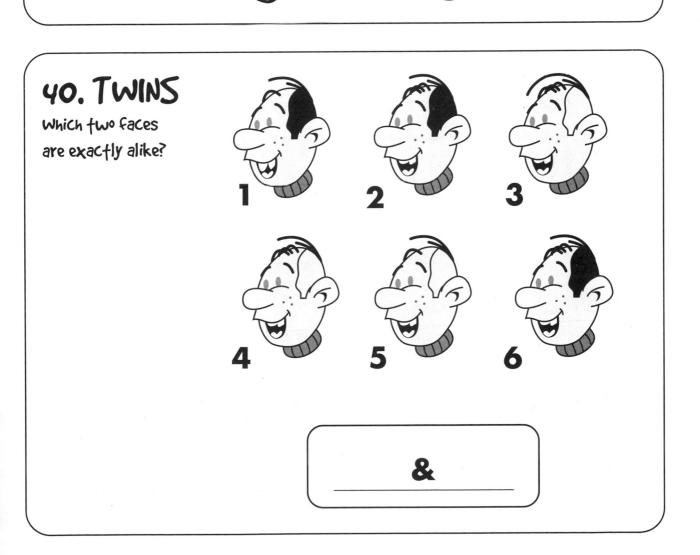

1  2  3

4  5  6

_____ & _____

# 41. SALT SIGNS

Shapes and signs have been used to take the place of letters of the alphabet. Can you work out what the words are? They are all things that could be found on a dining table. The first word is SALT.

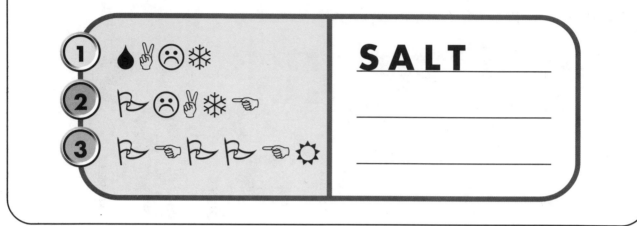

SALT

_____

_____

# 42. LINKS

Which word will go after the first word and before the second word?

**NORTH( _ _ _ _ _ )VAULT**

# 43. BACK WORDS

Solve the clues: the second answer is the first answer written backwards.

**DOMESTIC ANIMALS ✶ DANCE MOVEMENT**

# 44. CORNERED

The corner letters are in place. Use all the listed letters to complete the grid and form a word square in which words will read both across and down.

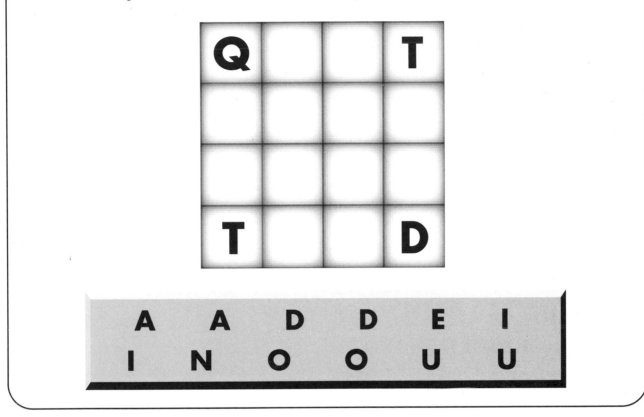

| Q |  |  | T |
|---|---|---|---|
|  |  |  |  |
|  |  |  |  |
| T |  |  | D |

A A D D E I
I N O O U U

# 45. FACE FACTS

Use the letters that make up the face to make a name.

## 46. ADDER

Using other words with the same meaning, can you create a new word from two separate ones?

ISN'T — — — —

+ FROZEN WATER + — — —

= POSTER = — — — — — —

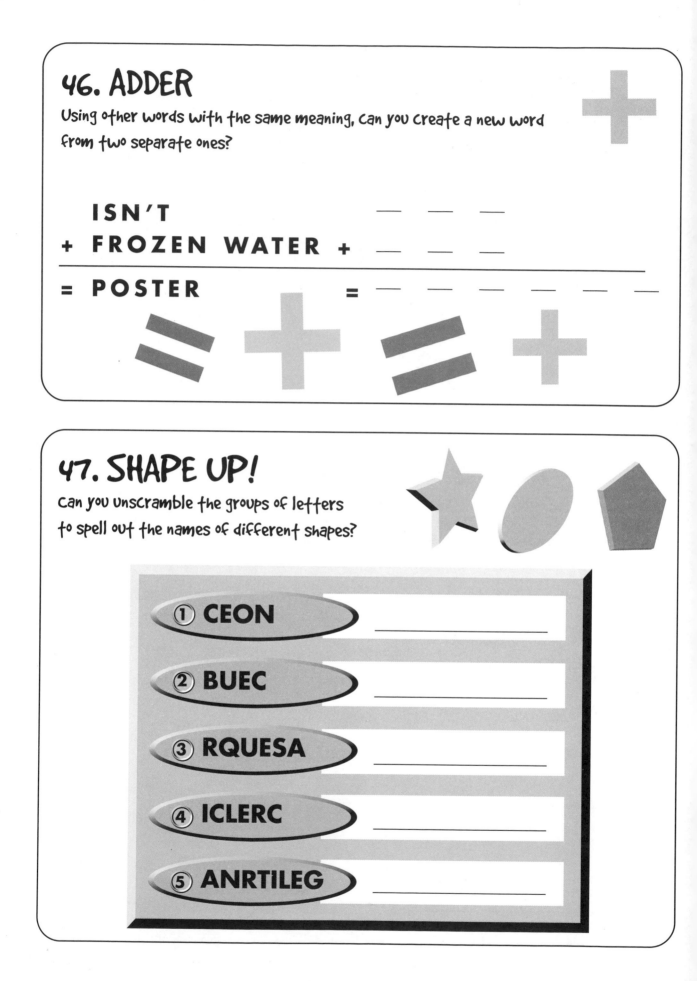

## 47. SHAPE UP!

Can you unscramble the groups of letters to spell out the names of different shapes?

① CEON _____

② BUEC _____

③ RQUESA _____

④ ICLERC _____

⑤ ANRTILEG _____

# 48. SECRET SEVEN
Rearrange the letters in the word below to make another word of seven letters.

P R O T E S T

_ _ _ _ _ _ _

**CLUE**

Think
CRAFTSMEN

# 49. STARTING BLOCKS
How many more blocks are needed to make the upper layer the same size and shape as the lower layer?

# 50. AFTER-WORDS
Which word can go after all these words to make new words?

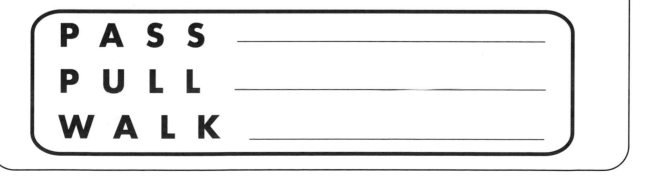

P A S S _____

P U L L _____

W A L K _____

# ANSWERS

## 1. CUBED

2

## 2. CLOTHES LINE

Jeans/Shirt.

## 3. JIGSAW

Danny went first and put in the piece bottom left. Tessa went second and put in the piece top left. Tim went third and put in the piece bottom right. Rosie went last and put in the piece top right.

## 4. AFTER-WORDS

out.

## 5. CREATURE CODE

Leopard.

## 6. CONNECTIONS

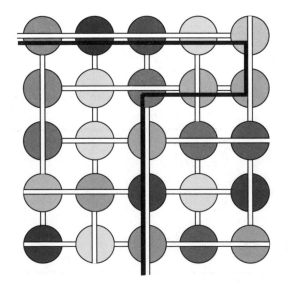

# 7. SECRET SEVEN

Pleased.

# 8. TOP TEN

one. This completes the word throne.

# 9. SPACE TREK

only portal 2 logs on to a path to the planet.

# 10. LINKS

Basket.

# 11. BACK WORDS

Spin * Nips.

# 12. ADDER

out + cry = outcry.

# 13. ACT 3

# 14. FRUIT SPLIT

orange is split between the words
HERO RAN GENEROUSLY.

# 15. SPIKE LIKES . . .

Spike likes things that sound likes letters of the alphabet. Ps, Is and Us.

# 16. FACE FACTS

George.

# 17. CRAZY CREATURES

1. Mare
2. Stoat
3. Goat
4. Deer
5. Leopard.

# 18. GOING BATS

## 19. FLY THE FLAG
Paris.

## 20. SILHOUETTE
C.

## 21. MIND THE GAP
Rot.

## 22. COUNTER
12.

## 23. SECRET SEVEN
Peanuts.

## 24. TRICKY SIGNS
caravan.

## 25. WHAT'S NEXT?
U. Letters are in alphabetical order, with three missed out at each move.

## 26. AFTER-WORDS
Back.

## 27. STARGAZER
1. Tall
2. Troy
3. Part
4. Trap
5. Ploy
6. Tool.

# 28. NUMBER FIT

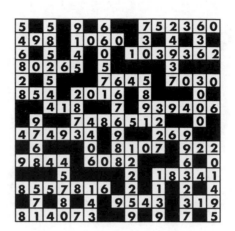

# 29. ON LINE

Paste.

# 30. SECRET PLACES

1. Spain
2. Chile
3. Canada.

# 31. PATTERN PLAY

# 32. BACK WORDS

Stun * Nuts.

# 33. SPLITZER

Brass/Steel.

# 34. MIDDLE MOVES

1. Oil/Owl
2. Jig/Jog
3. Hip/Hop
4. Shirt/Short
5. Leaning/Leaping.

## 35. MORE OR LESS?

On average there are 30 days in a month, so 6 x 30 gives 180 – more than the number of hours in a week, which is 168.

## 36. JUST JUICE

100. Coming back you looked at the same cartons again.

## 37. NAME GAME

Jennifer.

## 38. NEWS ROUND

1. News
2. Nets
3. Pets
4. Peas
5. Peal
6. Seal
7. Seas
8. Sews.

## 39. ALPHA-SEARCH

Peach.

## 40. TWINS

2 and 6.

## 41. SALT SIGNS

1. Salt
2. Plate
3. Pepper.

## 42. LINKS

Pole.

## 43. BACK WORDS

Pets * Step.

## 44. CORNERED

| Q | U | I | T |
|---|---|---|---|
| U | N | D | O |
| I | D | E | A |
| T | O | A | D |

## 45. FACE FACTS

Carol.

## 46. ADDER

Not + Ice = Notice.

## 47. SHAPE UP!

1. Cone
2. Cube
3. Square
4. Circle
5. Triangle.

## 48. SECRET SEVEN

Potters.

## 49. STARTING BLOCKS

16.

## 50. AFTER-WORDS

over.